To Mike—
with best wishes
from

and Ross!
(you lucky
guy!)

HIGH SOCIETY

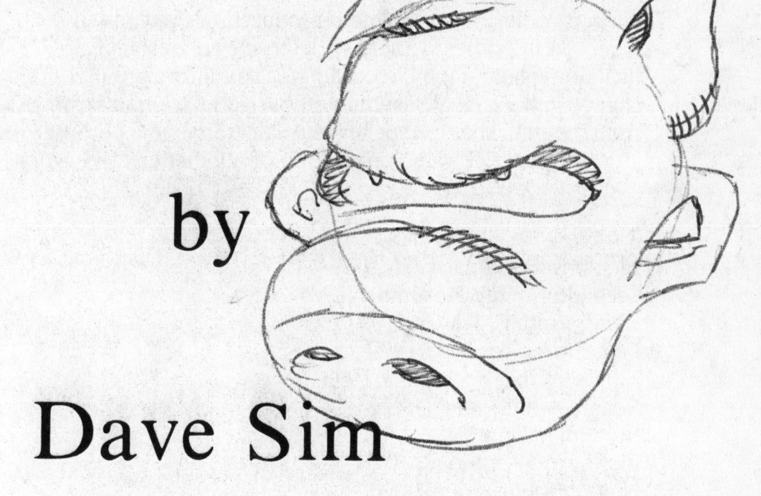

by

Dave Sim

Aardvark-Vanaheim Inc.
First printing, June 1986
Second printing, November 1987
Third printing, January 1991
Fourth printing, June 1992
Fifth printing, September 1993
Sixth printing, May 1995
Seventh printing, November 1997
Eight printing, July 2000
Ninth printing, July 2002
Tenth printing, September 2005

ISBN 0-919359-07-8

Printed in Windsor, Ontario by
Preney Print & Litho Inc.

PRINTED IN CANADA

to Barry Windsor-Smith who taught
me to dream big

to Neal Adams who broke barriers of
all kinds and made it look like fun
and

to Mike Kaluta who gave me the title
back when I was just little

CONTENTS

I began the five-hundred page novel you hold in your hands shortly before my twenty-fifth birthday, completing it shortly after my twenty-seventh birthday. It appeared in monthly twenty-page installments in the pages of my comic book, Cerebus.

There is a temptation to wax eloquent about the influences, interests and thinking that went into the making of the story, or to provide notes and afterwords and such-like on the fictional city-state of Iest and the election of 1414. It has been resisted.

I'm going to let this one sink or swim on its own merits, pausing only to thank Gerhard who took my blue pencil drawing of the Regency Hotel on the cover and brought it vividly to life and Karen McKiel who keeps the clockwork ticking and the money safe.

Welcome to the Regency.

I hope you enjoy your stay.

Dave Sim
May 26, 1986
Kitchener, Ontario

HIGH society

THE REGENCY-- IEST'S OLDEST AND MOST LAVISH HOTEL!...AND CEREBUS' LAST HOPE IN HIS SEARCH FOR A ROOM AND FOOD!

HE CARRIES WITH HIM A LAST FEW PIECES OF LOOT HE INTENDS TO SELL ON THE BLACK MARKET IN THE SPRAWLING PORT CITY...

HE PREPARES HIMSELF FOR THE INEVITABLE BATTLE WITH THE HOTEL GUARDS -- AN INCONVENIENCE THAT **ORDINARILY** KEEPS THE EARTH-PIG **AWAY** FROM SUCH SNOBBISH ESTABLISHMENTS...

HE IS GRATEFUL THAT HIS MOOD IS SO **GRIM** -- IT WILL MAKE THE JOB OF INTIMIDATING THE DESK CLERK **EASIER!**

AND THE EARTH-PIG'S MOOD, DAMPENED BY ENDLESS MILES OF SWAMP IS GRIM, INDEED! HE SCOWLS AT THE DESK CLERK EVEN AS HE ENTERS THE LOBBY...

"THEY MUST BREED THEM FOR ARROGANCE" THINKS THE AARDVARK AS HE APPROACHES, NOISILY...

NO ROOMS.
SORRY.

CEREBUS HAS JUST CARRIED THIS SACK OVER FIFTY MILES THROUGH THE WORST SWAMPS IN ESTARCION -- NOW -- IF YOU DON'T WANT CEREBUS TO FORCE-FEED YOU TO ONE OF THOSE STONE LIONS OUTSIDE, YOU...

CEREBUS?
DID YOU SAY 'CEREBUS,' SIR?
AYE-- CEREBUS THE AARDVARK.
HENRY! TAKE OVER FOR ME!
I'M SORRY, SIR, WE HAD NO ADVANCE NOTICE OF YOUR ARRIVAL. I'LL SHOW YOU TO YOUR ROOM...
ROOM?
uh...
OKAY.

IF YOU'LL LEAVE YOUR BAG DOWN HERE, ONE OF OUR BOYS WILL TAKE IT...
THAT'S WHY CEREBUS IS KEEPING IT WITH HIM...

UM...
...YES...
OF COURSE.

YOU'LL WANT A BATH BEFORE EATING...
NAY -- THE RIVER IS TOO FAR...
AND TOO COLD, NOW THAT THE SUN IS DOWN...

ACTUALLY, I WAS THINKING MORE ALONG THE LINES OF A BATH HERE IN YOUR ROOM, SIR
I TOOK THE LIBERTY OF HAVING ONE DRAWN FOR YOU...
OH
UH
AYE.

I'LL BE BACK WITHIN THE HOUR, SIR...
CEREBUS UNDRESSES SLOWLY--HE NOW HAD A ROOM AND WOULD SOON HAVE FOOD...
...WHY, THEN, WAS HIS MOOD GETTING WORSE INSTEAD OF BETTER?

SIR?
AH! THERE YOU ARE!
WHAT'S HAPPENED TO YOUR BOY?
HE LEFT.

WHEN CEREBUS' FUR GETS WET, IT TAKES A STRONG STOMACH TO STAY IN THE VICINITY...

I SEE WHAT YOU =KOFF= MEAN
SORT OF LINGERS IN THE AIR-- DOESN'T IT?
SHALL WE ADJOURN TO THE DINING ROOM?
JUST A MINUTE.

CEREBUS WANTS TO TALK ABOUT COST...
SIR?
THIS RED CARPET TREATMENT ...
HOW BIG A DENT IS IT GOING TO PUT IN CEREBUS' BANKROLL ...

WHY-- IF IT WOULDN'T INSULT YOU, OF COURSE THE MANAGEMENT WOULD BE HONOURED IF YOU WOULD STAY HERE AS OUR GUEST!
CEREBUS WOULDN'T BE INSULTED...

MEALS INCLUDED, EH?
MOST ASSUREDLY-- YOU'LL NEED TIE, HOWEVER

CEREBUS FIGURED THERE WAS A CATCH SOMEWHERE ...
THIS BETTER BE GOOD!

IT WAS ALL THE DESK CLERK'S FAULT, CEREBUS DECIDED! THE EARTH-PIG HAD ARRIVED QUITE READY TO FIGHT FOR A ROOM AND THE CLERK WAS TAKING PERVERSE SATISFACTION OUT OF MAKING THE WHOLE PROCESS TOO EASY... CEREBUS INTENDED TO START A FIGHT WITH **SOMEONE** IF IT TOOK THE WHOLE REST OF THE EVENING.

YOU EXPECT CEREBUS TO EAT IN THE MIDDLE OF A **CROWD?** WHAT KIND OF A...
CERTAINLY **NOT,** SIR...!

WE'VE SET ASIDE A PRIVATE ROOM FOR YOU, SIR.
TARIM.

CEREBUS WANTS PRIME RIB OF YAK WITH RUM AND RAISIN SAUCE...
YES, SIR
FOUR BOTTLES OF **CHATEAU DEHRSION...**
YES, SIR
FOUR DIFFERENT YEARS...

AND FOR DESSERT, ANY FRUIT THAT'S OUT OF SEASON
YES, SIR...
CEREBUS GIVES UP.

HADDEN-- HOLLAND M. HADDEN OF **HADDEN, HADDEN AND DIPP.** I SIMPLY CAWN'T **TELL** YOU WHAT AN **HONOUR** IT IS TO MEET YOU.
GO AWAY OR CEREBUS IS GOING TO STRIP-MINE YOUR **FACE.**
OH! HAHAHA! YAS. VERY GOOD. I WANT TO ASK YOU TO CONSIDER...
GOLD-PLATED STREETLAMPS!
YOU HAVE **FIVE SECONDS!**

FIVE SECONDS... HARDLY ENOUGH TIME FOR A FULL-SCALE PRESENTATION AS I'M SURE YOU'LL AGREE, SIR...
ONE!

...BUT! TIME ENOUGH TO MENTION HADDEN HADDEN AND DIPP ONE MORE TIME ...
TWO!

...TO REMIND YOU GOLD-PLATED STREET-LAMPS ARE A GOOD INVESTMENT AS WELL AS AN UNBEATABLE TOURIST ATTRACTION...
THREE!

...AND TO GIVE YOU THIS CERTIFIED CHEQUE FOR SEVEN HUNDRED IESTAN CROWNS PAYABLE TO...
FOUR!

FIIIVE...
...CEREBUS THE AARDVARK.

SEVEN HUNDRED CROWNS
YES, SIR.
FOR CEREBUS.
YES, SIR
AND ALL I ASK IS THAT YOU REMEMBER...
...HADDEN, HADDEN AND DIPP GOLD-PLATED STREETLAMPS.

I SEE THAT WE HAVE AN UNDERSTANDING--SORRY TO HAVE INTERRUPTED YOU

CEREBUS DOESN'T GET IT...
AH...
EXCUSE ME.

GREELY..
NED GREELY
OF GREELY, BLEAKER AND SPLEEN
...
DON'T TELL CEREBUS. LET HIM GUESS.

YOU WANT TO TELL CEREBUS SOMETHING.
WHY, YES I...
YOU WANT CEREBUS TO REMEMBER IT
WHY, YES I...
DID YOU BRING YOUR CHEQUE BOOK?
WHY, YES I...
SIT DOWN.

AN HOUR LATER.
CHEQUES AND BANK DRAUGHTS FOR OVER FIVE THOUSAND CROWNS...
...AND THEY HAVEN'T EVEN BROUGHT THE WINE YET.
TIME FOR CEREBUS TO ASK SOMEBODY SOME QUESTIONS.

FROM FAR AWAY HAVE I COME TO SEE FAMOUS THE AARDVARK CEREBUS PLEASE
MOST GREATLY!
CLOSE ENOUGH. HAVE A SEAT.
I AM TELLING YOU SOMETHING, OKAY?

I AM TELLING YOU THERE IS TOO MUCH SEWAGE! NAME WILL BE SCORZ OF SCORZ, SCORZ AND SONS, IEST, BEDUIN, SERREA SINCE 1266
AND WHAT DO YOU HOPE CEREBUS CAN DO FOR YOU...?

SEWAGE IS PROBLEM SOLVING -- BUILD PIPES UNDERGROUND! AWAY THE SEWAGE!

MUCH SAVING. EASY TO INSTALL. REDUCE TO PERCENT SMELL OF FIFTY! NO MORE!
TARIM.

AM ALL I ASKING IS FAMOUS THE AARDVARK...
...TO REMEMBER SEWAGE PIPES AND SCORZ, SCORZ AND SONS
FAMOUS THE AARDVARK PROMISES TO REMEMBER! NOW WATCH FAMOUS' LIPS...
WHAT-DO-YOU-WANT-FAMOUS THE-AARDVARK-TO-REMEMBER IT-FOR?

NATURALLY FOR TALKING AT LORD JULIUS! FAMOUS THE AARDVARK IS FAMOUS SUPERVISOR OF THE STAFF KITCHEN. TALK AT LORD JULIUS...
OHO
TALK AT LORD JULIUS "SEWAGE, SEWAGE, SEWAGE"

DRIVE IT RIGHT THROUGH HIS BRAIN!
WHY NOT DRIVE IT THROUGH HIS BRAIN YOURSELF?

ALREADY TRIED! SEND LETTERS, JUNIOR PARTNERS AND PROMOTIONAL BROCHURE ...
FINALLY GO TO PALNU CONTACT HEAD OF PURCHASING COMMA GOVERNMENTAL MYSELF
HOY!
IS VERY VERY LONG LONG STORY ...MAY BE BORING FAMOUS THE AARDVARK
DON'T WORRY, FAMOUS HASN'T EVEN HAD HIS YAK YET
DRIVE IT THROUGH FAMOUS' BRAIN.

HEAD OF PURCHASING COMMA GOVERNMENTAL TELL ME HE IS TAKE ONLY CARE OF DEPARTMENT OF INTERIOR TELL SCORZ "GO SEE BASKIN". GO SEE BASKIN. TALK AT BASKIN "**SEWAGE, SEWAGE, SEWAGE**" BASKIN SAY "INQUIRIES REGARDING PUBLIC UTILITIES ARE TO BE DIRECTED TO THE UNDERSECRETARY OF THE 'INTERNAL SECURITY TASK FORCE ON AGING IN THE HOME.'" SCORZ FILL OUT FORMS FOR HOUR AND A HALF. TWO WEEKS LATER SCORZ GET OFFICIAL COMMUNICATION FROM OFFICE OF THE UNDERSECRETARY OF THE "EXTERNAL AFFAIRS TASK FORCE ON AGING IN THE STREETS" INSIDE, SCORZ FIND FORMAL DECLARATION OF WAR AND INVITATION TO FESTIVAL OF PETUNIAS."

UNFORTUNATELY, SCORZ HAD NO ARMY AND NO PLACE TO RENT COSTUME. COMES IN NEXT COMMUNICATION SPECIAL ONE-TIME-ONLY, TOO-GOOD-TO-TRULY-BE OFFER! OFFICE OF COMMUNICATIONS AND OBFUSCATION MAKE AVAILABLE TO VALUED CUSTOMERS A DIRECTORY OF PALNU'S EXECUTIVES, STUDY GROUPS AND DEPARTMENT HEADS! SMALL CHARGE FOR HANDLING. WITH TAX, CONSULTING FEE AND LABOUR CHARGES, DIRECTORY COME TO ONLY FORTY-NINE CROWNS. TWO WEEKS LATER COMES NEXT NOTE "OWING TO INCREASED COSTS, DIRECTORY NOW COST **TWO HUNDRED** AND FORTY-NINE CROWNS. SEND MORE MONEY WITH COURIER."

NEXT LETTER ARRIVES FROM THE OFFICE OF CENTRAL INFORMATION. LETTER THANKS SCORZ, SCORZ AND SONS FOR CONTRIBUTION TO LORD JULIUS' STUDY GROUP EXAMINING METROPOLITAN FORESTRY. LETTER APOLOGIZED FOR DELAY IN ANSWERING. SCORZ WRITE LETTER TO STUDY GROUP DEMANDING COPY OF DIRECTORY. NEXT LETTER ARRIVE. STUDY GROUP DISSOLVED BY LORD JULIUS OWING TO LACK OF FOREST AREAS IN METROPOLITAN CENTRES. LETTER SAY LORD JULIUS CONSIDERING IDEA OF A DIRECTORY. WILL GET BACK TO SCORZ.

EVERY TIME MAIL ARRIVE SCORZ BREAK OUT IN HIVES.

WARMING TO HIS SUBJECT, SCORZ BEGINS TO MAKE A CASE FOR CEREBUS' BECOMING AN EMPLOYEE OF SCORZ, SCORZ AND SONS...
CHATEAU DEHRSION

BUT THE EARTH-PIG'S THOUGHTS ARE ALREADY **ELSEWHERE** AS HE THINKS BACK TO HIS DAYS IN PALNU.

HE IS NOT SO GREATLY SURPRISED BY HIS RECEPTION, NOW; HE REMEMBERS THE LINES OF BUSINESSMEN, CABINET MINISTERS AND UNDERLINGS THAT DAILY PASSED THROUGH THE DOORS OF LORD JULIUS' OFFICE. ALL WITH THE SAME DISGUSTING LOOK OF WELL-DRESSED BEGGARS WHINING FOR A HAND-OUT HE NOW SAW ACROSS THE TABLE.

SIPPING THOUGHTFULLY FROM HIS FINGER-BOWL, CEREBUS DECIDES THAT HE HAS HAD ENOUGH OF THIS AGGRAVATION. THERE WAS ONLY ONE THING THAT WOULD ALLEVIATE HIS FOUL MOOD.

CEREBUS HAD TO FIND SOMEONE TO BEAT UP.

TO TELL YOU THE TRUTH, LORD JULIUS ALREADY HAS A PLAN FOR PALNU'S SEWAGE -- HE INTENDS TO HAVE IT MOLDED INTO HUGE BALLS AND ROLLED DOWNHILL INTO ONLIU TERRITORY. CEREBUS HAS TO LEAVE NOW...
BUT...

I'LL BET YOU DON'T REMEMBER ME.
CEREBUS?
EXCUSE ME...
I KNOW YOU'RE BUSY, SIR
I MET YOU IN PALNU DURING THE FESTIVAL.
CEREBUS SIR IF I COULD JUST TALK TO YOU FOR...
SIR?
I'VE BEEN WAITING FOR AN HOUR! IF WE COULD JUST...
IF I COULD HAVE A MINUTE OR SO...
SIR?
CEREBUS! CEREBUS!
SIR? I REPRESENT THE GUILD OF
EXCUSE ME, CEREBUS
OVER HERE, CEREBUS.
BUT...

BELCH!

THE NERVES OF A RIVERBOAT GAMBLER!
EASILY ONE OF THE TOP THREE NEGOTIATORS IN ESTARCION
WHAT STYLE!
WHAT PANACHE!
IF I HAD SOMEONE LIKE HIM ON STAFF
YOU CAN SEE WHY LORD JULIUS TRUSTS HIM WITH SUCH A SENSITIVE CABINET POSITION

NOW WHO DOES CEREBUS HATE ENOUGH IN IEST TO BEAT UP...?

VON CROYDER! AVE
A FEW OLD SCORES TO SETTLE WITH THAT IDIOT ...

THERE'S AN EXTRA TWENTY CROWNS FOR YOU IF WE REACH THE DOCKS WITHIN THE HOUR...
SORRY, SIR. I'M WAITING FOR MR. CARRON ...

MR. CARRON WILL HAVE TO FIND HIMSELF ANOTHER CAB...
LET'S GO.
GET AWAY FROM THAT CAB, YOU SCRUFFY LITTLE HOODLUM!...

TAKE THAT!
AND BE GRATEFUL THAT I DON'T HAVE YOU ARRESTED, URCHIN...!

YOU JUST MADE A BIG MISTAKE, MISTER CARRON...!

OF ALL THE IMPERTINENCE!

MAYBE THIS WILL TEACH YOU TO NOT TALK BACK TO YOUR BETTERS!
NUK

AND...
...THIS!
CLOK

AND...
ALL RIGHT! THAT'S ENOUGH!
SNATCH!

YOU WANT TO FIGHT?
WE'LL FIGHT!...
WITHOUT
THIS!

THAT CANE HAS BEEN IN MY FAMILY FOR A HUNDRED YEARS, YOU MISSHAPEN LITTLE GUTTERSNIPE...
I WAS WILLING TO LET YOU GO AFTER A FEW PUNITIVE BLOWS...
NOW, ALTHOUGH I DEPLORE VIOLENCE IN THE STREETS ...

I AM AFRAID I SHALL HAVE TO THRASH YOU TO WITHIN AN INCH OF YOUR WORTHLESS LIFE
WHENEVER YOU'RE READY, BLONDIE!

I SHALL TRY MY BEST TO REFRAIN FROM CAUSING YOU ANY PERMANENT INJURY...
CEREBUS HAS BEEN WAITING ALL DAY FOR THIS, BLONDIE!

CEREBUS?

WELL, THIS IS A STROKE OF LUCK...
CARRON
OF CARRON, McKIEL AND BENNY.

STOW IT, BLONDIE!
CEREBUS IS GOING TO BEAT YOU TO A PULP!

OH, OF COURSE
IN FACT, I INSIST!
I'M SURE IT'S THE LEAST I CAN DO...
AFTER BEING SUCH AN ABSOLUTE PIG...

YOU MEAN YOU'RE JUST GOING TO STAND THERE WHILE CEREBUS BEATS YOU TO A PULP?

EXACTLY SO...
HERE, LET ME MAKE IT EASIER FOR YOU...
CEREBUS DOESN'T BELIEVE THIS...
ALL I ASK IS THAT YOU NOT HOLD THIS AGAINST MY COMPANY-- THEY CAN BE OF GREAT HELP TO PALNU...

GAH!

WAIT!
I'M LETTING YOU BEAT ME UP!
PLEASE!

MY COMPANY HAS BEEN TRYING TO GET A CONTRACT WITH PALNU FOR...
FIVE YEARS.

IF MY PARTNERS FIND OUT THAT I MET CEREBUS THE AARDVARK
AND THAT I H...H...
HIT HIM!

PLEASE
YOU'VE GOT TO BEAT ME UP.
TARIM.
DRIVER!

THE DOCKS!
PLEASE!

GIVE ME MY COPY OF THE DIRECTORY, YOU LITTLE SWINE
DO YOU HEAR?
SEVEN HUNDRED CROWNS ALREADY AND YOU HAVE THE NERVE TO ASK ANOTHER FIFTY FOR STAPLES!!
YOU'RE NOT FOOLING ANYONE!
YOU HEAR ME?
GIVE ME MY DIRECTORY OR I'LL... I'LL ...I'LL

ANY SPECIFIC ADDRESS, SIR?
AYE, BUT FIRST CEREBUS IS GOING TO NEED A FIFTY POUND SACK OF FLOUR.
THAT MIGHT BE DIFFICULT, SIR. ALL THE SHOPS ARE CLOSED...

CEREBUS IS WILLING TO PAY FIFTY CROWNS
EH?
THERE'S A GROCER IN THE NEXT STREET, SIR...
I CAN ASK HIM.

MUCH POUNDING LATER...
WHAT'S THIS ALL ABOUT?
DO YOU KNOW WHAT TIME...
NEVER MIND THAT--I GOT A LIVE ONE IN THE CAB...
...WILLING TO PAY FIVE CROWNS FOR A FIFTY POUND BAG OF FLOUR!

IF YOU'VE GOT ONE HANDY, I'LL SPLIT THE FIVE WITH YOU...
LET ME GET MY KEYS!

AND SO...
YOU'RE QUITE SURE THAT'S WHERE YOU WANT TO GO, SIR?
CEREBUS HIRED YOU TO DRIVE NOT TO ASK STUPID QUESTIONS.
VERY GOOD, SIR.

YOU'RE QUITE SURE YOU DON'T WANT ME TO WAIT HERE FOR YOU THEN, SIR?
NO--CEREBUS IS APT TO BE HERE FOR A WHILE...
AS YOU SAY, SIR.
THE RAM'S LORDS TAVERN.

SINCE THE TURN OF THE CENTURY, THE GATHERING PLACE FOR EVERY SADISTIC SEAMAN WITH THREE MONTHS' PAY AND SHORE LEAVE...
IT WAS SAID THAT THE RAMS LORDS HAD CLAIMED MORE LIVES THAN THE REVOLUTION IN UPPER FELDA...
BUT THEN...

RRIP!
CEREBUS WAS LOOKING FOR A FIGHT...

HEY! SCUM BAG! OVER HERE!!

THE INSULT IS NOT DIRECTED AT ANYONE IN PARTICULAR...
...AS A RESULT...

EVERYONE TAKES IT PERSONALLY.
FOR A MOMENT, THE ENTIRE TAVERN IS DEATHLY SILENT...

BUT ONLY FOR A MOMENT.
GET 'IM!
BREAK THE LITTLE RAT IN HALF...!
CRIPPLE 'IM!
PULL HIS EARS OFF!

IMPOSSIBLE ODDS; MENTALLY UNBALANCED FOES; CRAMPED QUARTERS FOR A GOOD PUNCH-UP...
AND PEOPLE SAY IEST HAS NO NIGHT LIFE...

FWEEEEEE

WHAT IN...?
THE DOCK POLICE!
DOCK POLICE!
IT'S A TRAP!
GET BACK!

DOCK POLICE?
CEREBUS THOUGHT THE DOCK POLICE NEVER CAME INTO THE RAM'S LORDS...
BAF
CRAK
CRUNK
WAK

CAPTAIN HILL-HODGES; WATERFRONT SPECIAL SECURITY, M'LORD!

WHAT DID YOU CALL CEREBUS?
DIRECTIVE TWENTY-THREE SLASH "A" RANKING DIPLOMATIC REPRESENTATIVE OF ANY SOUTHERN CITY-STATE, UNDER PROTECTION OF AND/OR OBSERVATION BY IESTAN GOVERNMENT FORCES INCLUDING CITY-GUARDS, BOROUGH CONSTABULARY OR SUCH INTERNAL SECURITY FORCES AS ARE DEEMED NECESSARY BY THE GOVERNMENT, SHALL BE ADDRESSED AT ALL TIMES AS "M'LORD"
DIRECTIVE TWENTY-THREE SLASH "B" RANKING DIPLOMATIC REPRESENTATIVE IS TO BE ADDRESSED ONLY BY THE HIGHEST RANKING MEMBER OF IESTAN GOVERNMENT FORCE IN QUESTION
I'M AFRAID WE LOST SIGHT OF YOUR CAB ABOUT THREE BLOCKS FROM HERE. SHALL I REPORT OUR FAILURE TO KEEP UP WITH YOU AND HAVE THE MEN FLOGGED, M'LORD?

NOT UNLESS CEREBUS GETS TO DO THE FLOGGING HIMSELF.
I'M SORRY, M'LORD-- DIRECTIVE TWENTY-THREE SLASH "C" SPECIFICALLY FORBIDS RANKING DIPLOMATIC...

RIGHT.
CEREBUS IS GOING TO GO BACK TO HIS HOTEL... OKAY?
RIGHT YOU ARE, M'LORD IT WILL JUST TAKE TEN MINUTES TO ASSIGN YOU A SECURITY TEAM.
GOOD. THAT WILL GIVE CEREBUS A TEN-MINUTE HEAD-START...

BUT...
BUT, M'LORD!

THIS IS A DANGEROUS CITY -- AT ANY MOMENT, A GANG OF DRUNKEN THUGS COULD COME AT YOU FROM OUT OF NOWHERE -- VICIOUS COWARDS WITHOUT SCRUPLES OR...
IT'S BEEN A BAD DAY, CAPTAIN...

DON'T TRY TO CHEER CEREBUS UP...

THE EARTH-PIG CONTINUES HIS RAPID ASCENT OF THE STAIRS JOINING GREATER AND LOWER IEST...
HIS OFFICIAL ESCORT IS IN HOT PURSUIT AND CEREBUS IS DETERMINED TO REACH THE REGENCY BEFORE THEY OVERTAKE HIM.
UNFORTUNATELY HE HAS BEEN WITHOUT SLEEP FOR TWO DAYS...
AND IT IS THE ONE-THOUSAND, THREE HUNDRED AND TWENTY-FOURTH STEP...

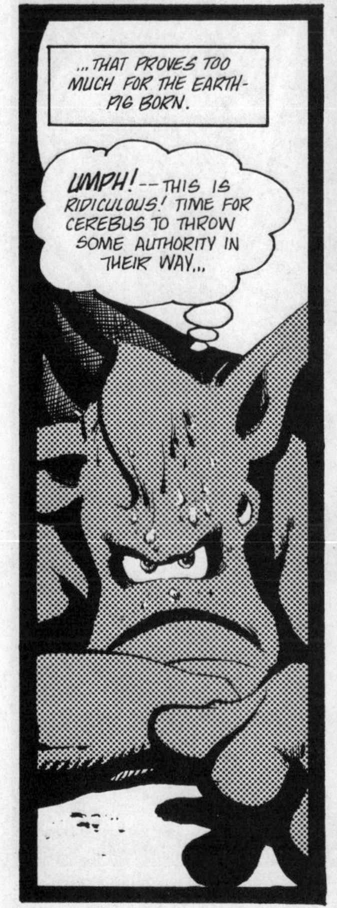
...THAT PROVES TOO MUCH FOR THE EARTH-PIG BORN.
UMPH!--THIS IS RIDICULOUS! TIME FOR CEREBUS TO THROW SOME AUTHORITY IN THEIR WAY...

RETURN TO YOUR CAPTAIN--CEREBUS HAS NO NEED OF...
UNH? ...

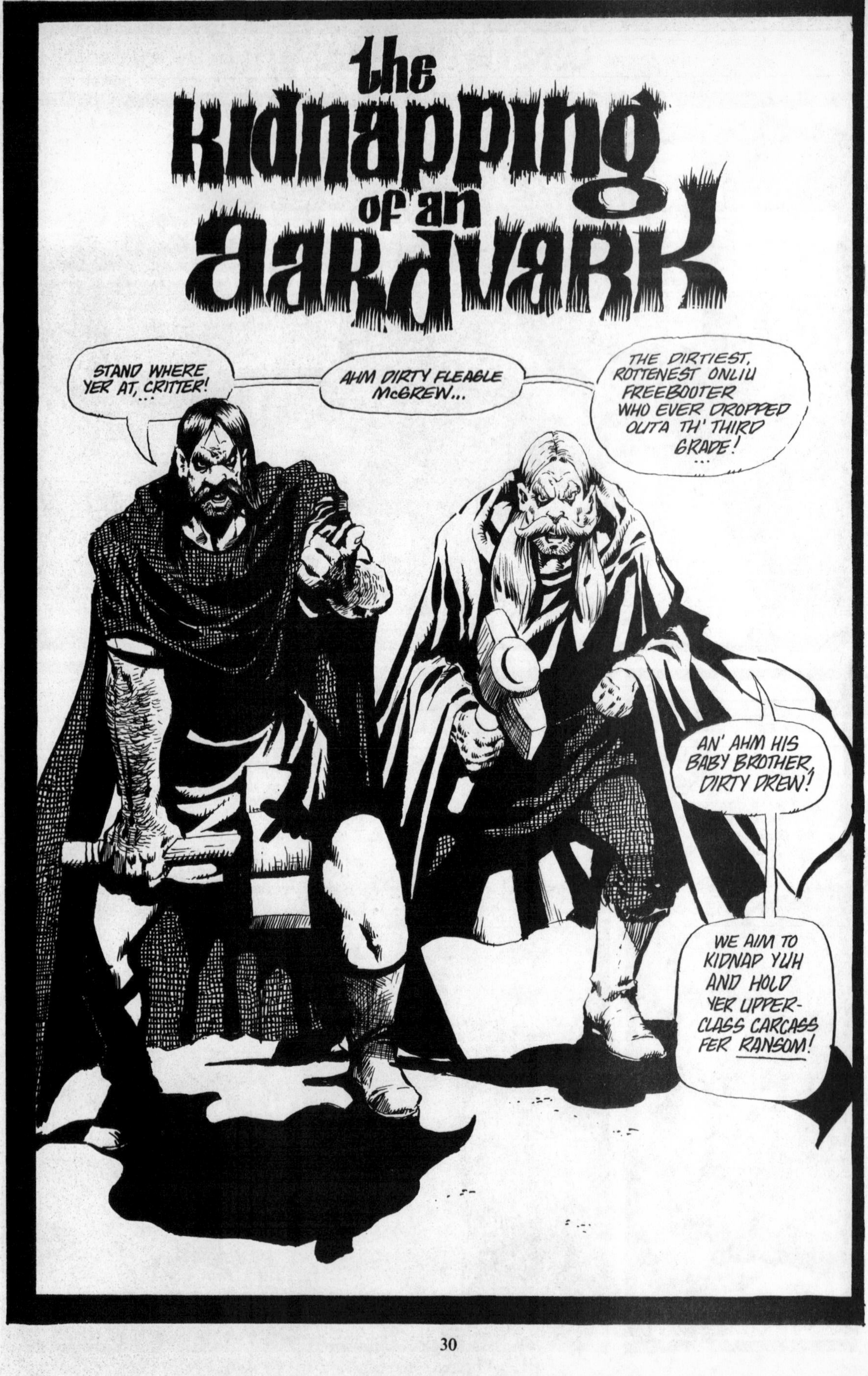

the Kidnapping of an Aardvark

CLOSE YER EYES, CRITTER! --THIS COULD GET A MITE MESSY!
HEH HEH
YAAAH!
CRAK
MUH LAIG! HE BROKE MUH LAIG!
OUCHIE! OUCHIE!
ARE YUH OKAY, DIRTY FLEAGLE?
OKAY?!?
OF COURSE AH AIN'T OKAY, IDJIT!
MUH LAIG'S BROKE!
JUST BRUISED ACTUALLY.
IF CEREBUS HAD MEANT TO BREAK IT, IT WOULD BE BROKEN ...
ANABODY HURTS DIRTY FLEAGLE McGREW
HASTA ANSWER TO 'IZ BLOOD KIN--MEANIN' ME! HIS BABY BROTHER DIRTY DREW!
SAY YER PRAYERS, VARMINT...
AHM FIXIN' TA BASH YER BRAINIES TA KINGDOM COME!
TARIM.

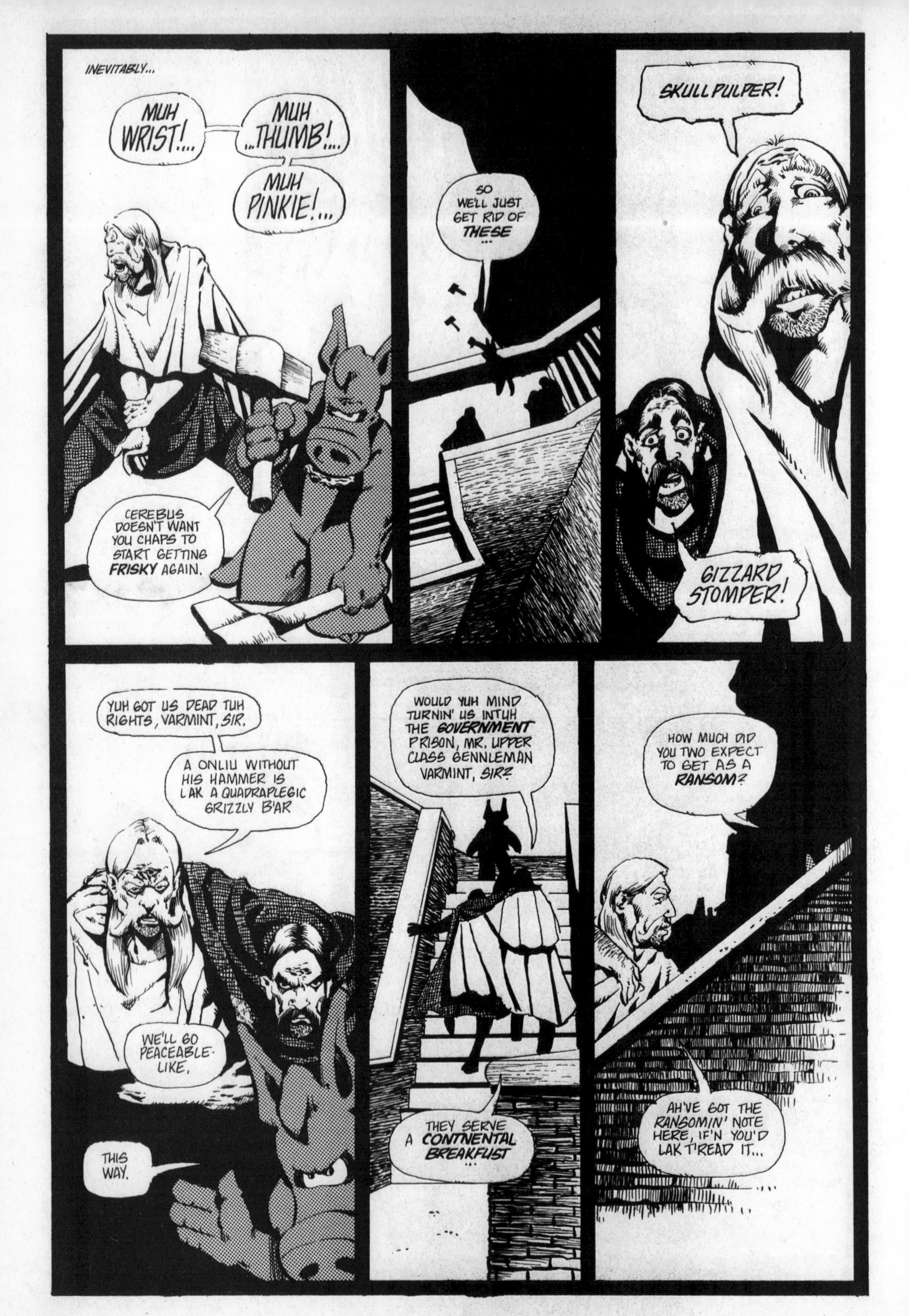
INEVITABLY...
MUH WRIST!...
MUH ..THUMB!...
MUH PINKIE!...
CEREBUS DOESN'T WANT YOU CHAPS TO START GETTING FRISKY AGAIN.
SO WE'LL JUST GET RID OF THESE ...
SKULL PULPER!
GIZZARD STOMPER!
YUH GOT US DEAD TUH RIGHTS, VARMINT, SIR.
A ONLIU WITHOUT HIS HAMMER IS LAK A QUADRAPLEGIC GRIZZLY B'AR
WE'LL GO PEACEABLE LIKE,
THIS WAY.
WOULD YUH MIND TURNIN' US INTUH THE GOVERNMENT PRISON, MR. UPPER CLASS GENNLEMAN VARMINT, SIR?
THEY SERVE A CONTNENTAL BREAKFUST ...
HOW MUCH DID YOU TWO EXPECT TO GET AS A RANSOM?
AH'VE GOT THE RANSOMIN' NOTE HERE, IF'N YOU'D LAK T'READ IT...

"TRESHERER OF IEST: BRING A HUNNERT GOLD PEESES TO TH DOG N DUCK OR YULL FIND TH CRITTER IN LITTLE BITS. COME ALONE. DIRTY FLEAGLE McGREW AND HIS BABY BROTHER D..."
YOU SIGNED THE RANSOM NOTE...?
COURSE AH SIGNED IT....
HOW ELSE WOULD HE KNOW WHO TA GIVE THE MONEY TUH?
STOOPID CRITTER
WHERE ARE YOU TAKING US, IF'N YA DON'T MIND ME ASKIN', YER UPPER CLASSNESS?
WE'RE ALMOST THERE

CEREBUS!
CEREBUS THE AARDVARK
TARIM! IT HAS TO BE TEN YEARS SINCE THE LAST TIME I LAID EYES ON YOU!...
GET THREE SLEEPING MATS FROM THAT CLOSET ...
...AND TAKE THEM TO THE ROOM AT THE TOP OF THE STAIRS...
CEREBUS NEEDS A CANDLE AND HOLDER, A SLATE, A BOX OF CHALK, A PEN, INK SOME NOTEPAPER
TWO FRESH DIAMONDBACK DECKS ...
A CROSSBOW
CEREBUS ALSO HAS A BANK DRAUGHT FOR EIGHT HUNDRED CROWNS THAT HE NEEDS FENCED ...
YOU SHOULD GET FOUR HUNDRED -- IT'S CURRENT AND CLEAN.
KEEP FIFTY FOR A WEEK'S RENT, FOOD AND ALE, GIVE ME THE REMAINDER IN SINGLE NOTES ...
POST A MAN ACROSS FROM THE REGENCY
CEREBUS IS TO BE NOTIFIED AS SOON AS THEY FLY A RED FLAG OVER THE FRONT DOOR
ONE MORE THING ...
IF YOU TELL ANYONE CEREBUS IS HERE, HE WILL CUT YOUR HEART OUT
JUST FINE THANKS
HOW ABOUT YOURSELF?
YOU'RE NOT THINKING OF FLEECING THOSE ONLIU CHAPS, ARE YOU?
THEY'RE NOT KNOWN FOR THEIR WEALTH...
THE IDEA ISN'T TO MAKE MONEY
CEREBUS JUST NEEDS SOMETHING TO DO ...
... WHILE HE WAITS FOR THAT RED FLAG.

to the attention of secretary of the treasury (city-state of IEST) ~ Place twelve thousand crowns in negotiable draughts on the central bank of Smina in a small boat; cover it with a red blanket and float it west on the river. Do not attempt to follow the boat or Cerebus' head will be sent to Lord Julius by special courier ...
SKRATCHA SKRITCHIE SKRITCH SKRIK
WUDDA YUH FIGGER'S GOIN' ON, DIRTY FLEAGLE?
NEAR AS AH KIN FIGGER, IN IEST TH KIDNAP-EE GOES TUH JAIL WITH THE KIDNAP-ERS
Fly a red flag over the front door of the Regency when the boat is released ....
the EYE in the PYRAMID
SKRITCH SKRITCH SKRITCH SK
EITHER THAT OR HE'S A SPECIAL GUARD
OR THE WARDEN MEBBE ...
SHORE WISH HE'D TELL US IF'N IT'S OKAY FER US TA MOVE
AHM GITTIN' A CRICK IN M'BACK ...

DIRTY FLEAGLE! DID YUH SEE THET? THE VARMINT JEST ...
QUIET, IDJIT -- HE'S A-WAITIN' OUTSIDE THE WINDUH -- LISNIN' TO WHUT WE SAY ...
HE IS? WHAR?
THAR!
WHAR THAR?

IT WOULDN'T BE AN EASY SHOT...
ALTHOUGH THIS WAS THE CLOSEST BUILDING TO THE REGENCY...
...THERE WAS STILL ALMOST A HUNDRED YARDS BETWEEN THE EARTH-PIG AND HIS TARGET...

FORTUNATELY, CEREBUS CONSIDERED HIMSELF ONE OF THE TOP THREE CROSS-BOWMAN IN ESTARCION...*
...AND THE DESK CLERK'S WINDOW WAS WELL-LIT AND STATIONARY...

*HE WAS ACTUALLY NUMBER SIX, BUT NO ONE HAD THE NERVE TO TELL HIM TO HIS FACE— Dave

THAR THAR?
NO NO-- OVER YONDER!
YONDER WHAR?
YONDER THAR!
CEREBUS DIDN'T TAKE YOU PRISONER
HE IS CUTTING HIMSELF IN FOR A SHARE OF YOUR LITTLE SCHEME...
CEREBUS JUST DELIVERED HIS OWN RANSOM NOTE. IN A COUPLE OF DAYS, THE RANSOM WILL BE FLOATING WEST ON THE RIVER IN A BOAT COVERED BY A RED BLANKET...
OH YEAH?
HOW BIG A SLICE ARE YUH CUTTIN' YERSELF IN FER?
HUNH?
NOT TOO BIG
YOU'LL MAKE A HUNDRED CROWNS EACH DOING IT CEREBUS' WAY

A HUNNERT EACH, UNH? WHUDD'RE WE SPOSEDA DO IN TH' MEANYWAL...?
CEREBUS THOUGHT WE COULD PLAY SOME CARDS...
WE AIN'T GOT NO MONEY!
THAT'S OKAY. CEREBUS WILL KEEP TRACK OF YOUR BETS ON THIS SLATE...
WE'LL DEDUCT YOUR LOSSES FROM YOUR SHARE OF THE RANSOM
CEREBUS WILL USE CASH!
WHY THAT'S RAGHT DECENT UV YUH, CRITTER
HEH HEH SUM CRITTERS IS SOO STOOPID
WHUD'LL WE PLAY?
OH I DON'T KNOW...
DIAMONDBACK?
DIAMONDBACK?!?
WAHOO!
AH LOOOVE DIAMONDBACK! DEAL THE CARDS!
YEAH!
DEAL THE CARDS
DEAL THE CARDS, VARMINT!

WHILE CEREBUS IS SHUFFLING At the time that I did the "Diamondback" story in ***Swords of Cerebus*** #1, it was my intention to provide only the barest details of the game as I imagined it; enough to keep the casual reader from feeling completely lost in the proceedings. There are a lot of you out there (judging by the mail) who are not satisfied with the barest details. Sometime in the future, we will be producing a diamondback deck that will contain rules for most of the major variations. For the moment, here is an outline of some of the more basic rules in the Onliu variation;

Match Diamondback

KARET, the variation described in Swords #1 was essentially a lower middle class variation popular in Lower Felda, lest and other major population centres. The act of ***doubling*** the initial wager was, in fact, a peculiarity of the emerging urban centres, reflecting the concentration of currency in the densely-populated capitals of the southern city states. The more money available in a city, the more frenzied the betting in its lower and upper-middle class taverns.

MATCH DIAMONDBACK, on the other hand, was the game of preference among the stingy military personnel of Onliu, and was much tamer when compared with its metropolitan cousin. Onliu soldiers were paid by the government a wage of twenty copper bits a month, out of which they were required to "kick-back" a [illegible] percentage for food, lodgings and other necessities. As a consequence, the Onliu soldier might have only three bits left for betting after his expenses were paid. Match diamondback was usually played with representative chips of varying denominations and it was not unusual for several hundred chips to be bet in a marathon game over several days for the sake of two or three copper bits that they represented.

THE DECK consists of 1 magician, 2 priestesses, 3 queens, 4 kings and 5 priests. For three players, the deck consists of 1 magician, 4 priestesses, 6 queens, 8 kings and 10 priests (two decks minus one magician). For four players, the deck consists of 1 magician, 6 priestesses, 9 queens, 12 kings and 15 priests (three decks minus two magicians).

THE HANDS magician-priestess 70 pts.; priestess-priestess 65 pts.; magician-queen 60 pts.; magician-king 55 pts.; priestess-king 50 pts.; priestess-queen 45 pts.; priestess-priest 40 pts.; queen-king 35 pts.; magician-priest 30 pts.; queen-queen 25 pts.; king-king 20 pts.; queen-priest 15 pts.; king-priest 10 pts.; priest-priest 5 pts.

THE GAME begins with a draw for high card. Winner deals the first hand, two cards face down to each player. Each placer examines his cards and the dealer makes a wager which must be matched by each of the other players (there is traditionally no ante in Match Diamondback. A player who folds on each hand can play all night and not lose a single coin). Each player then exposes one of his cards and the dealer initiates a new round of betting, each player choosing whether to match the dealer's wager or fold. Winning hand takes the pot. In the case of a tie between two players' hands, the pot is continued over into the next hand. If there are three players in the game and two are tied on a hand, the pot is split between the two players. If all three are tied, the pot is carried over into the next hand. If there are four players in a game and two players' hands are tied in points, the pot is split between the two tied players. If three or four players are tied in points, the pot is carried over into the next hand.

THE MOST UNIQUE FEATURE of Match Diamondback is the rule that the game must continue until a majority of the players involved agree to end it. (In a two-man game, both would have to agree, in a three-man game two would have to agree and in a four-man game, three would have to agree.) Very often another soldier would be asked to hold the contested coins in trust until a game was decided. "Coin-men" were responsible for organizing the closest approximation of a banking system ever to evolve in Onliu's loosely-knit military society, lending coins held in trust, fencing loot from military raids into neighboring countries, etc. It was not unusual for a game to drag on over several months, since a player leaving the game before a consensus was reached forfeited his winnings.

DAY ONE

CEREBUS HELD HOSTAGE

AH FOLD ...
BUNCHADAM CHEATERS RAZZA FRAZZIN
LOOKS LIKE IT'S JUST YOU AND ME, DIRTY FLEAGLE ...
THE BET'S A CROWN. MATCH OR FOLD!
DIRTY FLEAGLE?
AH CAIN'T THINK THAT FAST!
IT MAKES MUH HAID HURT!
LOOK; CEREBUS HAS A KING EXPOSED. THE BEST HE COULD HAVE IS FIFTY-FIVE POINTS
YOUR PRIESTESS MEANS YOU HAVE AT LEAST FORTY POINTS
ALL RIGHT! AH MATCH YER BET!
AN' YUH BETTER NOT O' BIN SWEET TALKIN' ME!
NERVES OF STEEL, THESE ONLIU.
QUEEN.
HAH!
NO GOOD LOWDOWN RAZNFN
THAT MEANS YOU GET A SHARE FROM DIRTY DREW
AND TWO CROWN NOTES FROM CEREBUS ...
GIMME THOSE!
SNATCH
AH WON! YAHOO! --A WHOLE TWO CROWNIES!
AH'M RICH! RICH! RICH!!!

DAY TWO

DAY TWO-- BY NOW ALL OF THE IESTAN BUSINESS COMMUNITY HAD BEEN NOTIFIED OF CEREBUS' ABDUCTION. UNLESS CEREBUS WAS MISTAKEN, THE BUSINESSMEN WERE INSISTING THAT THE GOVERNMENT PAY THE FULL RANSOM SINCE IT WAS GOVERNMENT SECURITY FORCES THAT HAD LOST TRACK OF THE EARTH-PIG. IF THE PRIME MINISTER DIDN'T HAVE THE BUSINESSMEN EXECUTED FOR TREASON, NEGOTIATIONS WOULD PROBABLY GO ON FOR SEVERAL HOURS.

DAY THREE

BY NOW, THE PRIME MINISTER WOULD BE GOING THROUGH THE CHARADE OF CONVENING A MEETING WITH HIS CABINET, OSTENSIBLY TO DISCUSS WHETHER OR NOT TO PAY THE RANSOM. IN ACTUALITY, HE WOULD BE SIZING UP HIS MINISTERS... TRYING TO FIND ONE WHO OWED HIM ENOUGH FAVOURS TO HIDE A TWELVE THOUSAND CROWN RANSOM IN HIS MINISTRY'S QUARTERLY STATEMENT OF EXPENSES TO THE SACRED CHURCH'S GOVERNMENT ACCOUNTING OFFICE. ONCE THE UNFORTUNATE LACKEY HAD BEEN SELECTED THE RANSOM WOULD BE PAID QUICKLY--NO ONE IN THE IESTAN GOVERNMENT RELISHED THE IDEA OF CEREBUS' HEAD BEING SENT TO LORD JULIUS (AT LEAST UNTIL CERTAIN TRADE AGREEMENTS HAD BEEN SIGNED).

DAY FOUR

***RIGHT HON. THE MINISTER OF EXPORT DEVELOPMENT*:** IF IT PLEASE YOUR REVERENCE, THE SPECIAL STUDY GROUP ON LONG-TERM GROWTH IN THE PRIVATE SECTOR HAS DELIVERED ITS QUARTERLY BUDGET YESTERDAY AND WE HAVE DETERMINED, THROUGH A CLOSE EXAMINATION OF THEIR EXPENSES INCURRED, THAT THERE IS A CONSIDERABLE ERROR IN THEIR CALCULATIONS OF INCOME VERSUS EXPENDITURES. WE REGRET TO INFORM THE HOUSE THAT THIS AMOUNT IS IN EXCESS OF TWELVE THOUSAND CROWNS.
***SOME HON. MEMBERS*:** OH! OH!
***HIS REVERENCE*:** ORDER, PLEASE.
***RIGHT HON. THE MINISTER OF EXPORT DEVELOPMENT*:** AN ORDER IN COUNCIL SIGNED BY THE PRIME MINISTER THIS MORNING AUTHORIZES THE EXECUTION OF THE CHAIRMAN AND ALL CIVILIAN MEMBERS OF THE STUDY GROUP, EXCEPTING, OF COURSE, THOSE MEMBERS OF THE STUDY GROUP UNDER THE PERSONAL PROTECTION OF HIS HOLINESS.
***SOME HON. MEMBERS*:** HEAR! HEAR!

HIS HOLINESS' PARLIAMENT OF IEST (excerpt of transcripts)

DAY FIVE

CEREBUS HELD HOSTAGE

HAH! AH'M STILL AHEAD BY ....uh
TWENNY CROWNSH.
HIC
AH'LL MATCH YER BET
AN' ALSO DISOWN YUH!
MAGICIAN AN'A QUEENIE!
HIC
TOP THAT, YUH FLEA-BITTEN IDJIT!
TWO PRIESTESSES!
HAH!
WHAR'S YER SMART TALK NOW, HUNH?
BEAT YER CRUDDY QUEEN DIDN'T AH?!
WHUTSA MATTER?
YUH GONNA CRY? HUNH? YUH GONNA...
HIC
WHY DON'T YOU JUST GIVE ME ALL OF YOUR MONEY AND I'LL REFUND WHAT'S LEFT...?
YER A SORE LOSER, DIRTY FLEAGLE

DAY SIX

BY NOW, WITH THE EXCEPTION OF SIGNING THE PROPER FORMS TRANSFERRING TWELVE THOUSAND CROWNS FROM THE VAULTS BENEATH THE IEST TREASURY BUILDING TO THE PRIME MINISTER'S SECRET ACCOUNT IN THE IEST OFFICE OF THE CENTRAL BANK OF SMINA, BURNING THE BUILDING HOUSING THOSE FORMS TO THE GROUND, AND HAVING THE LEADER OF THE OPPOSITION ARRESTED FOR ARSON AND EXECUTED FOR TREASON, ALL WAS IN READINESS...

DAY SEVEN

SHORTLY BEFORE NOON

SOMETIME AFTER DUSK

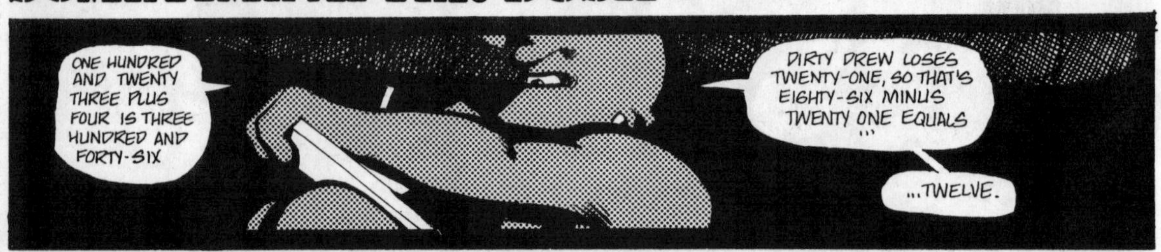

SUDDENLY, THAT EVENING

MOMENTS LATER

IN THE NEXT INSTANT

JUST THEN

HE'D NEED TWO HORSES. IF THERE WAS NO TROUBLE PICKING UP THE RANSOM, HE WOULD PAY OFF DIRTY FLEAGLE WITH A COUPLE OF HUNDRED CROWNS AND BE ON HIS WAY...

IF SOMETHING WENT WRONG AND SECURITY OR MERCENARY GUARDS WERE WAITING FOR THEM, HE'D TURN FLEAGLE IN FOR KIDNAPPING...

BEFORE CEREBUS CAN TURN

DIRTY DREW AN' AH WILL TELL 'EM WHAR TUH FIND YUH...
AN' PICK UP OUR RANSOM OURSELFS ...
NO HARD FEELIN'S AH HOPE...
Y'LONG EAR'D GALOOT

CONTINUED

Well, well, well. Good morrow to you.

Po.

So Cerebus is back in the Seventh Sphere.

Eighth, ***actually.***

Eighth, eh? How do you get to the Eighth Sphere?

Well, I got here by meditating for seventy-two years until I got the hang of it. I haven't got a clue as to how you managed it.

How long is Cerebus going to keep falling like this?

That's entirely up to you.

It is?

It's a matter of will power. Concentrate on slowing your breathing and pulse rate. Everything around you in the Eighth Sphere is a creation of your own mind.

Really.

Getting control of it is not really as difficult as it appears on the surface. The Adepts who have the most trouble tend to be those with only just a nodding acquaintance with their conscious mind.

Cerebus seems to be slowing down a little.

Your mind is apt to produce a number of pretty unusual environments. Just keep reminding yourself that it isn't real.

*Cerebus hopes you don't mind if he lumps **you** in with that theory.*

Excuse me?

If you met Cerebus in a tavern some place and Cerebus started telling you that the funniest thing has been happening lately. Cerebus has been hearing the voice of Suenteus Po in his head. Dead? Not a bit of it. He hangs around this strange grey and black place called the Seventh Spere. He's one hundred and eighty two years old, don't you know?

Ah.

Cerebus once saw an old woman who heard voices in her head. She used to sit outside the Ram and Peacock chewing on the hem of her dress and selling portraits of passersby she used to paint with her spittle.

I see.

No offense, But Cerebus figures its better all around if he keeps on thinking of this as a singularly dull dream.

Not at all. You don't mind if I continue to believe I exist?

*What **you** do with the voices in **your** head is **your** problem. Actually, Cerebus has a question about this .... dream.*

Yes?

Cerebus has been to this ... dreamworld on two different occasions now. Against his will.

Mm.

When you come here, Cerebus assumes that you do so on purpose.

Correct. What is your point?

*Cerebus can think of a dozen vacation spots that, if nothing else, are at least better **lit**.*

Well, you have to understand, to an Illusionist, the Seventh Sphere is, first, a retreat from the modern world -- a way of removing oneself from day-to-day living.

Escapism?

Hardly. We're engaged in finding the essence of life and living. Through meditation and the ingesting of certain illicit substances, we are seeking after Truth, Reality and Essence.

How exciting for you.

The Seventh Sphere is, second of all, a means of slowing the adept's bodily functions to such a degree that he needs only the smallest amounts of food and water to survive. His need for the material world in all its forms fades as he continues to meditate.

Must make Illusionism the belief of choice for tightwads.

I've never heard it expressed quite that way, but I suppose you could say that.

Cerebus still hasn't really gotten an answer to his question; what's so special about lots of black with strange grey scenery.

It would be easier to describe if you had some background in the sorcerous arts -- alchemy, levitation ....

Cerebus has studied.

Hmm. We're full of surprises, aren't we? With whom did you study?

Magus Doran.

Ah. For how long?

Three years.

How did you fare?

Cerebus ran the gauntlet of energy globes in Imesh. Twice.

Do you remember first and second meditation?

Aye.

**Well, you can look on the Eighth Sphere as an inten-
sive second meditation. The "strange, grey scenery" as you call it is a manifestation of your mental .... clutter? The first step toward eliminating this clutter is to ....**

.... focus on the black.

Good. Good. How long have you been away from your studies?

Ten years. Maybe more.

You'll need my help, then. I think you'll understand this sphere a little better with a practical demonstration of its nature.

Okay.

The Seventh Sphere is where one seeks his own equilibrium. Once attained, the world is seen as a cross-roads of an infinite number of paths. The Eighth Sphere is a specific path revealed at a more complex level.

Complex structurally or manifest?

That depends on the inividual. How are you doing with your clutter?

There isn't much grey scenery anymore. Cerebus is a little rusty at this, though.

Do you feel any motion?

It is like Cerebus is half-walking and half-sliding. Like trying to climb down an embankment of mud.

Let yourself sink, as if you're in a deep well. Your mind will seek its own level.

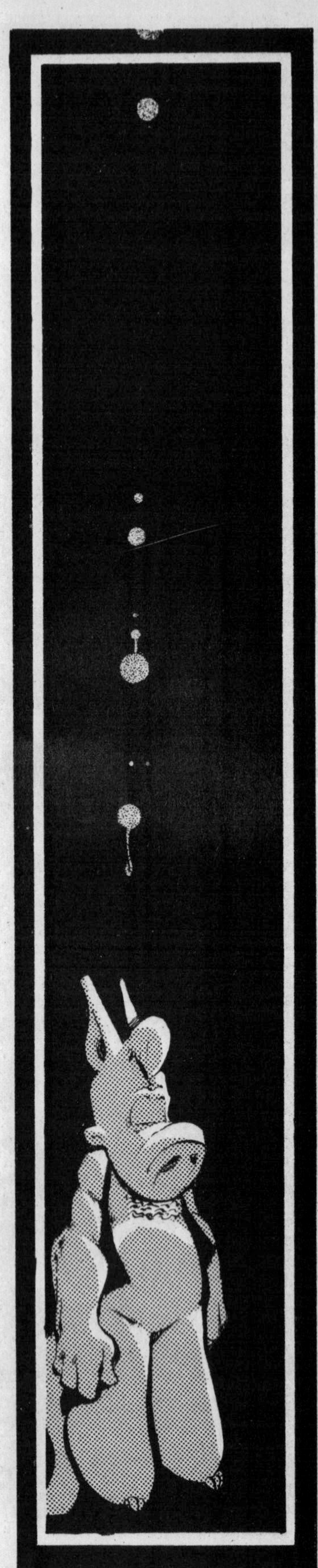

Very good. Very good.
Relax your muscles.

Breathe in.

Breathe out.

Let the weight of your arms pull you down and the buoyancy of your spirit pull you up.

The Eighth Sphere will lead you to the answers you seek if you just ....

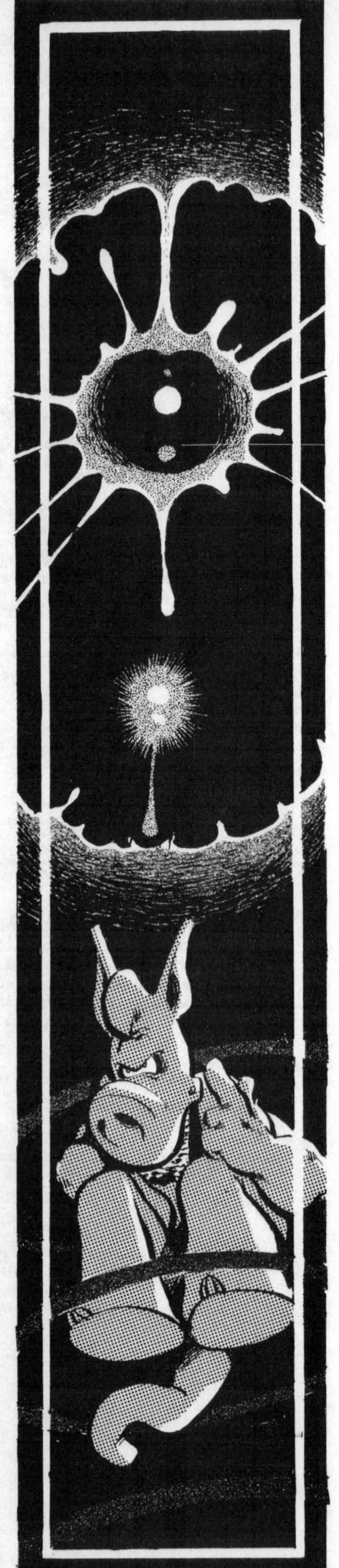

What Cerebus would like to know is how he got from Togith to Beduin the last time he visited this little resort.

****sigh* Can't you just meditate about it?***

Cerebus would rather ask you.

One minute you were talking to me in the Seventh Sphere and the next -- PFFFT -- You were gone. What else can I tell you?

Well, Cerebus was gone for almost a fortnight. He was drugged in Togith shortly before Concordance Eve and he woke up in Beduin several weeks later.

The Cirinists probably ....

*The Cirinists **had** Cerebus. Why would they make a fuss about building him a temple and then dump him in Lower Felda?*

You're asking** me **to explain the Cirinists?

Who knows why the Cirinists do *anything?* **They're fanatics for Set's sake!**

But that still doesn't....

Or it could have been the Kevillists possibly.

The Kevillists.

A rebellious faction that's only recently come to light in Upper Felda -- in Cirin's own government.

Aye?

A fanatic's fanatics. They believe in the death penalty for wearing clothing that isn't grey or brown.

Why would they be interested in Cerebus?

To keep the Cirinists from getting you .... to discredit Wenda .... Hell, maybe they just like grey fur, I don't know. Can't handle second meditation, mm?

Cerebus has a few things he wants to talk about.

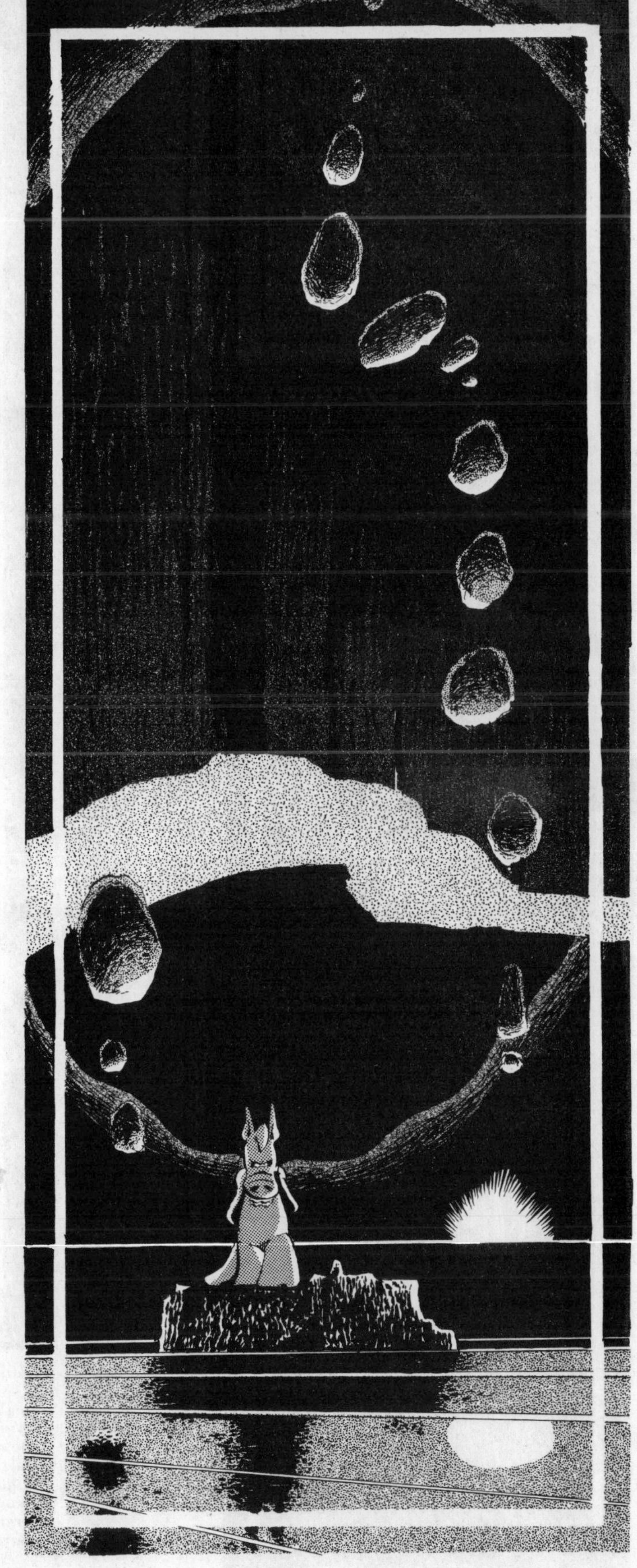

How's your mental clutter, by the way.

Cerebus can live with it.

I was afraid you were going to say that.

Cirinists, Kevillists, Illusionists. Without putting too fine a point on it, Cerebus can't figure out why you keep on trying to buck the system. Whatever small victories you might have from time to time, it's the Orthodox Tarimites who run the show, isn't it?.

That's not as true as it was in the past. The Church of Tarim feels it has solid grass-roots support and a general sense of unity prevails in Iest and Serrea to all outward appearances. The rift between the two Churches is quite permanent, however, by this point. Either pontiff could quite contentedly watch his conterpart sink screaming into the midst of a domestic revolution or foreign invasion. Would delight in fact, to an almost impious degree, in not lifting a papal finger.

Cirin has supported rebellions in Dehrsion, Eshnosopur and Enothas. She's supplying arms and equipment to the Borealan rebels in the Blood Wars and she has solid treaties with the neighbouring Feldwar States. Effectively surrounded on all sides by Cirinists and Cirinist allies, The Sepran Church will be facing a rapid demise over the next few decades. The Church and the Empire haven't enough legions between them to fight on all their borders simultaneously.

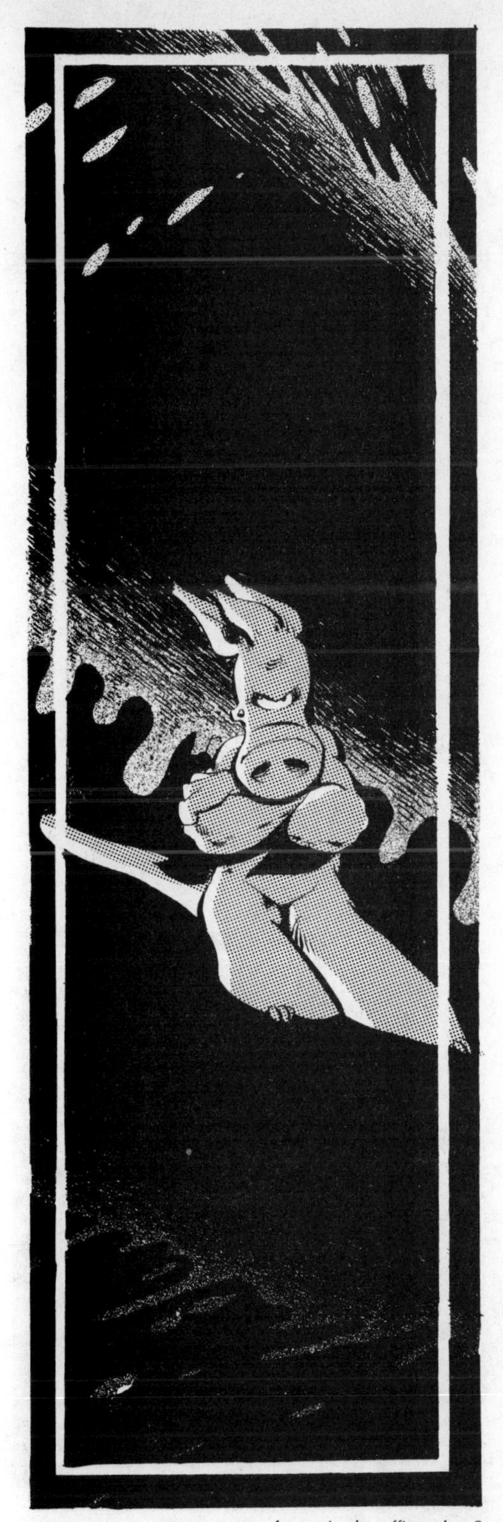

A war in the offing, then?

Hardly necessary. A prolonged war would drive down the value of the Sepran crown and Cirin would have a depressed economy to handle when she finally crushed the Empire. Her goal is containment of the Seprans on their present holdings while her Priestesses infiltrate the civilian population, re-instating the old Corn-King rituals. There's already a two-to-one ratio of Cirinist Priestesses to Tarimite Priests within the Sepran Empire's border territory.

What about your own little group?

The illusionists? We're not really a major force of any kind. More of a discipline, as I told you, for exchanging information.

Sort of a psychic social club.

I'm not sure I like your tone.

You don't have to sound so offended. Cerebus just finds it a little hard to believe that you carry around all these complex analyses of Estarcion politics just so you can chit-chat about it with your friends.

Naturally, we are interested in the ongoing state of our environment. But it is against our teachings to assume too extroverted a role. in our view, each individual needs to cast himself adrift from his surroundings. Or, to put it another way, interference in the process of self-illumination tends to pollute the essence of the process.

You haven't got the tiniest foothold anywhere --? There are no illusionists in the great councils of the governed world?

Followers of our disciplines have a great range of occupations. We don't find earning a living to be mutually exclusive of following Illusionist theory.

And if an Illusionist happened to be -- say -- secretary of the treasury for a large country -- if he decided, with no influence from you, to siphon off a few copper bits for the Illusionist coffers -- that would be **his** *business, no?*

There's no evidence that that has ever happened.

There's no "evidence" that Lord Julius is robbing his people blind, either, but I don't think either of us would be willing to give him the benefit of the doubt.

You have a keen mind, my friend.

Skip the flattery, Cerebus would rather have a straight answer.

What was the question? I must have missed it.

Cerebus wants to know if you really expect him to believe that Illusionists don't have influence with a number of Estarcion political leaders.

Oh. That question.

All right, let's suppose that the Illusionists are not what I say they are.

Mm.

What reason would I have for lying to you?

*Cerebus wouldn't know, but that wouldn't alter the fact that you **were** lying.*

Let me put it differently; what makes you** suspect **I'm lying.

Your view of the Cirinists for one.

View? What view? You can ask anyone with more than a passing interest in them -- they're dangerous.

The last time we talked, you were surprised when Cerebus told you the Cirinists had plans -- and even more surprised when he told you they were dangerous. Your exact words were "I thought their only goal was to wipe out fun in our lifetime."

Well, uh, see ....

Skip it. Cerebus doesn't really expect you to start telling the truth just because you were caught in one contradiction.

Well, actually ....

*Cerebus **would** like to know why you're pumping him for information, though.*

What? Pumping you for ....

You don't have to fall back on Gosh-wow surprise every time Cerebus asks you a pointed question.

All I'm doing is ....

.... playing stupid. But that's quite all right. Cerebus would just like to know how he got to be so important.

You were the Kitchen Staff Supervisor in Palnu. Is that what you mean by important?

That was just a job.

"Just a job"? That's like calling the Wyndmel Diamond "just a rock".

What is that supposed to mean?

You show up in Palnu, you get placed in the top cabinet position in the wealthiest city in Estarcion, you're given the run of the place, daily conferences with Lord Julius .... behind closed doors and off-the-record, I might add .... finally ending up in Iest as Ranking Diplomatic Representative of Palnu and you call that just a job?

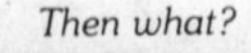

Then what, what?

What happened after Cerebus arrived in Iest?

Well, I'm sure I don't know.

That's funny, you seem to know every move Cerebus made before that.

Well, I only hear things after they're old news.

Mm.

You must have arrived in the last while.

Mm.

So, how's it going?

Fine.

I mean, Iest. It's a beautiful city, isn't it?

Walls, streets, buildings. It's definitely a city.

Find a nice place to stay?

A bed and a roof. You can't do better than that.

So.

So.

Is there some reason you don't want to talk about Iest?

Is there some reason you ***do?***

I'M JUST TRYING TO BE FRIENDLY, FOR SET'S SAKE!! HOW'S IT GOING?!!

Fine.

GOOD!! GREAT!!

*Come to that, what are **you** doing in Iest?*

Me? I don't remember saying that I ....

Having a good time?

Look, who said I was in ....?

No one. But you are, aren't you?

SO WHAT! IS THERE A LAW AGAINST IT?

No. Having a good time?

I DON'T KNOW WHAT YOU MEAN BY THAT!!!

Find a nice place to stay?

WHAT ARE YOU IMPLYING? WHAT? WHAT?

Mm. All of this only exists in Cerebus' mind.

ARE YOU ALRIGHT?

It's okay. Cerebus just forgot who was in charge here for a minute.

CEREBUS!!

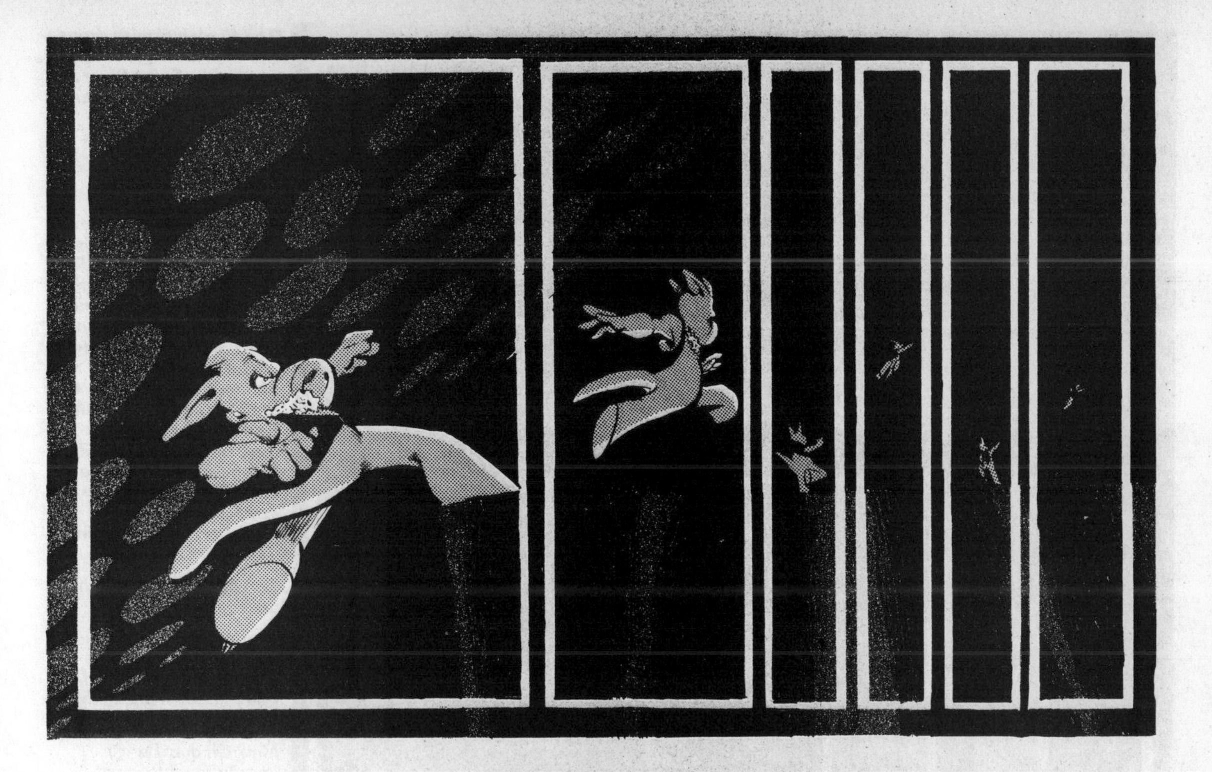

I STILL WANT TO KNOW WHAT YOU'RE IMPLYING! WHAT DID YOU MEAN BY "FIND A NICE PLACE TO STAY?"?!

The Regency Hotel.

I'VE-NEVER-SET-FOOT-IN-THE-REGENCY-HOTEL-IN-MY-ENTIRE ....

No. No. The Regency is where Cerebus is staying. You asked Cerebus where he was staying in Iest, remember?

AHA!

Aha, what?

AHA, NOTHING! IT'S A NICE PLACE, ISN'T IT?

How would you know?

I'VE HEARD .... ahem .... I've heard about it from many people. They all say it's a nice place.

Then there's the Pigts.

The Pigts? What about the Pigts? There are Pigts at the Regency?

You were asking Cerebus why he thought he was important. The Pigts had a statue that looked like Cerebus.

Statues? Who cares about statues. The Pigts are dying out. They used to be the best around at one time. At one time.

Cerebus heard. The Redeemer Dynasty. The Eastern Monoliths. The Black Tower Empire. Impressive.

That isn't the half of it. There was a time when every inch of the Red Marches was criss-crossed by the best roads in Estarcion. Cities that would rival Iest.

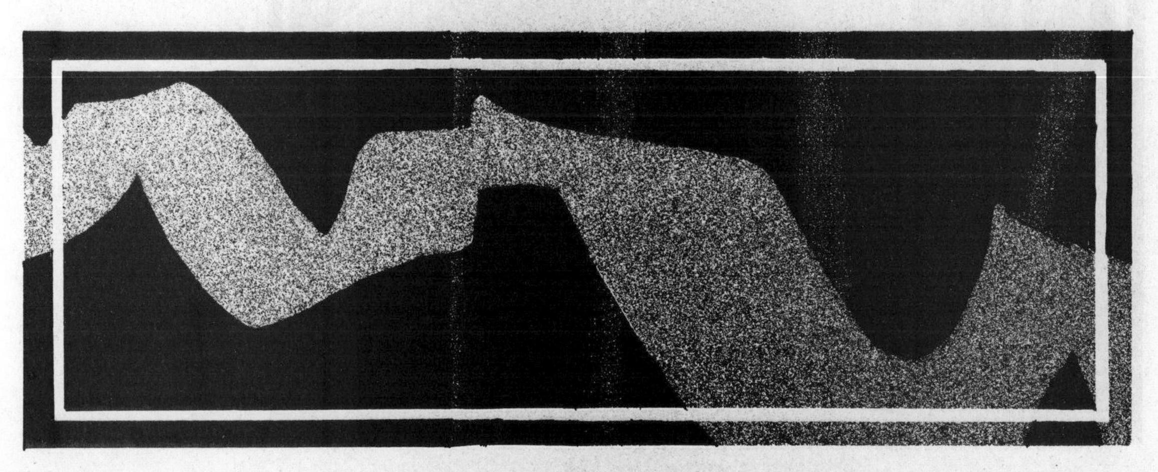

The Pigtish armies drove the Sepran Legions back across the Sofim River on dozens of occasions and I never saw one once wearing armour.

They're pretty well set, aren't they?

Oh, no. This was a long time ago. It was the Pigts who caused the Mystic Cataclysm that brought the Black Tower empire to an end and wiped out most of the known magic in the world. It was almost a century before a plant would grow in the Red Marches. To this day, the only Pigts still living on the Marches are bands of nomads, gradually losing their lands to the Conniptin Tribes.

Cerebus saw some of their underground city.

You mean the burrows? Yes. Yes. Damn Pigts burrow like gophers. Did you fall down one of their holes or something?

Mm? Oh aye. Barely enough room to stand.

And they had a statue that looked like you?

Aye, it was about a foot high. Cerebus gave one of the Pigts a copper piece and took it.

Well. It's a bit curious in its own way, but I don't know that I would say it was a sign of your importance.

Cerebus doesn't have anything against ambition.

Perhaps you're right.
Perhaps Cerebus isn't as important as he thinks he is.

The thought had crossed my mind.

Cerebus has a lot of trouble trying to figure out ***what*** *to believe, sometimes.*

What ***do you believe?***

Cerebus believes it is easier to see during the day than it is at night.

And not much else besides?

And not much else besides.

There are other things to believe in, you know.

That's what Cerebus has been thinking about. Maybe it's time to throw in his lot with some group.

Maybe it's a good time for Cerebus to find a course and stick to it. Maybe it's time for Cerebus to take stock of himself, set a few long-range and short-range goals. Cerebus thinks about that quite a bit lately.

So why have't you done it?

Because Cerebus also thinks this is a good time to get drunk every day and look for comfortable gutters to lie in.

As long as it doesn't interfere with Cerebus' drinking.

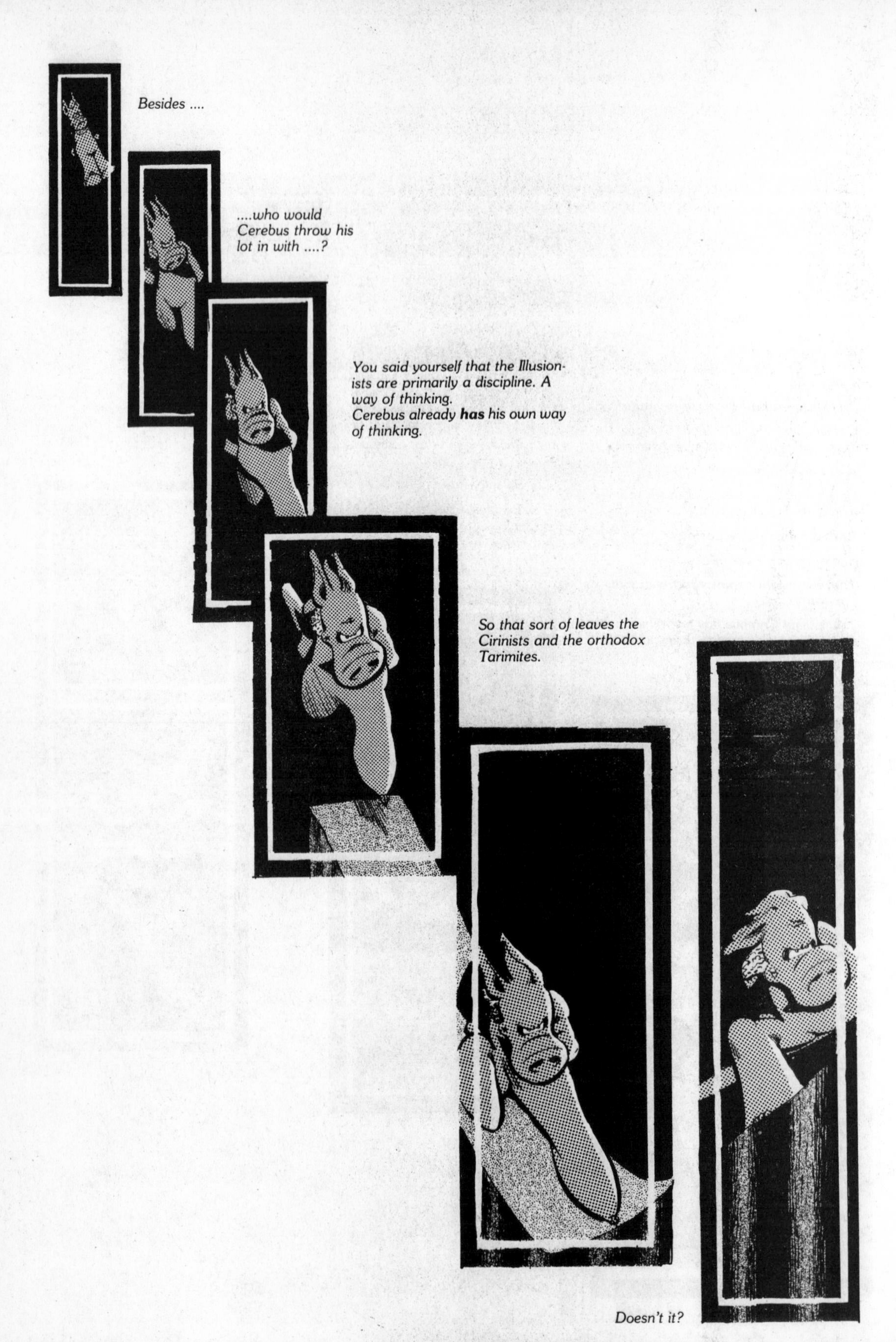
Besides ....
....who would Cerebus throw his lot in with ....?
You said yourself that the Illusionists are primarily a discipline. A way of thinking.
Cerebus already **has** his own way of thinking.
So that sort of leaves the Cirinists and the orthodox Tarimites.
Doesn't it?

Forgive me, but I have great difficulty picturing you as an orthodox Tarimite. Or a Cirinist for that matter.

You said yourself that times are changing. Last year, Cerebus played Diamondback with Leopold, the famous Gambling Priest. Ten years ago, he would have been burned at the stake for carrying a deck of cards. How many of Tarim's priests do you suppose have a few bottles of Borealan whiskey tucked away behind their holy books?

Perce is an inner circle Cirinist Priestess and also a prostitute. Exceeding the proscribed boundaries seems to have become a continent-wide phenomenon.

Who knows what advances would be made if Cerebus was around to assist in the decision-making; advocating his own variations on doctrine and discipline. Inside of five years, getting drunk and lying in the gutter could be sanctioned by the Church as an official means of worship.

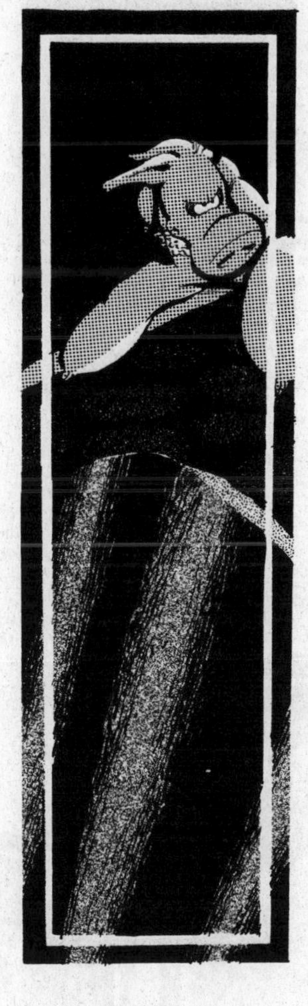

You're free to do what you want, of course, but I feel I should warn you. The flexibility you see in the Church of Tarim is a peculiarity of the Eastern Orthodoxy. So long as you never stray west of the Osiris River, you'll probably be reasonably safe.

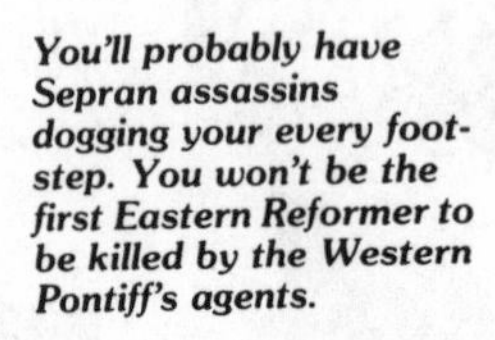

You'll probably have Sepran assassins dogging your every foot-step. You won't be the first Eastern Reformer to be killed by the Western Pontiff's agents.

The Cirinists are definitely more flexible, but they have also become more ruthless and brutal as their power and influence has grown. Cirin has purged her inner circle three times since seizing power in Upper Felda.

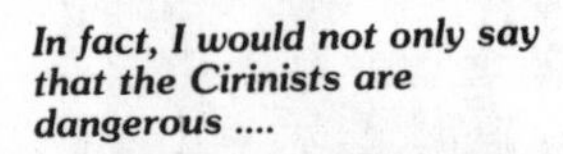

Po?

Let me finish.
As a matter of fact, I would not only say that the Cirinists are dangerous; even more than that, they are unstable. I mean, of course, that instability is the more lethal of the two traits. An Onliu soldier is dangerous, but he is at least consistent. He's a blood-thirsty, half-witted, foul-smelling savage one day and a blood-thirsty, half-witted, foul-smelling savage the next.

uh .... Po?

Let me finish.
The Cirinists. The Cirinists will sell anyone down the river if it will advance their cause. If you throw in with them and they decide you are no longer of use to them, they will snuff out your life like a candle flame. Do you understand?

Po, there's something Cerebus has been thinking of telling you, but he couldn't make up his mind whether he should or not.

Really? What is it?

After Cerebus arrived in Iest ....

Yes? Yes?

And after he met all of the businessmen who gave him money.

Yes .... go on.

Well .... Cerebus was kidnapped.

By the great Set! Who did it? It sounds like a conspiracy afoot!

Do you know who did it? Do you?

Aye. That was the reason Cerebus didn't know whether he should talk. He didn't know if he could .... trust you. Now he knows that you're on his side. Now he can tell you that he was kidnapped by ....

.... by whom? ....
.... Cerebus? ....
.... CEREBUS?! ....

M'Lord?

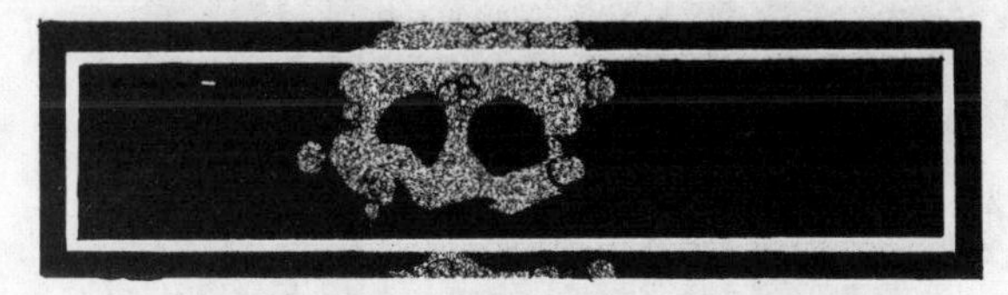

M'Lord, I don't wish to disturb you but I have an urgent message for you from the Prime Minister.

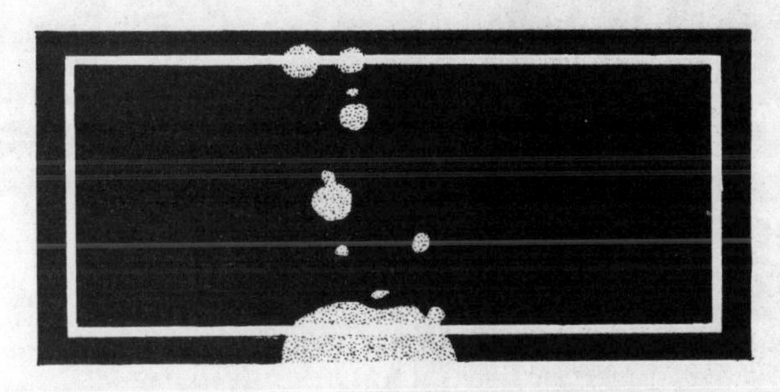

Cerebus isn't going to open his eyes until you tell him where he is.
Why, the Regency Hotel, M'Lord.
This is your room.

CEREBUS JUST WANTED TO BE SURE IT WASN'T A PUBLIC BENCH IN BEDUIN...
WHAT SORT OF URGENT MESSAGE?

REPERCUSSIONS

THE RIGHT HONORABLE PRIME MINISTER WISHES TO EXPRESS HIS SINCERE GOOD WISHES TO PALNU'S RANKING DIPLOMATIC REPRESENTATIVE ON HIS SAFE RETURN FROM SO TORTUROUS AN ORDEAL. THE...
PUT A CORK IN IT FOR A MINUTE, SON..

HEY!
HEY, KID!!
YEAH. YOU.
BRING UP A SIDE OF BEEF AND A BOTTLE OF BOREALAN WHISKEY
AND SOMEONE TO DRAW CEREBUS' BATH.

...THE PRIME MINISTER FURTHER EXPRESSES HIS SINCERE DESIRE TO DISCUSS REIMBURSEMENT OF THE RANSOM PAID ON M'LORD'S BEHALF...
...HE CONCLUDES WITH SINCERE WISHES FOR YOUR SPEEDY RECOVERY
GIVE US A HAND HERE WOULD YOU, SON?

I AM INSTRUCTED TO AWAIT A REPLY ...

OKAY OKAY
...uh...
"THE RANKING DIPLOMATIC REPRESENTATIVE OF PALNU THANKS THE RIGHT HONORABLE PRIME MINISTER FOR USING THE WORD 'SINCERE' THREE TIMES IN ONE LETTER...
"AS A RESULT OF HIS ABDUCTION, CEREBUS FINDS HIMSELF TO BE TEMPORARILY WITHOUT FUNDS..."

"PLEASE REST ASSURED, HOWEVER THAT THE NEXT TIME CEREBUS HAS TWELVE THOUSAND CROWNS HANDY, HE WILL NOT HESITATE TO DO HIS DUTY FOR THE PRIME MINISTER AND IEST..."
"AMEN."
KNOCK KNOCK
IT'S OPEN!

VEDDY SORRY, M'LAWD. I DIDN'T KNOW YOU WERE...
THE MUSTACHE WAS JUST LEAVING...
WEREN'T YOU, MUSTACHE?
em--OF COURSE
QUITE SO.

IF YOU KEEP THE FOOD COVERED WHILE YOU BATHE, IT SHOULD KEEP WARM, M'LAWD ...
AND MAY I SAY, ON BEHALF OF THE HOTEL STAFF, HOW GLAD WE ARE TO HAVE YOU BACK SAFE AND SOUND?

YASS.
WELL.
IF YOU WILL EXCUSE ME, M'LAWD ...

CLICK.
TARIM.

YOU KNOW WHAT I THINK?

I THINK THEY'RE UP TO SOMETHING ...

INNEC STARYM WAS KIDNAPPED ONE HUNDRED AND FIFTY-NINE YEARS AGO FROM THE REGENCY

AND THEY DIDN'T EXPECT *HIM* TO PAY BACK HIS RANSOM.

YOU'RE AN **AARDVARK** AREN'T YOU?

DID YOU KNOW THERE HASN'T BEEN AN *AARDVARK* AROUND HERE FOR EIGHT HUNDRED *YEARS?*

DO YOU KNOW WHAT YOU'RE GOING TO *DO?*
ABOUT THE *MONEY,* I MEAN.

THEY'RE, LIKE, APT TO BE *UPSET*...
IF YOU DON'T PAY THEM...
TWELVE THOUSAND CROWNS IS A LOT OF MONEY

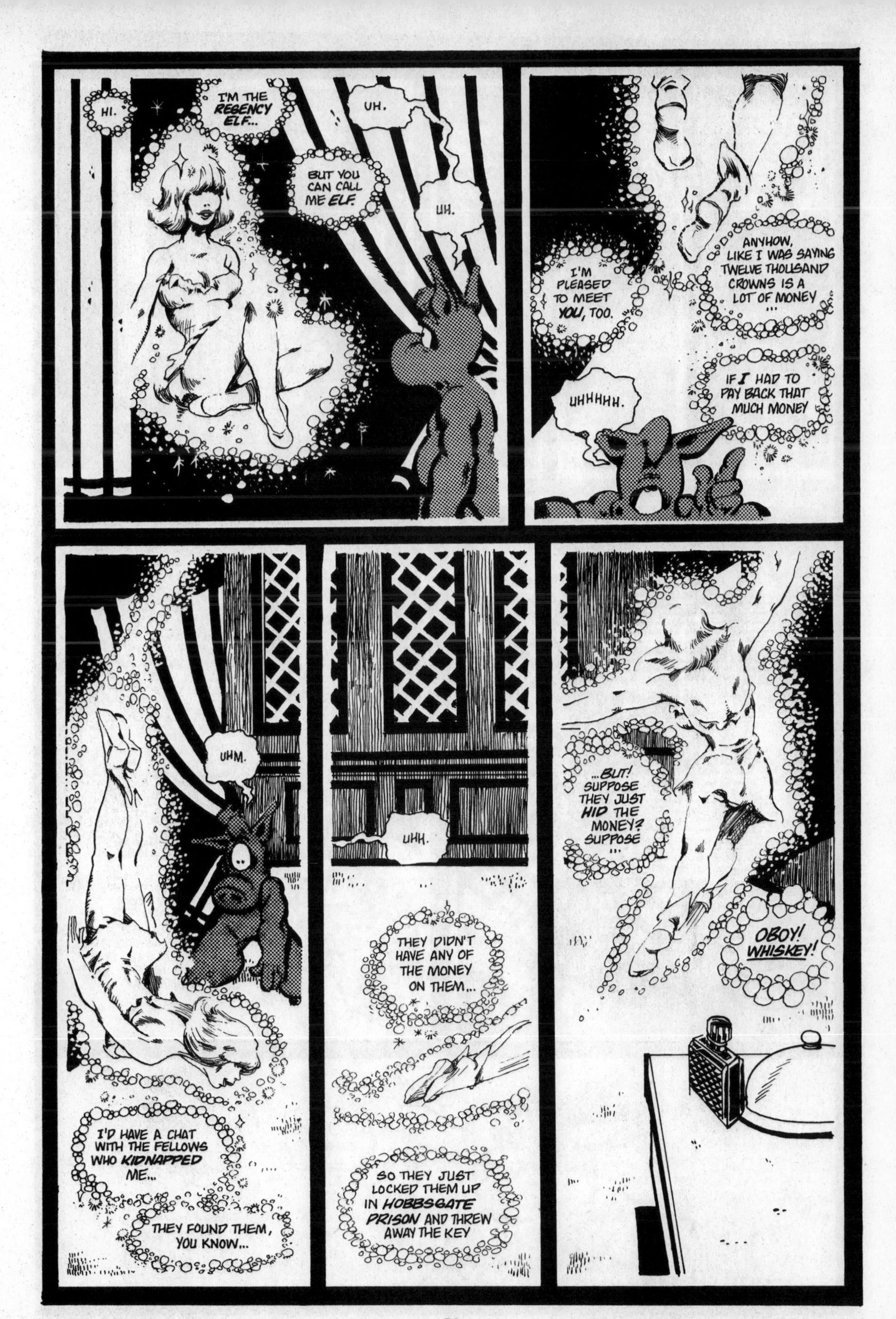

HI.
I'M THE REGENCY ELF...
UH.
BUT YOU CAN CALL ME ELF.
UH.
I'M PLEASED TO MEET YOU, TOO.
ANYHOW, LIKE I WAS SAYING TWELVE THOUSAND CROWNS IS A LOT OF MONEY ...
UHHHHH.
IF I HAD TO PAY BACK THAT MUCH MONEY
UHM.
I'D HAVE A CHAT WITH THE FELLOWS WHO KIDNAPPED ME...
THEY FOUND THEM, YOU KNOW...
UHH.
THEY DIDN'T HAVE ANY OF THE MONEY ON THEM...
SO THEY JUST LOCKED THEM UP IN HOBBSGATE PRISON AND THREW AWAY THE KEY
...BUT! SUPPOSE THEY JUST HID THE MONEY? SUPPOSE ...
OBOY! WHISKEY!

GULP! GULP! GULP!

GULP! GULP! GULP!

LOOK, 'ELF'... CEREBUS ...

CATCH!!
GAH!!

MMMMM.

HOBBSGATE PRISON... THAT'S THE PLACE TO START...
KNOCK KNOCK
IT'S THE ROOM CLERK, M'LORD
ARE YOU FINISHED BATHING?

HEY!
GET IN HERE!
HURRY UP!
LOOK AT THIS!!

YES, M'LORD? WHAT IS IT?!
SHE'S GONE!
SHE?
THE REGENCY ELF!
SHE WAS JUST HERE!
TALKING TO CEREBUS

CEREBUS WALKED OVER, PULLED THOSE DRAPES ASIDE AND THERE SHE WAS!
SHIMMERING! GLOWING!

AND THEN THE MOST AMAZING THING HAPPENED ...

...SHE SWOOPED AROUND THE ROOM LIKE A BIRD!
WOOSH!

"WOOSH" ...
... M'LORD?

AND THEN SHE DRANK ALL OF CEREBUS' WHISKEY!

DON'T LOOK AT CEREBUS THAT WAY...!
SHE'S YOUR ELF!

WILL THERE BE ANYTHING ELSE, M'LORD?

NO.
CEREBUS IS GOING TO BED...
AN EXCELLENT IDEA, M'LORD

CEREBUS HAD BROKEN INTO HOBBSGATE PRISON SOME YEARS BEFORE TO WIN A BET WITH A LOCAL TAVERN OWNER! IESTAN SECURITY FORCES HAD IMPROVED IN RECENT YEARS BUT THE EARTH-PIG WAS SOBER THIS TIME! HE HOPED THE ADVANTAGE WAS STILL HIS...
AS CEREBUS REACHES THE ROOFTOP LEDGE OVERLOOKING THE WEST COURTYARD, HE FREEZES! EVIDENTLY, NEW 'LAW AND ORDER' POLICIES IN IEST EXTEND TO THE CITY PRISONS ONCE GUARDED BY ILL-PAID THUGS AND LOW LEVEL BUREAUCRATS.

A SPECIAL SECURITY GUARD, USUALLY RESERVED FOR DUTY IN THE TURBULENT LOWER CITY. HIS EYES SWEEP THE COURTYARD, ONE HAND RESTING LIGHTLY ON THE HILT OF HIS SWORD...
MORE CAREFULLY NOW, CEREBUS BEGINS HIS DESCENT, PAUSING WHENEVER THE GUARD TURNS IN HIS DIRECTION. FOR THE FIRST TIME, HE WISHES HE HAD THOUGHT TO BRING A WEAPON...
EVEN AS THE GUARD TURNS, CEREBUS BEGINS A SOUNDLESS DASH FOR SHELTER
THE FOOTSTEPS STOP. THE EARTH PIG FLEXES HIS MUSCLES AS THE SOUND APPROACHES AND STOPS ONCE MORE...
A MOMENT LATER, CEREBUS HAS A BETTER IDEA...

TEN-SHUN
FIRST GUARD ELWYN SALICE, SIR!!
WEST COURTYARD DETAIL, SIR!!

I'M CEREBUS THE AARDVARK RANKING DIPLOMATIC REPRESENTATIVE OF THE GREAT CITY-STATE OF PALNU ...
YES, SIR.

YES WHAT?!

YES, M'LORD!
SORRY, M'LORD!

CEREBUS HAS THIS...
...PROBLEM
PERHAPS YOU CAN HELP CEREBUS WITH HIS PROBLEM. THEN CEREBUS CAN HELP YOU WITH YOUR PROBLEM.

CEREBUS WANTS TO SEE THE TWO MEN WHO HAVE BEEN CHARGED WITH HIS KIDNAPPING

OF COURSE THAT WOULD BE AGAINST REGULATIONS...
WOULDN'T IT?
YES, M'LORD!

WHICH BRINGS US TO YOUR PROBLEM ...
IS IT NOT, AFTER ALL, ALSO AGAINST REGULATIONS TO BE UNSHAVEN AT YOUR POST? ...
Y-YES M'LORD!!

THEN WOULD IT NOT BE ENTIRELY TO OUR MUTUAL BENEFIT TO FORGIVE EACH OTHER OUR...
...PROBLEMS?
YES, M'LORD!
IF YOU WILL FOLLOW ME, THEN, M'LORD

HOW MUCH TIME WILL CEREBUS HAVE?
FIVE MINUTES AT THE MOST, M'LORD ...
THAT'S WHEN THEY CHECK THESE CELLS ...
THEY'RE IN THE TORTURE CELL ON THE END...
STAY BACK FROM THE BARS, M'LORD. THEY'VE BEEN STANDING FOR TWO DAYS...
THERE'S NO TELLING HOW DESPERATE THEY MIGHT BE ...
LOOKEE HYAR, DIRTY DREW IT'S CEREBUS THE NO-ACCOUNT SCUMBAG DIRTY-DEALIN' DOUBLE-CROSSIN' SKONK!!
YEAH!
CEREBUS HAS A FEW QUESTIONS AND NOT MUCH ...

QUESTIONS?! WAL, WE AIN'T TALKIN' TUH NO LOW-DOWN ORN'RY POLECAT TH' LIKES UH WHICH YOU ARE, CRITTER!
YEAH! ASK SUMBUDDY ELSE, YUH UPPER CLASS HALF-PINT LONG-EAR'D GALOOT!!
GO TALK TUH YERSELF!!
YEAH!!
SIT ON YER THUMB AN' ROTATE!
HAWHAW!
HEY!! DON'T GO 'WAY MAD VARMINT!!
ASK US SOME MORE QUESTIONS HAW! HAW!
YEAH! HAW! HAW!
ASK US SUM MORE QUESTIONS, VARMINT
HEY!!
HEY!! ARE THOSE YER EARS OR WUZ YER MUTHER A RABBIT?
HAW HAW
CRAK
AP
OUCHIE OUCHIE
HEY! GUARD!
GUARD
OW OWCH!!
BAM
OW
AAG
MUH FOOT!
HEY!
SMAK
THAK
AAK
CR
WAM
SMAK!
AAG
OUC
GUARD!
OW

AH S'POSE, LONG'S WAR JEST STANDIN' HYAR ANYHOW THET WE COULD ANSWER A FEW QUESTIONS ...
AH S'POSE ...
THE RANSOM.
WHERE IS IT...?
RANSOM!?! THAT S'POSETA BE SUM KINDA UPPER CLASS JOKE!?!
NO JOKE.
CEREBUS WANTS TO KNOW WHERE THE RANSOM IS...
AH RIDE A HORSE FIFTY MILES INNA BLINDIN' THUNNERSTORM CHASIN' AFTER A DAM BOAT WITH A DAM RED BLANKET ON IT ONLY TO FIND NUTHIN' IN IT BUT A DAM STATCHOO OF A DAM DUCK!
AN' YOU WANNA KNOW WHAR TH' RANSOM IS?!
WAL AHM SORRY BUT I SOLD YER DAM DUCK TUH BUY SOME SADDLE-SORE REMEDY!!
WHY'N TH' HELL DINYA ASK FER MONEY, HUH?!
WHUT ARE YUH...?
SUM KINDA DAM DUCK LOVER?!
WHO HAS THE DUCK?
AH SOLD IT TUH BIG GARN!

LATER.

STEWARD, M'LORD.
DID YOU GET THEM?
FOUR POTATOES M'LORD ...

FOUR...
...RAW...
...POTATOES.
JUST SET THEM DOWN ON THE LITTLE TABLE...
THE NIGHTSTAND?
NO. THE LITTLE TABLE NEXT TO THE BED...
YES, M'LORD

NEXT TIME LEAVE THE SKINS ON!
THAT'S THE BEST PART!
YES M'LORD.

CLICK
CARUNCH

SO WHAT DID THEY SAY?
THERE WAS NO RANSOM
CRUNCH CRUNCH
JUST A STATUE OF A DUCK

GEE.
SO WHAT ARE YOU GOING TO DO NOW...
KNOCK KNOCK

STICK AROUND...
CEREBUS HAS A HUNCH SOMEONE IS ABOUT TO TELL HIM WHAT HE'S GOING TO DO NOW...

M'LORD CEREBUS?
I HAVE A MESSAGE FROM THE PRIME MINISTER
BY ALL MEANS.. COME IN BEFORE THE INK DRIES ...

THE PRIME MINISTER IS RESPONDING TO YOUR LETTER OF THIS MORNING ...

"WHILE THE CITY-STATE OF IEST IS MOST SYMPATHETIC TO YOUR DESTITUTE SITUATION, RECENT YEARS HAVE BROUGHT AN INORDINATE NUMBER OF CROP FAILURES IN OUR IMMEDIATE AREA...
AWW.
WE ARE THEREFORE IN THE UNFORTUNATE POSITION, FOR THE SAKE OF OUR STARVING POPULACE, OF HAVING TO DEMAND RESTITUTION" ...
AND YOU'RE INSTRUCTED TO AWAIT A REPLY.

UH...
"CEREBUS WISHES TO COMMEND THE PRIME MINISTER FOR HIS UNNECESSARILY QUICK REPLY, AND FOR WHATEVER MINOR DEGREE OF SINCERITY HE INTENDED TO CONVEY..."

"PLEASE REST ASSURED THAT CEREBUS INTENDS TO PAY BACK EVERY CROWN OF HIS RANSOM..."
"EVEN IF HE HAS TO HOLD DOWN THREE JOBS FOR EIGHTY-SIX YEARS."

UNFORTUNATELY YOU HAVE TO BE GOING.
er..
YASS.

TIME FOR CEREBUS TO WRITE A FEW LETTERS OF HIS OWN!

DO YOU REALIZE YOU JUST THREW A CABINET MINISTER OUT OF YOUR ROOM?
MM.
LORD JULIUS SAYS YOU CAN MEASURE A MAN'S WORTH BY THE BREED OF PERSON HE THROWS OUT OF HIS OFFICE
FIRST LETTER.
"MR. NED GREELY -- GREELY, BLEAKER AND SPLEEN. DEAR SIR; OWING TO HIS RECENT ABDUCTION, CEREBUS FINDS HIMSELF IN NEED OF IMMEDIATE CASH RESERVES TO REIMBURSE YOUR GOVERNMENT. CEREBUS IS THEREFORE ASKING YOU AT THIS..."
...HM. NO...
"IS THEREFORE URGENTLY REQUESTING..."
HM.
BOY-- IF I WAS WRITING TO GREELY, I KNOW WHAT I'D ASK HIM
I'D ASK HIM WHY HE KEEPS BRINGING THAT SLEAZY SECRETARY OF HIS UP HERE EVERY AFTERNOON
...WHEN HE'S GOT A PERFECTLY RESPECTABLE WIFE AT HOME.
SAY THAT AGAIN...
...SLOWLY.
SAY WHAT AGAIN SLOWLY?
CRUMPLE CRUMPLE CRUMPLE

OKAY-- HERE'S THE FINAL DRAUGHT;
"DEAR SIR: IT HAS COME TO CEREBUS' ATTENTION THAT HE IS EXPECTED TO REIMBURSE THE CITY STATE OF IEST FOR THE RANSOM PAID ON HIS BEHALF. SINCE CEREBUS WAS ROBBED OF ALL HIS CURRENCY, HE FINDS HIMSELF UNABLE TO COMPLY WITH THIS REQUEST..."
"... CEREBUS SINCERELY HOPES THAT YOU WILL GIVE SERIOUS CONSIDERATION TO INTERVENING ON HIS BEHALF WITH THE GOVERNMENT AGENCIES INVOLVED..."
"CEREBUS' HAS ALWAYS ADMIRED YOU FOR YOUR SENSE OF MORALITY AND HIGH STANDARDS OF DECENCY..."
"... QUALITIES THAT RANK VERY HIGH WITH BOTH CEREBUS AND LORD JULIUS" ...
"QUALITIES THAT WOULD FIGURE PROMINENTLY IN THE GRANTING OF CERTAIN LUCRATIVE GOVERNMENT CONTRACTS..."
"YOU ARE, HOWEVER, A BUSY MAN."
"IF YOU SHOULD FIND YOURSELF UNABLE TO INTERVENE IN THIS MATTER BECAUSE OF YOUR FULL SCHEDULE, IT WOULD PLEASE CEREBUS IMMENSELY..."
"...TO MEET WITH YOU AND YOUR VERY CHARMING YOUNG WIFE ON ONE OF YOUR AFTERNOON VISITS HERE..."
"PLEASE CONVEY CEREBUS' COMPLIMENTS TO HER. CEREBUS IS MOST ANXIOUS TO SEE YOU BOTH AND HOPES YOUR REPLY WILL NOT BE LONG-DELAYED. SINCERELY YOURS, ETC. ETC."
CEREBUS ONLY WISHES HE COULD BE THERE WHEN GREELY READS THAT LAST PART....
LIFE IS JUST FULL OF LITTLE FRUSTRATIONS FOR YOU, ISN'T IT?

THE NEXT MORNING.

DASH IT ALL -- IT'S GETTING TO THE POINT WHERE A RANKING DIPLOMATIC REPRESENTATIVE CAN'T PLAY AN UNINTERRUPTED GAME OF WICKETS WITH HIS ELF! ...
THIS HAD BETTER BE IMPORTANT
A LETTER, M'LORD.
FROM THE PRIME MINISTER'S OFFICE...

WELL DON'T JUST STAND THERE ...
READ IT, MAN... YOU'RE HOLDING UP CEREBUS' GAME!

THE PRIME MINISTER WISHES TO THANK YOU FOR YOUR RECENT LETTER OF INTENT AND HOPES YOU WILL NOT BE FORCED TO SEEK EMPLOYMENT TO REPAY THE RANSOM ...
MM

THE PRIME MINISTER ALSO WISHES TO CONVEY GREETINGS TO YOU FROM YOUR GOOD FRIEND NED GREELY WHO STOPPED BY FOR A CASUAL VISIT IN THE MIDDLE OF THE NIGHT. MR. GREELY ALSO HOPES THAT THE MATTER CAN BE SETTLED WITH AS LITTLE PERSONAL DIFFICULTY TO YOURSELF AS POSSIBLE. HE SPOKE MOST PERSUASIVELY AND AT SOME LENGTH ON THIS VERY POINT...

THE PRIME MINISTER HAS ENCLOSED AN INVITATION TO JOIN HIM IN HIS WEEKLY PHEASANT HUNT THE DAY AFTER TOMORROW...
...WHERE HE HOPES THE TWO OF YOU MAY BE ABLE TO REACH A MUTUALLY SATISFACTORY AGREEMENT ON REIMBURSEMENT ...

TELL THE PRIME MINISTER CEREBUS WILL BE DELIGHTED TO JOIN HIM ...
... AND HAVE A DOZEN ROSES SENT TO MRS. GREELY.
YES, M'LORD.

HE DOESN'T KNOW I EXIST YOU KNOW.
OBVIOUSLY.
THEN WHY TALK ABOUT ME? HE'LL ONLY THINK YOU'RE...
...CRAZY.
CEREBUS KNOWS THAT.
BUT WHY WOULD YOU ...
LORD JULIUS ALWAYS SAID THAT INSANITY WAS THE LAST LINE OF DEFENCE FOR THE MASTER BUREAUCRAT
I DON'T GET IT.
IT'S HARD TO GET A REFUND WHEN THE SALESMAN IS SNIFFING YOUR CROTCH AND BAYING AT THE MOON ...
OH-- I GET IT NOW.
INSANITY IS A VIRTUALLY IMPREGNABLE GAMBIT...
BUT YOU HAVE TO LAY THE GROUNDWORK EARLY IN THE GAME...
CRAK
REMATCH?
SURE.

SO WHAT ARE YOU GOING TO DO NEXT?
CEREBUS IS GOING TO FIGURE OUT HOW TO GET SOMEONE TO GIVE HIM THE MONEY TO PAY BACK HIS RANSOM.
AND THEN?
AND THEN CEREBUS IS GOING TO PAY IT BACK
YOUR SHOT ...
AND THEN?
THEN CEREBUS IS GOING TO GET AS MUCH MONEY FOR HIMSELF AS HE CAN GET...
AND THEN?
AND THEN CEREBUS IS GOING TO BUY EVERYTHING HE ALWAYS WANTED...
LIKE WHAT?
LIKE A QUIET ELF
HUH!?
SHUT UP AND PLAY ...

MISS
MISS
MISS
MISS

RATS.
THAT'S TWENTY-NINE GAMES TO TEN... CARE TO TRY FOR BEST THIRTY-ONE OUT OF SIXTY-ONE?
WHY DON'T WE WAIT 'TIL THE SUN COMES UP AGAIN? ...

DEBTS

YOU ADMIT THAT CEREBUS BEAT YOU?
I ADMIT THAT YOU HAVE BETTER NIGHT VISION ...
IT WAS SIX-SIX BEFORE THE SUN WENT DOWN ...

ARE YOU ACCUSING CEREBUS OF CHEATING?
HOW COME YOU AREN'T OUT LOOKING FOR YOUR DUCK?

CEREBUS HAS A ROOF OVER HIS HEAD AND FIVE SQUARE MEALS A DAY...
SOMEONE ELSE HAS CEREBUS' TWELVE THOUSAND CROWN RANSOM
SOMEONE ELSE HAS CEREBUS' DUCK!
AS FAR AS CEREBUS IS CONCERNED, THE SOMEONE ELSES GOT THE LOUSY TWO-THIRDS OF THE DEAL

BUT SUPPOSE THE DUCK IS WORTH MONEY?
A ZILLION TRILLION CROWNS
I MEAN, JUST ...
...SUPPOSE.

IT ISN'T
BUT HOW DO YOU KNOW...?
HOW MUCH COULD A DUCK STATUE BE WORTH?
IF IT WAS MADE OUT OF DIAMONDS?
CEREBUS IS GOING TO BED...

THE PRIME MINISTER'S PRIVATE GAME PRESERVE, SOMEWHERE EAST OF IEST....
...IT IS MIDDAY...
SO YOU SEE, I HAVE A LARGE PROBLEM. HIS HOLINESS HAS ORDERED A PAPAL AUDIT OF MY GOVERNMENT'S BOOKS
...AND I'M IN THE UNFORTUNATE POSITION OF HAVING TO RECTIFY A CERTAIN NUMBER OF BOOK-KEEPING ERRORS ...
... BEFORE THE AUDIT BEGINS NEXT WEEK.
HOW MUCH DO THE "ERRORS" AMOUNT TO...?
THREE QUARTERS OF A MILLION CROWNS
I'VE LIQUIDATED MOST OF MY ASSETS TO PAY THE INTEREST ON TWO DOZEN LOANS FROM FOREIGN BANKS
TUNG!
DAM.
WITH INTEREST RATES GOING UP AS FAST AS THEY ARE, I SHOULD BE ABLE TO KEEP MYSELF SOLVENT FOR NINE DAYS...
WHAT IF THE AUDIT TAKES MORE THAN NINE DAYS?
WELL, THAT'S JUST THE POINT, ISN'T IT?
I CAN'T AFFORD TO ALLOW ANY DEBTS TO GO UNPAID AT THIS POINT IN TIME...
THE TWELVE THOUSAND CROWN RANSOM PAID ON YOUR BEHALF WOULD COVER A DAY'S INTEREST ON MY PERSONAL LOANS...
SHH-- I THINK I SEE A PHEASANT ...

IT'S THE BLOODY CHURCH'S OWN FAULT, YOU KNOW. THEY USED UP ALL THEIR CASH RESERVES.
THE PRICE OF WHEAT WENT UP...
THERE WERE A FEW BAD CROP YEARS
BINGO! STARVING PRIESTS AND AN AUDIT OF MY GOVERNMENT.
TUNG
DAM.
I AM NOT OVERLY CONCERNED, HOWEVER ...
REPLENISHING CASH RESERVES IS MOSTLY JUST A MATTER OF SQUEEZING THE RIGHT PEOPLE IN THE RIGHT PLACES
I MEAN AT LEAST IT'S AN AUDIT AND NOT A PURGE.
LET'S TRY OVER HERE ...
AND SQUEEZING PEOPLE IN THE RIGHT PLACES IS AN ACQUIRED SKILL
LIKE
SHOOTING
A
TUNG!
DAM.
SO HOW AND WHERE DO YOU PLAN ON SQUEEZING CEREBUS?
WELL, TO BE HONEST, I GAVE UP HOPE OF BEING REIMBURSED AFTER YOUR FIRST LETTER
SO WHY DID YOU INVITE CEREBUS HERE?

NED GREELY, ACTUALLY... IF YOU COULD ONLY HAVE SEEN HIS FACE WHEN HE PLEADED WITH ME TO CANCEL YOUR DEBT ...
I HAD NEVER BEFORE SEEN HIM EVEN PERTURBED ...
YOU CRACKED HIM LIKE A WALNUT--
JUST BETWEEN YOU AND ME ...
... HOW'D YOU DO IT?
CEREBUS HAD SOME LEVERAGE ...
LEVERAGE! YES! AND THAT'S WHAT I WANT TO TALK TO YOU ABOUT...
YOU'VE ESTABLISHED QUITE A REPUTATION FOR YOUR "LEVERAGE"
I CAN USE SOMEONE WHO USES LEVERAGE ...
PROPERLY USED, LEVERAGE CAN WORK TO OUR ADVANTAGE...
AND NEEDLESS TO ADD
IT CAN WORK TO THEIR DISADVANTAGE
CEREBUS HAS A QUESTION ...
YES?
WHAT THE HELL ARE YOU TALKING ABOUT?

GETTING NED GREELY TO COME AND SEE ME WAS ATTENTION-GETTING--IMPRESSIVE.
BUT NOT VERY PRACTICAL...
GREELY IS A GOOD FRIEND OF MINE, YOU SEE.
HOWEVER I CAN APPRECIATE THAT YOU WANT ME AND MY GOVERNMENT OFF YOUR BACK SO YOU CAN GET ON WITH YOUR BUSINESS.
I DON'T KNOW WETHER IT'S FOR LORD JULIUS, FOR PALNU OR IF YOU'RE JUST LINING YOUR OWN POCKETS
I DON'T REALLY CARE, EITHER...
I'VE GOT MY OWN SCHEMES TO JUGGLE
YOU CAN TAKE MY WORD FOR IT, THOUGH
GREELY CANNOT HELP YOU.
HOWEVER, HOLLAND M. HADDEN ...
HOLLAND M. HADDEN CAN DO YOU SOME GOOD ...

THE ONE WHO GAVE CEREBUS SEVEN HUNDRED CROWNS TO TALK TO LORD JULIUS ...
...ABOUT GOLD-PLATED STREET LAMPS...
... IT'S SORT OF A PET PROJECT OF HIS...
MY GOVERNMENT OWES HADDEN AND HIS LOANS OFFICER TWENTY-NINE THOUSAND CROWNS...
AND YOU OWE ME TWELVE THOUSAND CROWNS ...
IF YOU CAN PERSUADE HADDEN TO CANCEL MY GOVERNMENT'S DEBT
I WON'T NEED THE MONEY YOU OWE ME.
ALL THAT'S MISSING FROM THE EQUATION IS ...
...LEVERAGE.
DO YOU SUPPOSE YOU COULD FIND SOMETHING AS...EFFECTIVE... AS WHAT YOU USED ON NED GREELY?
CEREBUS KNOWS JUST WHO TO ASK...
GOOD.
SHALL WE HEAD BACK?
I'M AFRAID HUNTING WEARS ME OUT ...

AT LEAST SIX COURSES... TWO VEGETABLES
A COUPLE OF BOTTLES OF WINE...
DRINKING BOWLS.
YES M'LORD
ELF?
C'MON, ELF...
CEREBUS HAS TO TALK TO YOU...
SO? DID THE PRIME MINISTER KNOW ANYTHING ABOUT YOUR DUCK?
WILL YOU FORGET THE DAMNED DUCK?
HOLLAND M. HADDEN WILL BE HERE IN A FEW MINUTES...

OF HADDEN, HADDEN AND DIPP?
RIGHT.
NOW CEREBUS HAS A QUESTION
WHAT IS THE SINGLE MOST VULNERABLE AREA IN HADDEN'S BACKGROUND?
THE BIGGEST SCANDAL THAT HE WOULD PAY ANY PRICE TO COVER UP?

I GIVE UP.
WHAT?

WOULD YOU MIND LEAVING?
CEREBUS HAS A LOT OF IMPROVISING TO DO IN THE NEXT THREE AND A HALF MINUTES
POIT
YOU SURE ARE MOODY SOME DAYS AREN'T YOU?

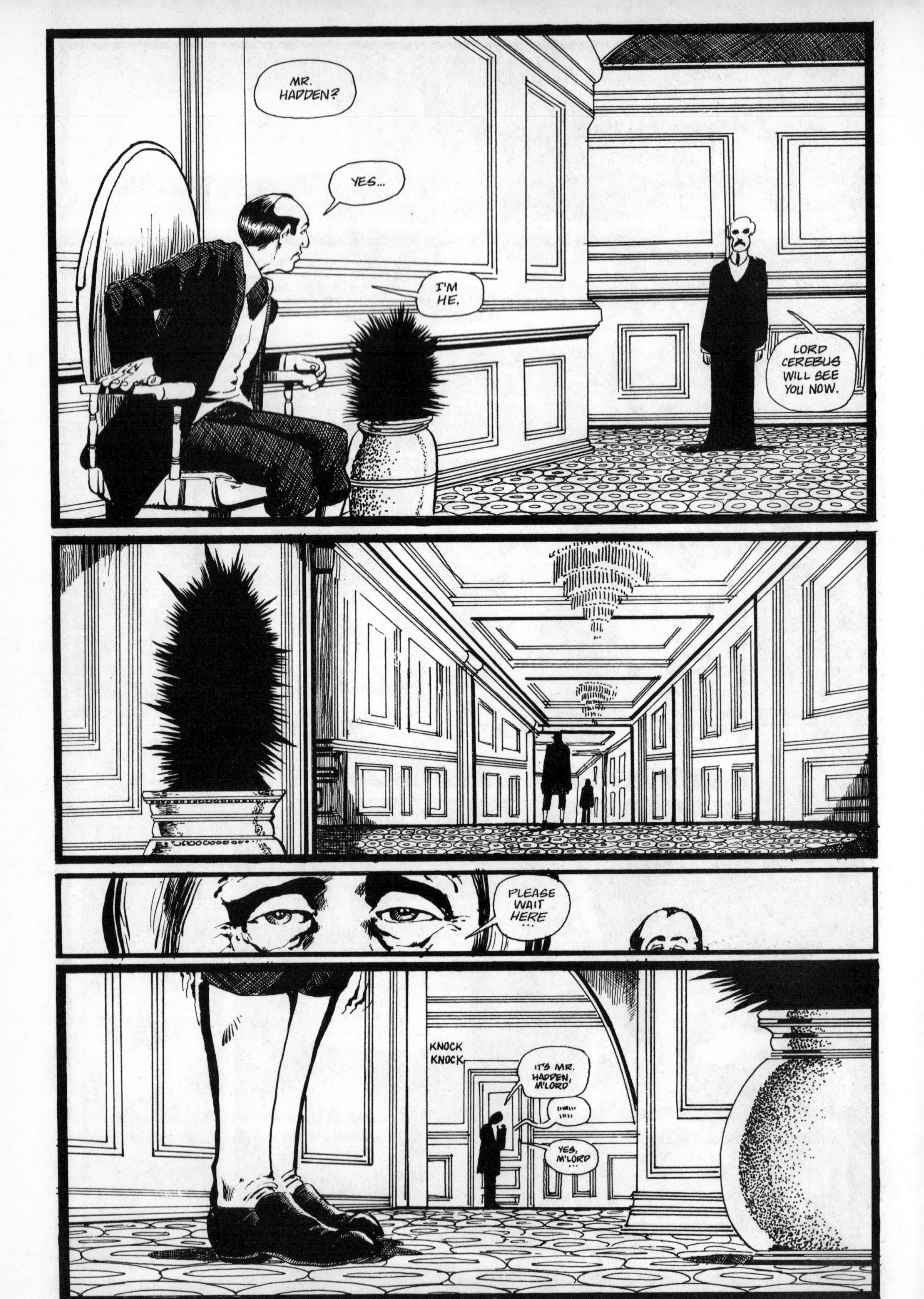
MR. HADDEN?
YES...
I'M HE.
LORD CEREBUS WILL SEE YOU NOW.
PLEASE WAIT HERE ...
KNOCK KNOCK
IT'S MR. HADDEN, M'LORD'
YES, M'LORD ...

MR. HADDEN? ...

HADDEN, MY BOY...
SIT DOWN
SIT DOWN
THANK YOU, M'LORD... THANK YOU VERY MUCH

HADDEN?
M'LORD?
YES SIR, M'LORD ...
CEREBUS HAS BEEN GIVING THESE STREET-LAMPS OF YOURS A LOT OF SERIOUS THOUGHT ...

HEH HEH HEH
BET I CAN GUESS WHAT YOU'VE DECIDED, M'LORD

HEH HEH HEH
BET YOU CAN'T ...
THERE'RE SOME QUESTIONS IN CEREBUS' MIND ABOUT SOME ASPECTS OF A PRODUCT LIKE THIS...

OF COURSE OF COURSE OF COURSE
THE EXPENSE!
WELL, M'LORD ...

EXPENSE?
MY BOY, THE LAST THING WE ARE WORRIED ABOUT IN PALNU IS HOW MUCH SOMETHING COSTS ...
WHISKEY?
HEH HEH
DON'T MIND IF I DO...
CLINK
GLP GLP GLP GLP GLP
THANK YOU! THAT'S ...
FINE I...
FINE. THANKS.
uh. THANKS.

SUPPOSED TO BE FOR BRANDY ...
BUT THEY'RE THE ONLY GLASSES IN THE HOTEL THAT WILL HOLD A HALF BOTTLE OF WHISKEY EACH...
YES. WELL.
THE NEXT TIME I WANT TO DRINK A HALF-BOTTLE OF WHISKEY, I'LL KNOW WHAT KIND OF GLASS TO USE
WON'T I?

AS CEREBUS WAS SAYING, COST IS THE LEAST OF HIS PROBLEMS, STREET-LAMP-WISE ...
PALNU IS A VERY VERY IMPORTANT CITY...
CEREBUS IS A FIRM BELIEVER IN THE OLD SAYING THAT YOU CAN TELL THE IMPORTANCE OF A CITY BY ITS STREET-LAMP SITUATION...
NOW THERE, M'LORD, WE ARE IN COMPLETE ...
CEREBUS ISN'T FINISHED.
SORRY.

THE STREET LAMPS WOULD BE A LANDMARK ...THEREFORE, THEY HAVE TO BE ENDURING ...IMPRESSIVE...AMAZING ...
CEREBUS FEELS IT WOULD BE BETTER ALL AROUND IF THE STREETLAMPS WERE...

...SOLID...
...GOLD.
SSPRTZ

SOMETHING WRONG, HADDEN?
NO, M'LORD ...
I--uh--JUST GOT A LITTLE WHISKEY--uh
...UP MY NOSE.

OF COURSE CEREBUS WOULD NEED A COMPLETE COST BREAK-DOWN FOR A SINGLE STREET ...
...AS SOON AS POSSIBLE.

CERTAINLY, CERTAINLY.
THE DAY AFTER TOMORROW, I'LL HAVE ...

AS
SOON
AS
POSSIBLE!

HEH. WELL...
GOOD THING I BROUGHT MY NOTEBOOK, THEN
ISN'T IT, THOUGH?

THIS IS THE FINAL COST BREAKDOWN?
YEPSIR, MLORD--THASSIT DOWN'TA LAS' COBBER BIT...
ALL WERKED OUT...
YEP.
YEP.

HADDEN?
MM?
THIS DEAL IS GOING TO MAKE YOU A VERY WEALTHY MAN...

HEE HEE
I KNOW!
HOLLAND M. HADDEN, RICH AND FAMOUS CREATOR OF THE FAMOUS...PALNU... STREET...OF...GOLD!

MMM.
IT'S UNFORTUNATE THAT WE WON'T BE ABLE TO START FOR TWO YEARS ...

WHA'?
WHA' WUZZAT?
YOU DON'T MIND WAITING FOR TWO YEARS, DO YOU, HADDEN?

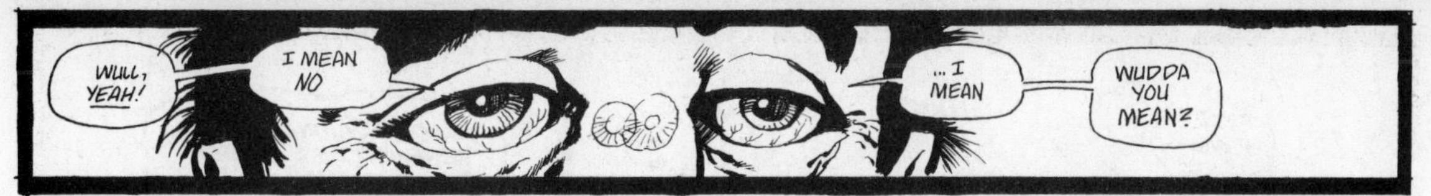
WULL, YEAH!
I MEAN NO
...I MEAN
WUDDA YOU MEAN?

DO YOU TRUST CEREBUS, HADDEN...?
YES
DO YOU?
YES! YES!

IEST IS IN GRAVE DANGER ...
AND SHE NEEDS YOUR HELP, HADDEN ...

M-HIC-ME?
THERE IS A CONSPIRACY AFOOT TO DESTROY IEST'S ECONOMY...
WE HAVE NAMES, DATES, PLACES, FACTS, FIGURES, AND SPECIFICATIONS...
EVEN AS WE SPEAK, GOVERNMENTS ACROSS ESTARCION ARE CANCELLING THEIR DEBTS WITH IEST AS A COUNTER-MEASURE ...
A TREMENDOUS CASH RESERVE MUST BE BUILT IN A HOPELESSLY SHORT PERIOD OF TIME TO ENABLE US TO WEATHER THE STORM...

EVERYONE...
EVERYONE!
...MUST DO HIS SHARE, HADDEN

CANCEL THE DEBT THE CITY OWES YOUR COMPANY!
DON'T EVEN THINK OF WHAT IT WILL MEAN TO YOU, PERSONALLY...
THE LARGEST GOVERNMENT CONTRACT EVER SIGNED!
YOUR DREAM COME TRUE...!
FAME!
IMMORTALITY!

FAME?
IMMORTALITY?
BY CONTRIBUTING TO THE RENEWED LIFE OF IEST, I CAN PROMISE YOU THAT THE STREETLAMPS WILL BE DISCUSSED IN TWO WEEKS-- NOT YEARS...
THAT INTERESTS YOU, DOESN'T IT?
RIGHT! DON'T EVEN THINK ABOUT THAT!
THERE ARE EVEN GREATER REWARDS, HADDEN! ...
BUT THERE ARE GREATER REWARDS, STILL, HADDEN!
DO YOUR SHARE NOW, AND YOU WILL NOT BE FORGOTTEN BY THE MAJOR POLITICAL LEADERS AND MILLIONAIRE BACKERS INVOLVED
YOU COULD EVEN...
YOU COULD EVEN GET TO BE ONE OF THE...
...INSIDE PEOPLE.
OOOOOH
I'VE ALLUS =HIC= WANTED T'BE AN INSIDE PEOPLE
WELL.
THAT'S GOOD.
CEREBUS IS GLAD WE HAD A CHANCE FOR THIS LITTLE TALK.

THIS WAY.
THAT'S IT.

SIT RIGHT HERE.
NO. CLOSER TO THE CHAIR.
THAAT'S IT.

NOW YOU'RE GOING TO HAVE TO WRITE YOUR NAME WITH THIS PEN.
"HOLLAND"
"HOLLAND..."
"...M..."
TWO BUMPS.

CEREBUS CAN'T IMAGINE WHAT HE DID WITH THAT CONTRACT.
IT SPELLED OUT ALL THE TERMS FOR THE INITIATION OF A FEASIBILITY STUDY ON SOLID GOLD STREETLAMPS
UH?
WELL, AS SOON AS CEREBUS CAN DRAW UP ANOTHER ONE...

HE'LL HAVE IT SENT TO LORD JULIUS FOR AN INTERIM STUDY...
BY THAT TIME, WE'LL HAVE THE PUBLIC WORKS' RECOMMENDATIONS AND THE TRANSPORT MINISTRY'S GO-AHEAD.
BUH! BUH!--

AFTER THAT THERE'LL BE FORMAL HEARINGS, IMPROMPTU GATHERINGS, TOP LEVEL NEGOTIATIONS AND CLOSED-DOOR SESSIONS...
BUT...
AS LONG AS WE CAN AVOID A HEAD-ON COLLISION WHEN WE'RE EYEBALL-TO-EYEBALL
BU...
...THERE SHOULD BE NO PROBLEM IN RAMMING IT THROUGH WITH AN OVERWHELMING MAJORITY THAT WILL GIVE US THE MANDATE WE SEEK...

NO!
NO!
GIVE ME AN I.O.U. FIRST!
A RECEIPT!
SOB
A LETTER OF RECOMMENDATION
I JUST SIGNED AWAY ALMOST THIRTY THOUSAND CROWNS...
PLEASE!
YOU'VE GOT TO GIVE ME SOMETHING!
HADDENZ
HSSSS.
OH NO.

"UNORTHODOX ECONOMIC REVENGE"
SCREAMS THE LARYNX OF THE MERELY MAGNIFICENT ...
MOON ROACH!
continued

CHASING COOTIE!
HOLLAND M. HADDEN IS DEAD, CRUSHED BENEATH A GIANT CRESCENT MOON OF STONE.
THE RANKING DIPLOMATIC REPRESENTATIVE OF PALNU IS SOMEWHAT LESS THAN PLEASED...
A THING LIKE THAT CAN REALLY HURT YOUR CREDIT RATING...
HSSSS
GET BACK HERE, YOU IDIOT BUG!

GIVE IT UP, COOTIE, AND YOU MIGHT GET OFF WITH ONLY FORTY YEARS HARD LABOUR ...
EAT-MY-ROACH-ARANG, MONEY-LEECHING OPPRESSOR OF THE MASSES!!
THE DIVERSION ALLOWS THE MOON ROACH TO SLIP AWAY, UNDETECTED ...
HIS ROACH CAPE IS NOT QUITE SO FORTUNATE...
COOTIE?
WHEN I THINK OF HOW POOR SOME PEOPLE ARE ...
... I COULD JUST PUKE ...
HE SAYS THE MOST EXTRAORDINARY THINGS, DOESN'T HE?

YOU DON'T OFTEN FIND A MAN HIS SIZE WITH A CONSCIENCE ABOUT SOCIAL ISSUES.
YOU HIS KEEPER, LADY?
IN A MANNER OF SPEAKING ...

I AWOKE ONE NIGHT TO FIND HIM STANDING AT THE FOOT OF MY BED, HOLDING HIS SIDE. I WAS TERRIFIED-- HE LOOKED LIKE SOME SORT OF JET AND SILVER DARKNIGHT CAPED CRUSADER. HIS EYES SEEMED TO BURN LIKE TWIN FLAMES. HE SPOKE TO ME FOR THE FIRST TIME...
SORRY, LADY...
MY GUT SEEMS TO BE LEAKING ALL OVER YOUR CARPET ...
AND I FELL INSTANTLY... MADLY... IN LOVE.

HE COLLAPSED ACROSS THE BED. I GOT BANDAGES AND OINTMENT AND I DRESSED HIS WOUND...
YOU RICH BROADS SURE GOT SOFT HANDS
HE TURNED MY HEAD WITH FLATTERY AND THEN...

SUDDENLY, HE GRABBED ME...
HEY-- WHAT D'YUH THINK YER DOIN'?
I STRUGGLED IN HIS ARMS
HEY!
BUT HE WAS TOO STRONG.
HEYYYMPH!
THE NEXT DAY...

...I TOLD HIM HE COULD STAY...
HE HAD RAVISHED ME, TRUE...
BUT I SENSED THERE WAS SOMETHING DECENT IN HIM...
I WANTED TO GIVE THAT DECENCY A CHANCE ...

I AWOKE THE NEXT NIGHT TO HEAR HIM CRYING OUT IN A COMPLETELY DIFFERENT VOICE...

"KILL THEM, MOON ROACH! GIVE THEM ONE FOR ME!" IT WENT ON FOR A GOOD HOUR. VILE THREATS MINGLED WITH ACCUSATIONS OF "MONETARY GENOCIDE" -- DEMANDS FOR "REVENGE"
IT WAS A COMPLETELY DIFFERENT PERSON LIVING INSIDE THE MOON ROACH ...
HE CALLED HIMSELF KEVITCH AND HE CLAIMED TO BE THE MOON ROACH'S BIGGEST FAN.
IT BECAME OBVIOUS THAT THIS WAS THE PERSONALITY THAT DROVE THE MOON ROACH TO ACTS OF PETTY VANDALISM...
IS THERE SOME REASON HE CAN'T DRESS HIMSELF?
I WAS JUST GETTING TO THAT...
I COULDN'T PERSUADE KEVITCH TO LET THE MOON ROACH RETIRE -- AND THE MOON ROACH HIMSELF WAS COMPLETELY BEYOND MY CONTROL...
...I DID THE ONLY THING I COULD.
I STARTED BUILDING ANOTHER PERSONALITY ...
ARTEMIS.
ARTEMIS STRONG.

IT WAS ARTEMIS WHO TOLD ME ABOUT THE PAST NEITHER KEVITCH NOR THE MOON ROACH COULD REMEMBER.
HE TOLD ME OF HIS LIFE AS A GARDENER FOR AN IMPORTANT FELDAN GOVERNMENT OFFICIAL, CARING FOR HIS HOUSEPLANTS AND ANTIQUE DRAPERIES...
HOW ONE DAY, HE HAD HEARD A STRANGE SOUND IN THE GREENHOUSE...
INVESTIGATING...
HE WAS SUDDENLY CONFRONTED BY THE MOON ROACH'S COSTUME, GLOWING WITH AN EERIE LIGHT...
THE COSTUME REACHED OUT AND GRABBED HIM ...
HE WRESTLED WITH IT...
TRIED DESPERATELY TO EXTRICATE HIMSELF...
BUT THE COSTUME PREVAILED.
IT FELT, ARTEMIS SAID, LIKE HE WAS HAVING AN ORIGIN...

YOU SEE HOW HIS FACIAL MUSCLES RELAX WHEN HE'S ARTEMIS ...
I'VE TRIED TO HELP HIM ESTABLISH DIPLOMATIC CONTACTS TO AID THE FELDAN PEOPLE. SINCE I HAVE FOUND THAT CONCERN FOR THEIR WELFARE IS WHAT CAUSED HIS...
CEREBUS HATES TO INTERRUPT ...
BUT DID YOU KNOW THE COOTIE DROPPED A BIG MOON ON HOLLAND M. HADDEN TONIGHT?
OH DEAR ...
...AND
CEREBUS FIGURES IF THEY LINE HIS BIRD CAGE WITH PADDING, HE WON'T BE ABLE TO HURT HIM...
...SELF.
HEY!
HEY! STOP THAT!!
LOOK, SISTER-- YOUR BOY-FRIEND HAS TO GO TO THE GALLOWS ...
IT'S NOT LIKE CEREBUS WANTS THE COOTIE DEAD...
AND YOU'VE ... COME TO
ARREST HIM
I BELIEVE YOU
TAKE HIS COSTUME THEN
WHAT?!
HIS COSTUME. WITHOUT IT HE COULD NEVER BECOME THE MOON ROACH AGAIN.

I SHOULD NEVER HAVE KEPT IT -- SOMEWHERE IN THE BACK OF MY MIND, I ALWAYS HOPED HE COULD GIVE UP THE MOON ROACH VOLUNTARILY ...
NONE OF THAT MATTERS NOW...
DON'T YOU SEE? YOU CAN END HIS THREAT TO YOU JUST BY...
...WALKING AROUND IEST WITH A LUNATIC ASSASSIN'S LONG UNDERWEAR UNDER MY ARM...
WHY DON'T YOU KEEP IT TO REMEMBER HIM BY...?
YOU CAN WEAR IT TO BED AT NIGHT ...
THIS SNIFF
THIS IS JUST SNIFF A--A--
JOKE TO--TO YOU...
ISN'T IT?
YOU'LL NOTICE CEREBUS HASN'T LAUGHED ONCE SINCE HE GOT HERE
SNIFF
IT ISN'T GOING TO WORK, LADY ...
CEREBUS WANTS HIM OUT OF THE WAY BEFORE HE RUINS CEREBUS' REPUTATION ...
I...
I UNDERSTAND
NOTHING PERSONAL, BUT BUSINESS IS BUSINESS
I...
I UNDERSTAND
THEN YOU SHAN'T FEEL TOO BADLY
WHEN I KILL MYSELF ...

MOMENTS LATER, CEREBUS CROSSES THE PLAZA TO HIS WING OF THE REGENCY
"SO KILL YOURSELF" CEREBUS SHOULD HAVE SAID
"LET ME HELP YOU" CEREBUS SHOULD HAVE SAID.
HAVE TO BURN THE COSTUME
M'LORD CEREBUS?
WHAT IS IT, FATHER? CEREBUS IS BUSY.
I UNDERSTAND. I HAVE BEEN ASKED BY HIS HOLINESS TO SPEAK WITH YOU...
ABOUT MR. HADDEN'S DEATH TONIGHT
I AM LUZZO, RANKING DIPLOMATIC REPRESENTATIVE OF ESHNOSOPUR
OH.
THOSE TWO GENTLEMEN YOU PASSED OUTSIDE...
INQUISITION.
CEREBUS RECOGNIZED THE CAPES.
YOU ARE IN GRAVE DANGER
TREATIES BETWEEN PALNU AND HIS HOLINESS PROHIBIT YOUR ARREST.
BUT HOLLAND M. HADDEN WAS A WARD OF HIS HOLINESS.
THE CHURCH MUST BE REASSURED THAT YOU HAD NO PART IN HIS DEATH
IN A MOMENT, I WILL ASK YOU A QUESTION THAT WAS GIVEN ME BY HIS HOLINESS IN PRIVATE
WHEN I HAVE ASKED IT...
YOU MUST GO TO THOSE TWO MEN AND ANSWER "YES" OR "NO"...
THE QUESTION IS "DID YOU AT ANY TIME TODAY RECEIVE FROM HOLLAND M. HADDEN A SIGNED AND DATED CONTRACT?"

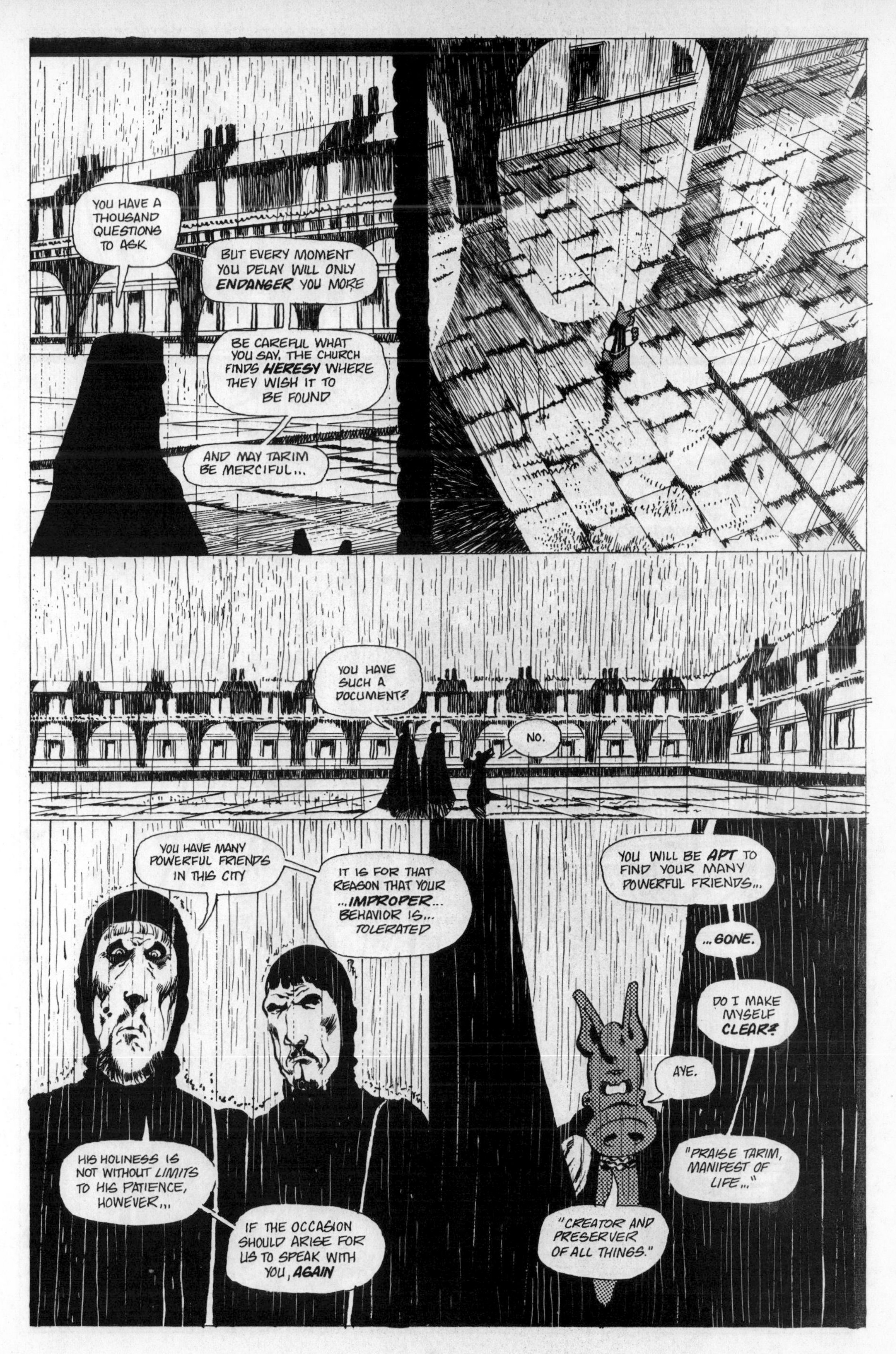
YOU HAVE A THOUSAND QUESTIONS TO ASK
BUT EVERY MOMENT YOU DELAY WILL ONLY ENDANGER YOU MORE
BE CAREFUL WHAT YOU SAY. THE CHURCH FINDS HERESY WHERE THEY WISH IT TO BE FOUND
AND MAY TARIM BE MERCIFUL...
YOU HAVE SUCH A DOCUMENT?
NO.
YOU HAVE MANY POWERFUL FRIENDS IN THIS CITY
IT IS FOR THAT REASON THAT YOUR ...IMPROPER... BEHAVIOR IS... TOLERATED
HIS HOLINESS IS NOT WITHOUT LIMITS TO HIS PATIENCE, HOWEVER...
IF THE OCCASION SHOULD ARISE FOR US TO SPEAK WITH YOU, AGAIN
YOU WILL BE APT TO FIND YOUR MANY POWERFUL FRIENDS...
...GONE.
DO I MAKE MYSELF CLEAR?
AYE.
"PRAISE TARIM, MANIFEST OF LIFE..."
"CREATOR AND PRESERVER OF ALL THINGS."

CRUNK
UNORTHODOX ECONOMIC REVENGE
BELLOW THE BRONCHI OF THE SIMPLY SENSATIONAL...
MOON ROACH!
THIS IS GOING TO COMPLICATE MATTERS SOMEWHAT...
YOU KNOW CEREBUS WOULDN'T BE A BIT SURPRISED?

ALL RIGHT, BUG!
SECONDS LATER...
CEREBUS GAVE YOU A CHANCE...
SO--AN ENEMY FROM MY PAST!
ONCE THE SON OF THE GREATEST AERIAL TEAM IN ESTARCION, HIS MIND WAS WARPED WHEN EXPLOITIVE MONEY-LENDERS SAWED THROUGH HIS PARENTS WHILE THEY WERE SWINGING ON A TRAPEZE...
THANKS, KEVITCH.
DON'T MENTION IT...
IT WOULD SEEM YOU HAVE ME, NOW.
USING HIS CAPE TO CONCEAL HIS MOVEMENTS, THE MOON ROACH TAKES HOLD OF HIS ROACH-ROPE...
HIS MUSCLES ROLL AND SHIFT BENEATH HIS CLOTHING, LIKE...
LIKE...?
LIKE FIRM BREASTS?
THANK YOU, KEVITCH
SUDDENLY...
HEY!
FOLLOW ME, IF YOU CAN, MONEY TYRANT!
THE MOON ROACH LEAPS INTO SPACE
WHY DOES CEREBUS KEEP THINKING THE COOTIE IS ABOUT TO HAVE AN ATTACK OF MENTAL HEALTH?
HIS FOE IS AWE-STRUCK
YOU'RE CRAZY, BUG --DO YOU KNOW THAT?!
HSSS.

CAN IT BE TRUE? IS THE MOON ROACH REALLY FLEEING HIS MOST FEARSOME FOE?
MEANWHILE, WHAT OF HIS GIRL FRIEND? WILL LEAPING AROUND ALL NIGHT CONTINUE TO CAUSE VIRILITY PROBLEMS?
GIVE IT A REST, KEVITCH
SORRY, MOON ROACH.
GIVE UP, COOTIE! ...
WHY ARE YOU RUNNING?
CEREBUS JUST WANTS TO KILL YOU A LITTLE ...
SUDDENLY HIS ROACH HAND DROPS TO HIS ROACH BELT...
HE TURNS
AND HURLS A ROACH-ARANG...
... WITH UNERRING...
WHACK!
...ACCURACY
INTERESTING LITTLE DEVICE.
YESSIR.
CEREBUS ONLY HOPES FOR YOUR SAKE THAT IT TASTES GOOD, TOO.

C'MON COOTIE -- YOU'RE BOXED IN THIS TIME!
THERE'S NOWHERE TO HIDE, BUG!!
IF YOU COME OUT RIGHT NOW, CEREBUS WON'T MAKE YOU EAT IT ALL IN ONE BITE!!
HSSS!
UH?
IF YOU WOULD HAVE THE MOON ROACH FOR YOUR CAPTIVE ...
YOU MUST FOLLOW WHERE HE LEADS
AS THE RAIN TRICKLES DOWN HIS CHEST AND INTO HIS SHORTS, THE MOON ROACH BEGINS TO THINK OF SHELTER
THE MOON ROACH CAN ALMOST READ THE ASTONISHMENT ON THE FACE OF HIS ADVERSARY
THE OUTER RAMPART IS AT LEAST THIRTY FEET FROM THE ROOFTOPS...
CEASE YOUR EXPLOITATION OF THE POOR, DESPOT ...
OR FACE THE FRANKLY FABULOUS FURY OF THE MOON ROACH!!
TARIM! HOW DID HE DO THAT?

LOOK-- BUG!
LET'S-GET-ONE-THING ...
STRAIGHT!
RIGHT NOW!
CEREBUS IS BROKE!
AND DO YOU KNOW WHY CEREBUS IS BROKE?
CEREBUS WILL TELL YOU WHY HE'S BROKE ...
BECAUSE YOU DROPPED A DAMN MOON ON HOLLAND M.HADDEN
AND MADE THE CONTRACT HE SIGNED WITH CEREBUS USELESS
WHAT DO YOU SAY TO THAT, BUG?!
WHAT?
WHAT?
UNORTHODOX
ECONOMIC
REVENGE
HSSSSSSS.

YOU THINK YOU'RE SMART, DON'T YOU, BUG?
YOU FIGURE YOU GOT CEREBUS A GOOD ONE
MAYBE YOU DID, MAYBE YOU DIDN'T...
THAT'S NOT IMPORTANT
WHAT IS IMPORTANT, BUG-- WHAT MATTERS MOST OF ALL HERE...
IS THAT CEREBUS IS HOLDING THE WINNING HAND...
YOU SEE, YOU FORGOT ONE THING-- YOU FORGOT ABOUT YOUR GIRL FRIEND
YES, BUG! YOUR GIRL FRIEND.
CEREBUS KNOWS WHERE HER APARTMENT IS, BUG!
CEREBUS IS GOING THERE RIGHT NOW AND HE'S GOING TO DRAG HER TO PRISON!
THAT'LL BE THE END OF YOUR COZY LITTLE HIDE-OUT, WON'T IT?
THE START OF A WHOLE NEW LIFE FOR YOU!
YOU CAN JUMP AROUND UP HERE MORNING, NOON AND NIGHT
HOW DO YOU LIKE THAT?
YOU'RE OUT OF YOUR DEPTH THIS TIME, BUG!!
STAY OUT OF CEREBUS' WAY OR HE'LL STEP ON YOU...
HARD!
HAVING LEFT ASTORIA ENOUGH TIME TO MOVE TO AN ALTERNATIVE ROACH NEST...
UNDERSTAND, BUG?!
THE MOON ROACH HASTENS TO THE NEW HIDEOUT

RIGHT LADY!
NO TALK!
JUST COME ALONG QUIETLY AND...
CRASH

CEREBUS IS NOT GOING TO GIVE UP...
THE CHURCH WILL JUST HAVE TO BE DEALT WITH.
THE PRIME MINISTER WILL JUST HAVE TO BE DEALT WITH...
THE INQUISITION WILL JUST HAVE TO BE DEALT WITH...
THE MOON ROACH.
THE MOON ROACH DEFINITELY HAS TO BE DEALT WITH...

CRASH

THEY'RE NOT REALLY GETTING THE BEST OF CEREBUS...
THEY THINK THEY ARE ...
BUT CEREBUS ISN'T WITHOUT RESOURCES YOU KNOW... NOT BY A LONG SHOT...
CEREBUS HAS A KEEN INTELLECT AND AN INSTINCT FOR MANIPULATION ...
ONE LUCKY THROW! THAT'S ALL IT WAS. THE RAIN MADE IT HARD TO SEE ...

IF THAT BUG KNOWS WHAT'S GOOD FOR HIM, HE'S HALFWAY TO BEDUIN BY NOW ...
WITH THAT GIRL FRIEND OF HIS SLUNG OVER ONE SHOULDER ...
PLOP!
AS FOR THE INQUISITION, THERE ISN'T MUCH CEREBUS CAN DO...
ASIDE FROM BRUSHING UP ON HIS PRAYERS ...
MONEY IS THE KEY. IF CEREBUS WAS RICH, HE COULD START BUYING HIS WAY OUT OF THESE PROBLEMS
SO THAT'S THE NEXT STEP...
MONEY.
LOTS OF IT.

FOR STARTERS, THE PRIME MINISTER CAN FIND SOMEONE ELSE TO CLEAR UP HIS LITTLE "INDISCRETIONS"

HOLLAND M. HADDEN DIES AND CEREBUS IS UP TO HIS ARM-PITS IN AGGRAVATION...
ALL FOR THE BENEFIT OF A POWDER-PUFF CAUGHT WITH HIS PERFUMED FINGERS IN THE TILL!

FROM NOW ON CEREBUS IS IN BUSINESS FOR HIMSELF...

NO MORE FAVOURS
NO MORE TRADE-OFF'S
NO MORE DOING BUSINESS WITH DAMN FOOLS!!

FROM NOW ON...
CEREBUS INTENDS TO BE TAKEN SERIOUSLY...

WHEN HE HEARS FROM THE PRIME MINISTER'S OFFICE CEREBUS IS GOING TO LAY DOWN THE LAW...
BACK OFF!
CEREBUS KNOWS ENOUGH ABOUT YOUR CROOKED LITTLE SCHEMES TO GET YOU DEMOTED TO AN EMBASSY IN BOREALA!
THIS ISN'T SOME AMATEUR YOU'RE DEALING WITH, YOU KNOW...
CEREBUS HAS A LOT OF VERY POWERFUL FRIENDS IN THIS CITY...
YOU SOLVE YOUR PROBLEMS...
...AND CEREBUS WILL SOLVE HIS OWN PROBLEMS
THAT'S IT!
END OF DISCUSSION ...
END OF ARGUMENT
GET OUT OF CEREBUS' LIFE...
PERIOD!
OH, CERTAINLY. YES. I KNOW EXACTLY WHAT YOU MEAN...
"FLUFFY."

'FLUFFY'

HAAHAA
HAAHAA
HAHAAA

HEEHEE
HEEHEE
HEEHEE

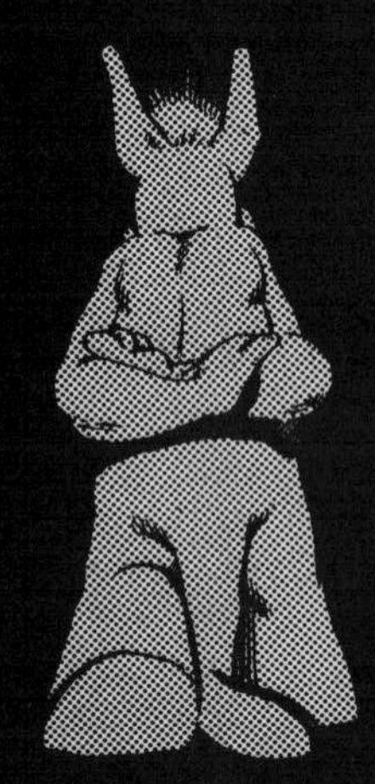

knock knock
I'M FROM THE PRIME MINISTER'S OFFICE, M'LORD...
TARIM.
IT'S PROBABLY ABOUT HADDEN'S CONTRACT
WHAT CAN CEREBUS TELL THEM?
WHY NOT TRY THE TRUTH?
CERTAINLY A NOVEL SUGGESTION
BUT CEREBUS NEEDS SOMETHING MORE EFFECTIVE ...
THE PRIME MINISTER WISHES TO REASSURE THE GOVERNMENT OF PALNU THAT THERE IS NO MALICE IMPLIED BY HIS DECISION TO...
WHY DON'T YOU SAVE US BOTH SOME AGGRAVATION AND JUST GIVE CEREBUS THE BOTTOM LINE...
YES, M'LORD. IF YOU DON'T COME UP WITH THE CONTRACT OR THE TWELVE THOUSAND CROWNS, WE'RE GOING TO THROW YOU TO THE INQUISITION.
CEREBUS NEEDS A HALF-HOUR TO THINK ABOUT IT...
THE PRIME MINISTER IS WAITING IN HIS CARRIAGE DOWNSTAIRS
I'LL ASK HIM IF THAT'S ALL RIGHT.

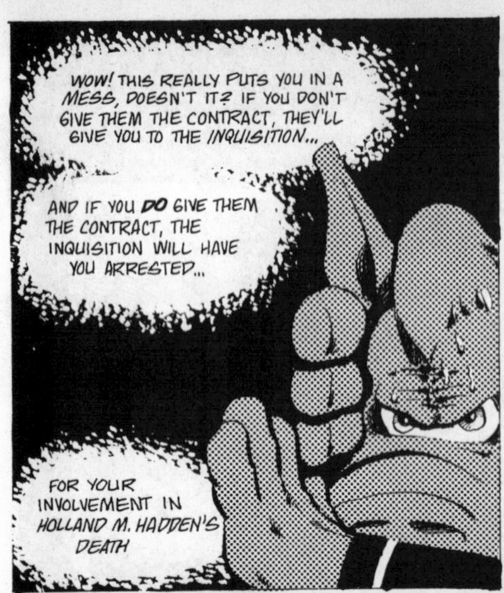
WOW! THIS REALLY PUTS YOU IN A MESS, DOESN'T IT? IF YOU DON'T GIVE THEM THE CONTRACT, THEY'LL GIVE YOU TO THE INQUISITION...
AND IF YOU DO GIVE THEM THE CONTRACT, THE INQUISITION WILL HAVE YOU ARRESTED...
FOR YOUR INVOLVEMENT IN HOLLAND M. HADDEN'S DEATH

HMM.

I HAVE TO ADMIT I'M STUMPED ON THIS ONE.
SO WHAT ARE YOU GOING TO DO?

HMM?
CEREBUS?

UM. ELF? CEREBUS HAS TO DO SOME THINKING ON THAT, ACTUALLY...
...BY HIMSELF. CEREBUS DOESN'T WISH TO APPEAR...
...RUDE OR ANYTHING...

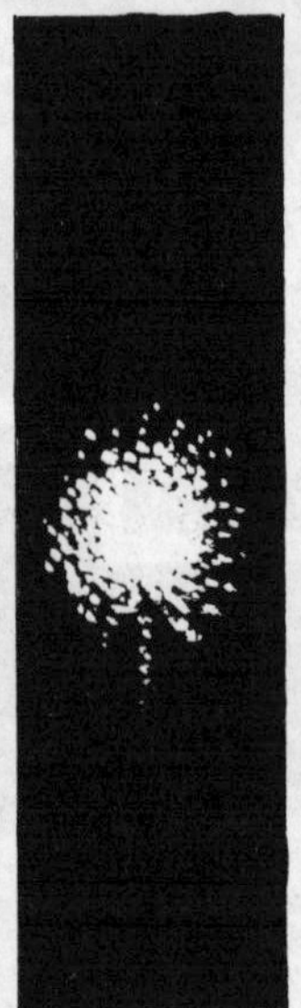

AT LEAST HE WAS LEARNING TO SUPPRESS HIS TEMPER. HE HAD HAD ONE ELF MAD AT HIM, ONCE, WHILE STUDYING IN IMESH. IT WAS AN UNPLEASANT EPISODE HE WAS NOT EAGER TO RELIVE..
FOR NOW, HE COULD ONLY TRY TO STAY CALM THROUGH IT ALL
AND HOPE THAT THE ELF FINDS SOME TROLLS OR SOMETHING TO PLAY WITH

RIGHT NOW, HE HAD ONLY MINUTES TO SOLVE AN INSOLUBLE PROBLEM ...THE PRIME MINISTER'S MAN HADN'T EVEN MENTIONED THE DEATH OF THE INQUISITION PRIEST...
...IF THE MAN DIDN'T KNOW ABOUT IT, CEREBUS COULD BE IN EVEN MORE DANGER VERY SHORTLY.
ALL BECAUSE OF THAT DAMNED BUG! ALL BECAUSE OF...

...YOU!
I APOLOGIZE FOR BREAKING INTO YOUR SUITE, BUT I'M AFRAID IT WAS NECESSARY...
I'VE A BUSINESS PROPOSITION TO OFFER YOU.
BUSINESS PROPOSITION?!
YOU KNOW WHAT YOU CAN DO WITH YOUR DAMNED BUSINESS PROPOSITION!!
BUG!!
TYRANT!!

EAT CARPET, TYRANT!
KNOCK KNOCK
YOU HEAR THAT, COOTIE?! IT'S THE PRIME MINISTER'S OFFICE, ABOUT TO TURN CEREBUS OVER TO THE INQUISITION!!
AND YOU HAVE A BUSINESS PROPOSITION?!
GK!
CEREBUS WILL...
HE DOESN'T HAVE A BUSINESS PROPOSITION.
I HAVE A BUSINESS PROPOSITION.
TELL THEM YOU'RE AUTHORIZING A THREE PER CENT INCREASE IN TARIFFS ON PALNAN GOODS ENTERING IEST...
TARIFFS?
YOU THINK IT WILL WORK?
OF COURSE.

I'M SORRY, M'LORD-- THE PRIME MINISTER INSISTS ON YOUR...
ARTEMIS.
CEREBUS AUTHORIZES A THREE PER CENT INCREASE IN TARIFFS ON PALNAN GOODS ENTERING IEST--OKAY?!
ARTEMIS, DARLING, IT'S TIME FOR YOU TO WAKE UP, NOW... ARTEMIS?
YOU HAVE SOME FURNITURE TO REARRANGE...
MM?
OH. YES.
THE PRIME MINISTER AGREES TO YOUR TERMS, M'LORD...
SORRY TO HAVE CAUSED YOU ANY TROUBLE.
NO TROUBLE!
NO TROUBLE AT ALL!!

THEY'RE GONE.
WHERE'S THE BUG?
YOU'RE WELCOME.
I TOLD HIM TO GO AWAY UNTIL I NEED HIM AGAIN.
I'M AFRAID I LIED TO YOU ABOUT THAT
I'VE LIED TO YOU ABOUT A GREAT MANY THINGS...
CEREBUS THOUGHT YOU COULDN'T CONTROL THE MOON ROACH...
THAT'S ALL OVER WITH, NOW.
I'M GOING TO MAKE YOU AN EMBARASSINGLY WEALTHY AARDVARK
YOU'LL LIKE THAT, I'M SURE! I WILL WARN YOU, NOW, THAT I AM USED TO BEING OBEYED. MAKING YOU WEALTHY IS A MEANS TO AN END FOR MY ORGANIZATION... IF YOU COOPERATE, WE'LL ALL GET WHAT WE WANT. IF YOU CHOOSE TO FIGHT ME, YOU WILL VERY PROBABLY WIND UP DEAD.
I REALIZE THAT YOU WISH TO KNOW MORE, AND I WILL ACCOMODATE YOU... UP TO A POINT.
YOU HAVE MY PERMISSION TO ASK ANY FIVE QUESTIONS YOU WISH TO HAVE ANSWERED...
HEY! WHERE DID THAT DOORWAY COME FROM...?

THIS DOORWAY HAS BEEN HERE FOR COUNTLESS GENERATIONS. IT WAS CONSTRUCTED BY THE LABOUR OF ENSLAVED PIGTS.
IT LEADS TO A SMALL ANTECHAMBER WITH A FEW MODEST FURNISHINGS ...
FOR THE SAKE OF PROPRIETY, I WILL USE IT FOR MY BEDROOM WHILE I AM ASSISTING YOU...
SINCE YOU DIDN'T KNOW IT WAS HERE...
... I SHANT IMAGINE YOU WOULD HAVE ANY OBJECTIONS WHATSOEVER.
YOU HAVE FOUR QUESTIONS LEFT...
THE EARTH-PIG HAS BEGUN TO FORMULATE HIS SECOND QUESTION.
EVEN AS THE SLIDING PANEL CLICKS INTO PLACE...

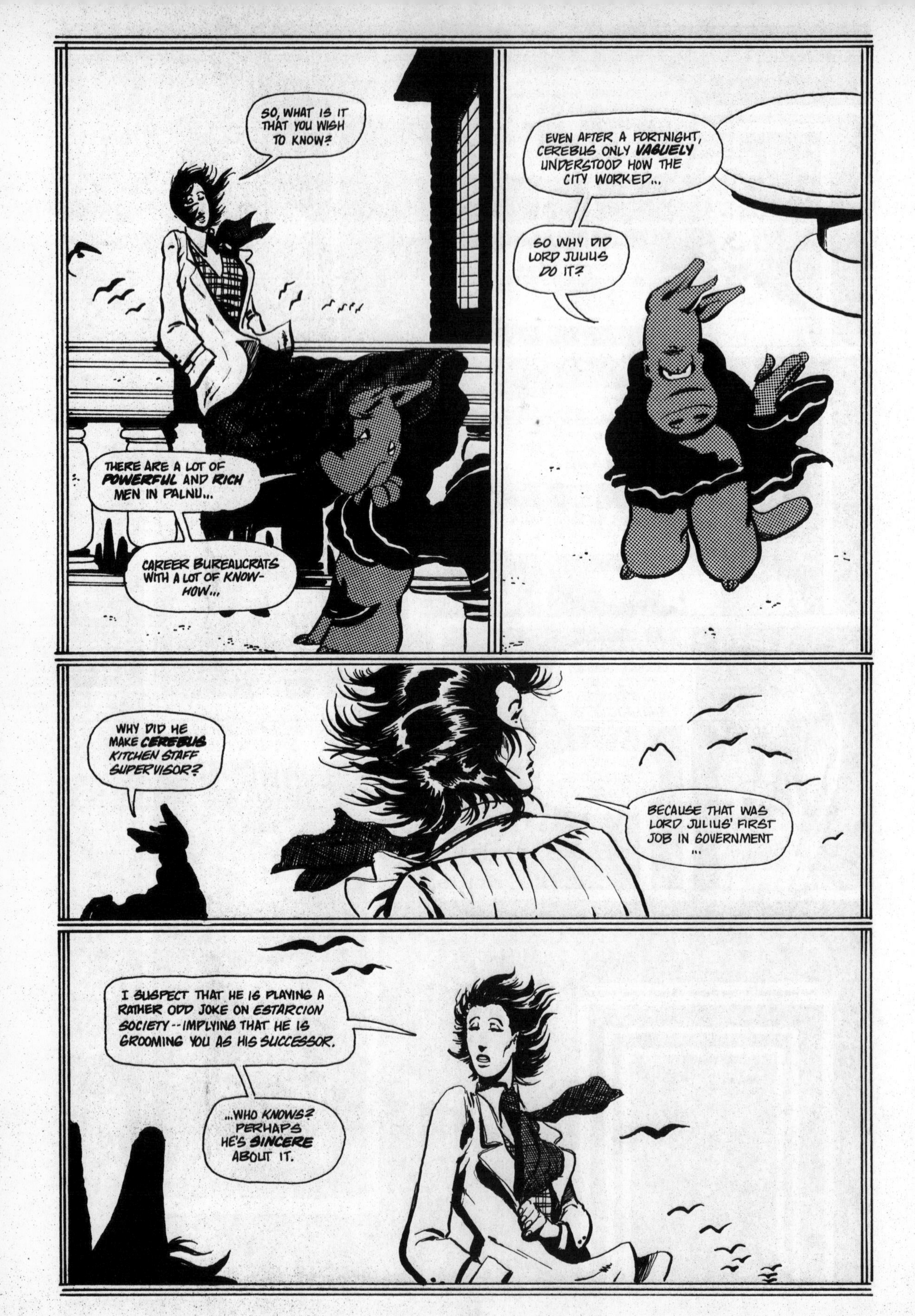
SO, WHAT IS IT THAT YOU WISH TO KNOW?
THERE ARE A LOT OF POWERFUL AND RICH MEN IN PALNU...
CAREER BUREAUCRATS WITH A LOT OF KNOW-HOW...
EVEN AFTER A FORTNIGHT, CEREBUS ONLY VAGUELY UNDERSTOOD HOW THE CITY WORKED...
SO WHY DID LORD JULIUS DO IT?
WHY DID HE MAKE CEREBUS KITCHEN STAFF SUPERVISOR?
BECAUSE THAT WAS LORD JULIUS' FIRST JOB IN GOVERNMENT ...
I SUSPECT THAT HE IS PLAYING A RATHER ODD JOKE ON ESTARCION SOCIETY -- IMPLYING THAT HE IS GROOMING YOU AS HIS SUCCESSOR.
...WHO KNOWS? PERHAPS HE'S SINCERE ABOUT IT.

IT MIGHT EVEN BE WORTH YOUR WHILE TO GO BACK TO PALNU AND STAKE YOUR CLAIM...
DEFINITELY NOT! ALL CEREBUS WANTS IS MORE MONEY THAN ANYONE ELSE HAS. AND THERE'S PLENTY OF MONEY...
...RIGHT HERE.
ASTORIA!
ARTEMIS, DARLING.
WHAT IS IT?

WAS I SUPPOSED TO DROP THIS ON THE EXPLOITIVE ASSISTANT IMPORTS ADMINISTRATOR ...
...OR ON THE EXPLOITIVE EXECUTIVE IMPORTS ADMINISTRATOR
THE EXECUTIVE IMPORTS ADMINISTRATOR
I TOLD YOU SO!
SHUT UP, KEVITCH.

AREN'T YOU GOING TO ASK ME WHAT THAT WAS ABOUT?
CEREBUS ONLY HAS THREE QUESTIONS LEFT AS IT IS...
NICE TRY, THOUGH

FOR NINE DAYS CEREBUS WATCHES IN FASCINATION AS ASTORIA WRITES HUNDREDS OF LETTERS, ADDRESSES APPLICATIONS AND PETITIONS, COMPOSES CONTRACTS AND RECORDS TRANSACTIONS! MESSENGERS, AT ALL HOURS, DELIVER AND PICK UP ENORMOUS AMOUNTS OF CASH IN ORDINARY ENVELOPES...
AT LAST, UNABLE TO HIDE HIS CURIOUSITY ANY LONGER, THE EARTH-PIG ASKS HIS THIRD QUESTION...
"IS CEREBUS **RICH**, YET?"
"HOW MUCH DO YOU WANT RIGHT NOW?" IS ASTORIA'S ONLY REPLY. CEREBUS PAUSES TO THINK.
"A THOUSAND CROWNS."
"HERE."
AS HE COUNTS THE BANK NOTES, CEREBUS WONDERS WHAT WILL HAPPEN TO MAKE HIM POOR **THIS** TIME...

WOW!
THAT'S A LOT OF MONEY!
WHERE'D YOU GET IT?
A WOMAN NAMED ASTORIA ...
SHE'S HELPING CEREBUS WITH HIS BUSINESS DEALS.
ASTORIA!?!
BOY--I'D TRUST HER ABOUT AS FAR AS I COULD THROW HER...
CEREBUS KNEW THIS WAS GOING TO HAPPEN
EVERY TIME CEREBUS GETS A FEW CROWNS, SOMETHING HAPPENS!!
EVERY TIME!!
CEREBUS FINALLY FINDS SOMEONE WHO KNOWS WHAT THEY'RE DOING...
AND NOW HE FINDS OUT SHE CAN'T BE TRUSTED...!

YOU DON'T HAVE TO TAKE IT SO HARD.
RIGHT! SURE! CEREBUS JUST LOST THE ONLY PERSON WHO CAN GET HIM AS MUCH MONEY AS HE WANTS...
EITHER THAT OR HE'D HAVE TO RISK THE INQUISITION FINDING OUT SHE'S HERE.
THAT'S ALL CEREBUS NEEDS, TO BE FOUND CONSORTING WITH A... A...
WHAT IS SHE ANYWAY?
...A DRUG SMUGGLER?
I DON'T KNOW ANYTHING ABOUT HER ...
... EXCEPT, I GET THIS SORTA CREEPY FEELING WHENEVER I SEE HER.
... SORTA...
... CREEPY?...
FEELIN'?
DON'T GET MAD AT AN ELF.
ANYWAY, IF YOU DO HAVE TO GET RID OF HER, YOU CAN COMPOSE YOUR OWN LETTERS...
YOU'RE REALLY GOOD AT COMPOSITION ...
DON'T GET MAD AT AN ELF.
DON'T GET MAD AT AN ELF.

YOU'RE ONLY SAYING THAT BECAUSE YOU THINK YOU'RE SO HOT!!
EEP!
WELL!!
UH-OH.

THERE'S SOMETHING I HAVE TO TALK OVER WITH YOU... THE LEGISLATURE IS DEBATING WHETHER OR NOT TO TO ACCEPT YOUR OFFER...
THEY'VE BEEN PUSHING FOR A RAISE IN THE TARIFFS FOR SEVERAL YEARS NOW BUT THERE IS SOME QUESTION INVOLVED THAT COULD CAUSE US TROUBLE.
THE ELF WAS MAD. AT HIM. CEREBUS WAS SURE OF IT. SOMEHOW SHE HAD FIGURED OUT THAT HE WAS MAD. AT HER.
AND SURE AS TARIM'S JUDGEMENT SHE WAS OUT THERE SOMEWHERE. PLOTTING REVENGE.
KNOCK KNOCK
WHO CAN THAT BE?
HE WOULD JUST HAVE TO KEEP HIS EYES OPEN. BECAUSE WHEN THE ELF DID DECIDE TO STRIKE...
YES?
PACKAGE FOR CEREBUS, MA'AM...
...IT WOULD BE SOMETHING GUARANTEED TO CAUSE THE EARTH-PIG NO END OF TROUBLE.
EDMONDS, LORD FRANCIS... THAT'S VERY ODD...
NEVER HEARD OF HIM...
EDMONDS? LORD FRANCIS.
E...L...

MUST BE ONE OF THOSE EXPATRIATE ...
HEY!
CEREBUS!
WHAT IN THE WORLD DID YOU DO THAT...
KLICK-KLAK

PAPAL DIRECTIVE THIRTY SEVEN AUTHORIZES PRIESTS OF THE HOLY ORDER OF MORAL INQUISITORS TO ENTER ANY RESIDENCE IN THE MOST HOLY CITY-STATE OF IEST...
... IF A PRIEST OF THE HOLY ORDER DEEMS THERE TO BE REASONABLE CAUSE TO SUSPECT THAT SAID RESIDENCE IS BEING USED IN THE COMMISSION OF ANY CRIME AGAINST THE LAWS OF IEST, OR THE MORAL PRECEPTS OF THE SACRED CHURCH OF THE LIVING TARIM...
WE HAVE RECEIVED A MESSAGE THAT THERE ARE FIVE KILOGRAMS OF ILLICIT NARCOTICS ON THE PREMISES...
...M'LORD.
ASTORIA, DEAR.. IT SEEMS A LITTLE CHILLY IN HERE. WOULD YOU MIND...
...STIRRING THE FIRE A BIT?
WHAT?
OH.

AN ORDER-IN-COUNCIL FROM THE OFFICE OF HIS HOLINESS SIGNED THIS DATE, AUTHORIZING THE TEMPORARY SUSPENSION OF YOUR DIPLOMATIC **IMMUNITY**...

PENDING A THOROUGH SEARCH OF THESE PREMISES BY A DULY SWORN MEMBER OF THE HOLY ORDER OF MORAL INQUISITORS... ***M'LORD?***

ORDER IN COUNCIL

YES--EVERYTHING SEEMS TO BE IN ORDER.

HOW'S THE FIRE COMING, *ASTORIA?*

SMASH

CRACK

SWSH

SNAP

BASH

SMAK

IN THAT CASE, *FATHER*...

FEEL FREE TO HAVE A LOOK AROUND.

LATER...
IT WOULD SEEM THAT OUR INFORMATION IS INACCURATE...
IF YOU WILL EXCUSE US, THEN, FATHER ...
COLOURS!
KLIK
KLAK

R'THEY GONE?
YEAH.
OH, GOOD...

HEY!
ARE YOU SICK OR SOMETHING?
SICK?

NO.
NO.
I THINK I J'ST BREATHEDED IN TOO MUCH
WHILST I WAS BURNIG THE PACKAGE ...

IT WAS AN ACCIDENT. TRY TO NOT GET UPSET...
WHO'S UPSET...?
YOU SHOULD LIE DOWN FOR A WHILE
OKAY, BUT ONLY IF YOU LIE DOWN WITH ME...
JUST TRY TO RELAX, ASTORIA...
WHY DON'T WE LIE DOWN RIGHT HERE?
IF I RELAX ANY MORE, I'LL START DROOLING...
ASTORIA! QUIT KIDDING AROUND! THIS IS...

MMPH!
ASTORIA! WHAT ARE YOU...

...DOING?! HAVE YOU GONE...
OUCH!!
STOP BITING CEREBUS' NECK THIS INSTANT!!

STOP IT, ASTORIA
RIGHT NOW
OR CEREBUS IS GOING TO HAVE TO HURT YOU...
OOOOH! THAT SOUNDS LIKE FUN!
SMASH!

WHAT'S
GOING
ON
HERE?

FRICTION
STAND ASIDE, ASTORIA
GO AHEAD! THROW AWAY EVERYTHING WE'VE WORKED FOR!

IT WON'T WASH THIS TIME, ASTORIA...!
GET OUT OF THE WAY...!
HE HAS MONEY. MONEY FOR THE PEOPLE...
MONEY FOR YOUR PEOPLE!
IT DOESN'T HAVE TO BE WITH HIS MONEY!! ...
IT WILL BE DONE, ARTEMIS, DEAR...
WITH WHOMEVER I CHOOSE!
NOT-WITH-HIM!
WITH...
...WHOMEVER...
...I CHOOSE.

PLEASE, ARTEMIS, I'M TIRED.
YOU'RE TIRED...
GO BACK TO THE ROACH LAIR AND I'LL JOIN YOU AS SOON AS I CAN ...
PLEASE.
PLEASE.
YEAH, BUG, LEAVE CEREBUS ALONE WITH HER FOR A HALF-HOUR ...
... AND WE'LL THROW A FEW CRUMBS AT YOUR ORPHANS.

LISTEN, YOU!...
ARTEMIS!!
PLEASE!
I'LL BE THERE AS SOON AS I CAN.
THAT WAS COMPLETELY UNNECESSARY AND CRUEL!
IT LOOKED GOOD ON HIM...
HE'S AN ARROGANT SON OF A BITCH.
I SEE.
HAVE YOU EVER HEARD THE EXPRESSION "IT TAKES ONE TO KNOW ONE"?

HAVE YOU? ...
WE'RE QUITE THE TRIO, AREN'T WE?
BY THE WAY, WHAT MAKES YOU THINK YOU DESERVE A HALF-HOUR ALONE WITH ME?
GROW UP, ASTORIA...
CEREBUS ONLY SAID THAT TO BUG THE BUG...
YOU KNOW WHAT YOU ARE? YOU'RE A CYNICAL LITTLE MANIPULATOR WHO DOESN'T CARE ABOUT ANYONE EXCEPT HIMSELF!!
YOU SEEM TO HAVE COME UN-DRUGGED PRETTY QUICKLY...

WHAT?
OH.
ISN'T THAT SILLY? IN ALL THE EXCITEMENT I SEEM... SEEM...
...TO HAVE...
OH.
OH DEAR.
MY... MY HEAD.
YOU WERE RIGHT... BEST THING FOR ME... LYING DOWN... MUST... REST ...SLEEP.
YOU DO THAT.
TOMORROW WE CAN TALK SOME MORE ABOUT CYNICAL MANIPULATORS AND HOW THEY DON'T CARE ABOUT ANYONE BUT THEMSELVES.

RAIN, LIKE SOME RELENTLESS ARMY OF DROPLETS, POUNDS THE BROODING FIGURE OF THE MOON ROACH...
HIS EYES NARROW TO ICY SLITS AS THEY SWEEP THE MERCILESS LIGHTS AND RAIN-SLICKENED COBBLES
BUT TONIGHT THERE IS MORE THAN JUST THE COLDNESS OF THE RAIN -- MORE THAN THE MERE ELEMENTS AT PLAY...
THERE IS EVIL! EVIL THAT HANGS IN THE AIR! EVIL SWIRLING ALL AROUND HIM...
HIS ROACH-SENSE, HONED TO PERFECTION, TELLS HIM THAT THE EVIL IS NEARBY; GROWING FASTER BY THE MOMENT...
HE STEELS HIMSELF --READYING MIND AND BODY FOR THE CONFRONTATION...
HIS FEATURES BETRAY NO EMOTION...
BUT DEEP WITHIN HIS ROACH-MIND HE WONDERS ...
CAN IT BE THAT THE EVIL IS ALREADY HERE... NOW... OR...?
...OR IS HE JUST JEALOUS BECAUSE AN OVER-SIZED RABBIT IS HUSTLING HIS CHICK?

MEANWHILE BACK AT THE REGENCY

IT ISN'T TRUE, OF COURSE ...
NO, M'LORD! I DIDN'T THINK...
...THAT IS... NOT FOR EVEN A... MOMENT.
CEREBUS KNOWS WHAT A TOILET IS FOR. CEREBUS HAS USED THEM MANY TIMES...
... MANY TIMES INDEED!
YES, M'LORD... I'M SURE YOU ...
...HAVE.
SO, IF ANYONE ASKS, YOU CAN TELL THEM CEREBUS SAID IT ISN'T TRUE.
HEH.
I'M QUITE SURE, M'LORD, THAT NO ONE IS LIKELY TO...
IF- ANYONE- ASKS ...
"CEREBUS SAYS IT ISN'T TRUE."
I'LL REMEMBER, M'LORD.

Cerebus wee-wees in the sink
(you-know-who)
THE WORKMEN WILL BE HERE TO PAPER OVER IT IN A WHILE.
YOU!...
YEAH!-- YOU!
WIPE THAT GRIN OFF YOUR FACE... OR CEREBUS WILL DO IT FOR YOU!

ANY MOMENT NOW, ASTORIA WOULD APPEAR, HASTENING TO THE ROACH-LAIR, UNAWARE THAT ROACH-EYES WERE WATCHING HER EVERY MOVE ...
WHAT WOULD SHE DO WHEN SHE FOUND HIM GONE?
THE MOON ROACH INTENDED TO FIND OUT...
HE WOULD NOT BE CRUEL, THOUGH! WHEN SHE STARTS TO CRY, HE WILL BE AT HER SIDE IN AN INSTANT, CONSOLING HER. HE...
THE SOUND OF SPIKED HEELS ON PAVEMENT BRINGS HIS ROACH SENSE TO FULL ALERT.
SO! SHE HAD MANAGED TO STAY AWAY FOR ALMOST A FULL HOUR! BUT SOON, NOW...
CLICK
CLACK
CLICK
CLACK
...SOON SHE WOULD BE BEGGING HIS FORGIVE-NESS...
PLEADING WITH HIM TO LET HER STAY...
IMPLORING HIM TO...
CLICK
CLACK
CLICK
A CLEVER PLOY!...
BUT THE MOON ROACH WILL NOT BE FOOLED BY A MERE LOOK-ALIKE ...
CLACK
CLICK
CLACK
CLICK
CLAK
CLIC

Noon The Legislature:

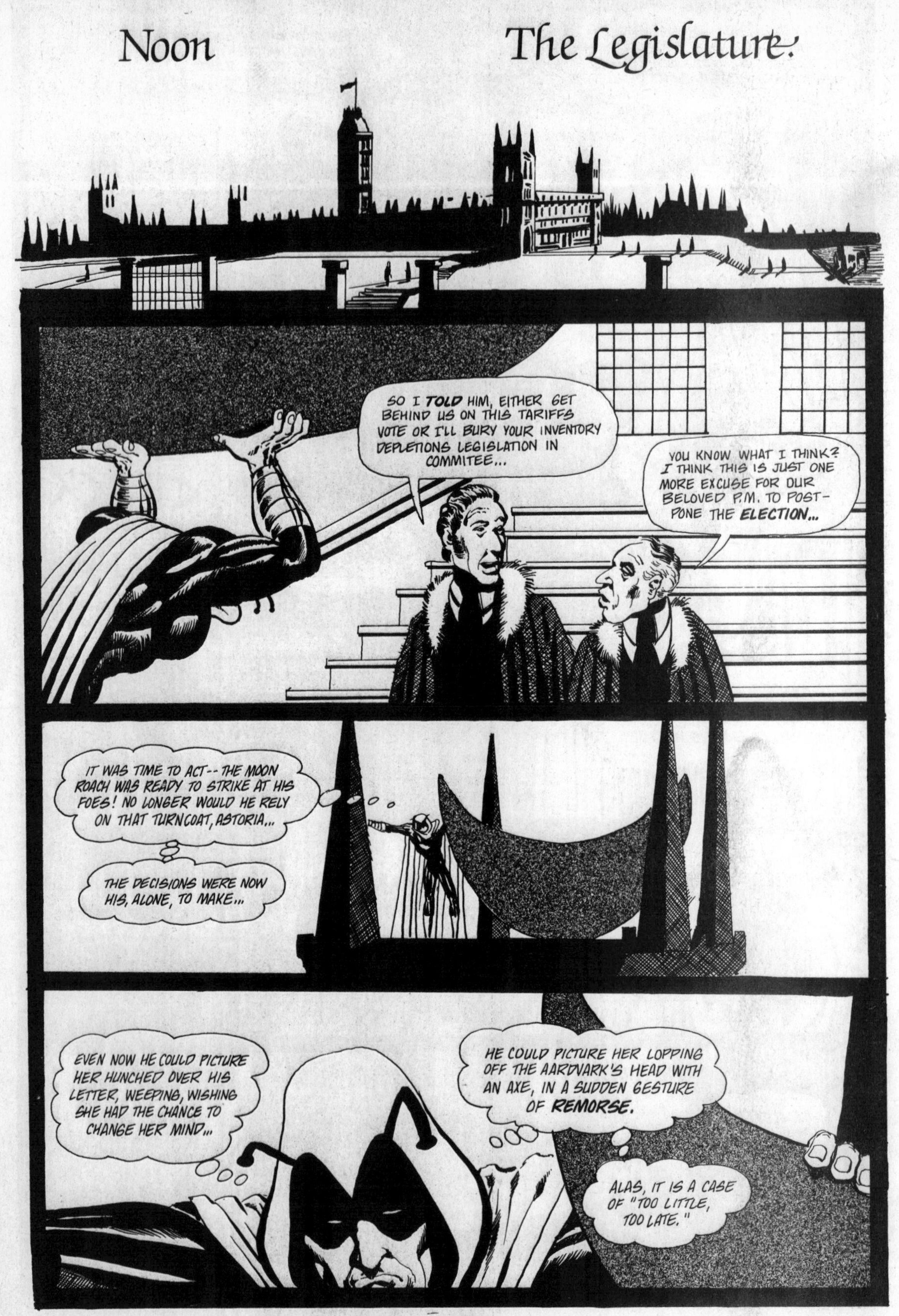

MAYBE A BATHTUB FULL OF WHISKEY.
WHAT ELSE DO THE DAMN THINGS LIKE?
TOADSTOOLS, PIXEE DUST... PIXEE DUST!
MM. NO...
THAT'S COVERED UNDER THE CONTROLLED SUBSTANCES ACT.
A BOY-ELF, MAYBE?
TOO HARD TO...
KNOCK KNOCK
COME!
MESSAGE FOR ASTORIA, M'LORD!
CEREBUS WILL TAKE IT...
I'M AFRAID IT'S "EYES ONLY," M'LORD
HOW LONG HAVE YOU BEEN DELIVERING MESSAGES, SON.
TWO YEARS, M'LORD
EVER DELIVERED A MESSAGE TO THE WRONG PERSON?
NO, M'LORD.
WELL CEREBUS IS WILLING TO BET ONE HUNDRED CROWNS
THAT THIS TIME, YOU DO!
HEH.
HERE YOU ARE, M'LORD
YOU NOW OWE CEREBUS A HUNDRED CROWNS...
BEAT IT, OR CEREBUS WILL HAVE YOU FIRED FOR GAMBLING...!

Astoria:
The Governor of the Legislature died today beneath a giant stone moon.
Please Advise
Yrs. truly
Blake
THE COOTIE AGAIN...
CEREBUS HAS TO GIVE HER FULL MARKS. ANYONE WHO CAN KEEP THAT LUNATIC ON A SHORT LEASH IS...
KNOCK
KNOCK
WHAT IS IT? CEREBUS IS BUSY!
IT'S THE DESK CLERK M'LORD
WHAT ABOUT "OUR PROBLEM"
THEY'VE TRIED PAPERING OVER THE WORDS, M'LORD, BUT THEY SEEM TO GLOW RIGHT THROUGH ...
HAVE THEM TRY ANOTHER LAYER OF WALLPAPER, THEN.
THEY WERE JUST FINISHING THE SIXTH LAYER WHEN I LEFT, M'LORD.
GAK
AND--uhm-- M'LORD.... THERE'S... uh.
THERE'S MORE.
THE WORDS HAVE APPEARED ELSEWHERE ...AS... WELL.
ELSEWHERE? WHERE ELSEWHERE?
OVER THE uh... GATE ...
OF THE HOTEL...!?
NO, M'LORD...
THE GATE TO THE --uh-- CITY.
TARIM.

WELL, WELL. WE'RE UP EARLY TODAY. FEELING AMBITIOUS OR DO WE JUST WANT TO GET A HEAD-START ON OUR SULKING...?
OH, GOOD.
JUST WHEN CEREBUS WAS RUNNING OUT OF ANNOYING DISTRACTIONS.
DON'T TELL ME --LET ME GUESS.
DOES IT HAVE ANYTHING TO DO WITH THE COLLECTED WRITINGS OF "YOU-KNOW-WHO"?
CAN WE CHANGE THE SUBJECT, PLEASE!
SUIT YOURSELF.
THERE ISN'T A POLITICIAN IN THIS CITY WHO DOESN'T WISH HE HAD THAT HARMLESS A SKELETON RATTLING AROUND HIS CLOSET, THOUGH.
BELIEVE ME, IF THAT'S ALL THEY HAVE ON YOU, YOU SHOULD TRY FOR HIS HOLINESS' JOB...

NOW THAT WE'RE FINISHED CHANGING THE SUBJECT...
CAN WE CHANGE-THE-SUBJECT!!
SURE, HOW ABOUT...?
WHAT'S THAT YOU'VE GOT IN YOUR HAND?
A MESSAGE. IT CAME IN WHILE YOU WERE SLEEPING ...
UH-OH!
"UH-OH"?
WHAT DO YOU MEAN "UH-OH"?
WE'RE IN TROUBLE.
WE'RE IN TROUBLE AND IT'S THE BUG'S FAULT!...
RIGHT?

THAT MORON.
"PLEASE ADVISE."
YOU CAN TELL CEREBUS.
CEREBUS CAN TAKE IT.
I THINK IT'S TIME I SHOWED THESE SHEEP HOW TO KEEP A BILL ALIVE PAST THE FIRST READING...
WE'RE BROKE ...
CEREBUS GUESSED IT, RIGHT?
REVENUE FORECASTS ...REVENUE FORECASTS ...
WHERE ON EARTH ARE THE...
AH!...
THE BUG DROPPED A BIG MOON ON SOMEONE HE WASN'T SUPPOSED TO AND NOW CEREBUS IS BROKE!
... AND IS ABOUT TO BE ARRESTED ...
... AND EXECUTED FOR BEING POOR, RIGHT?

GO AHEAD! SAY IT...
CEREBUS CAN HANDLE IT...
I'VE GOT EVERYTHING I NEED.
I'LL BE AT THE LEGISLATURE 'TIL QUITE LATE... HAVE ANY MESSAGES RELAYED TO ME THERE...
HAVE THE DESK CLERK CANCEL ALL MY APPOINTMENTS FOR THE DAY.
THE INQUISITION! HAS THIS GOT ANYTHING TO DO WITH THE INQUISITION?
THEY'RE GOING TO GET CEREBUS, RIGHT?
MY DEAR, THE ONLY DANGER YOU FACE AT THE MOMENT IS YOU YOURSELF
IF YOU CAN MANAGE IT, DO TRY NOT TO GET INTO TROUBLE UNTIL I'M BACK.

ARE YOU INFERRING...
THAT CEREBUS CAN'T TAKE CARE OF HIMSELF?

NO, DEAR.
I'M IMPLYING THAT YOU CAN'T TAKE CARE OF YOURSELF.

CLICK

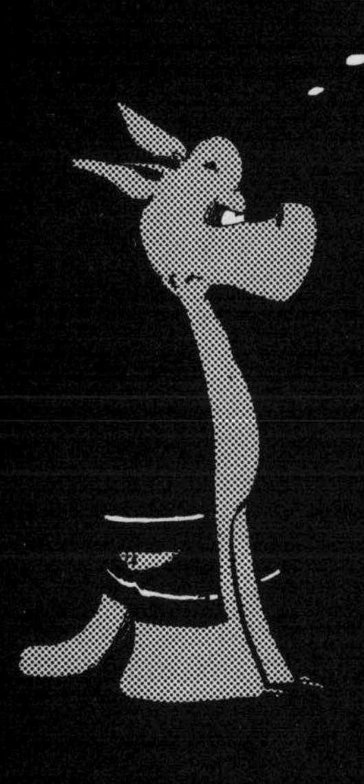
CEREBUS CAN SO TAKE CARE OF HIMSELF ...
ANY LITTLE PROBLEM THAT COMES HIS WAY...

CEREBUS HAS NEVER HAD TROUBLE BEING THE ONE IN CHARGE...
HEY!.. AH SAY..
HEY, YOU...!
Y'ALL SEEN A KID IN A BUNNY SUIT AROUND H'YAR?
LOCALLY, THAT IS...
WITH ANY LUCK AT ALL, CEREBUS WILL HAVE A HEART ATTACK AND DIE IN THE NEXT FIVE SECONDS
WHAT IS IT, SON? Y'GUMS'RE FLAPPIN' BUT NOTHIN'S COMIN' OUT..
AH SAY.. Y'LL HAVE T'SPEAK UP, SON AH DON'T READ LIPS...

'three days before'

WELL, DIP ME IN BREAD CRUMBS AND QUICK-FRY ME FO' THE **HOLIDAYS**-- IF IT AIN'T MUH OLD FRIEND **CEREBUS**...

WHEN AH READ Y'ADVERTISEMENT OVER THE FRONT GATE, AH SAID, *"ELROD, YOU OWE IT TO Y'BUNNY-SUITED LITTLE AMIGO TO DROP IN AND* ***CONSOLE*** *HIM ABOUT HIS DEFECTIVE PLUMBING..."*

URINARY, THAT IS. *AH FIGURED Y'ALL NEEDED* SOMEONE WHO WOULDN'T "TEE-HEE" ABOUT Y'"WEE-WEE," SON.

THIS--AH SAY-- THIS SHORE IS THE PERFECT HOTEL FOR A LITTLE GET-TOGETHER...
DID Y'ALL GET THE NAMEPLATES DONE? IF THERE'S ONE THING THE LAST RULER OF A DYING RACE ABSOLUTELY DETESTS...

baf!

TAXI!

YES, M'LORD? OFF TO THE RAM'S LORDS TAVERN, M'LORD?
ACTUALLY, THIS ALBINO CAME TO IEST TO MAKE TROUBLE FOR CEREBUS ...
MM.
JUST BEFORE HE FELL ASLEEP, HE HAD A CHANGE OF HEART AND ASKED CEREBUS TO GIVE YOU THIS FIFTY CROWNS TO PUT HIM ON THE NEXT BOAT GOING ANYWHERE FAR AWAY...
VERY GOOD, M'LORD ...

CEREBUS CAN TAKE CARE OF HIMSELF. THE TRICK IS TO MAKE SURE THEY DON'T GET THROUGH THE DOOR ...
M'LORD CEREBUS.

"IN HIS TWENTY-EIGHTH YEAR HE WILL LAY WASTE TO THE RICH AND POWERFUL; BENDING THEM TO HIS WILL..."
"THE SHADOW OF THE EARTH-PIG WILL SPREAD FROM THE CENTER AND A NEW AGE WILL DAWN."
IF THAT'S SUPPOSED TO BE POETRY, IT DOESN'T RHYME.

NOT POETRY...
PROPHECY.
I SEE YOU DON'T REMEMBER ME...

MY NAME IS MACMUFIN...
BRAN MACMUFIN...

CEREBUS ONLY LEANED AGAINST YOUR STATUE...
IT WAS AN ACCIDENT!
CEREBUS DIDN'T MEAN TO BREAK IT *
* CEREBUS No.5

ON THE CONTRARY, M'LORD YOU DID WHAT YOU FELT **HAD** TO BE DONE FOR THE GREATER GOOD OF **PIGTDOM...**
WE LIVE TO SERVE THE EARTH-PIG... YOU HAVE BUT TO **COMMAND** AND ...
CEREBUS IS **BUSY** RIGHT NOW...
IF CEREBUS COMES UP WITH ANY GOOD **COMMANDS**, HE'LL LET YOU KNOW.
I QUITE *UNDERSTAND*, M'LORD -- I'M IN ROOM ONE-FIFTY FIVE OF THE WEST WING ...
WHENEVER YOU'RE **READY**
IT'S A **TEST**.
SURE. **THAT**'S IT. ASTORIA IS TRYING TO PROVE TO CEREBUS THAT HE CAN'T STAY OUT OF **TROUBLE**
THE FIRST TIME CEREBUS LET'S ONE OF THESE JERKS TALK HIM INTO SOMETHING
BAM!

SHE'LL BE THERE LIKE A **SHOT!**
"I TOLD YOU SO! I TOLD YOU SO!"
"NYAH! NYAH!"
JUST WAIT'LL SHE GETS BACK AND FINDS OUT CEREBUS STAYED OUT OF TROUBLE.
WE'LL **SEE** WHO GETS THE LAST *"NYAH-NYAH"*, ASTORIA.

SLAM

THE **TRICK** IS TO MAKE YOURSELF COMPLETELY UNAVAILABLE...

WITH CEREBUS IN **HERE** AND ALL OF THEM OUT **THERE**...

TROUBLE IS GOING TO HAVE A JOB FINDING ...

GAH!

HAVE YOU -- *I SAY* -- HAVE YOU GOT A **TOWEL**, SON? I SEEM TO'VE GOTTEN M'SELF **IRRIGATED**...

... **SOAKED**, THAT IS. HEH-HEH -- I'M DAMPER THAN A BUSINESSMAN'S ARM-PITS DURING A TAX AUDIT

THAT'S A **WITTY**, SON

IF WE'RE GONNA BE ROOMIES Y'ALL ARE GONNA HAVE TO PAY **ATTENTION**...

I DON'T -- *I SAY* -- I DON'T HAVE TIME TO DO **SUB-TITLES**...

LISTEN. ALBINO.
CEREBUS IS TRYING TO KEEP HIMSELF OUT OF TROUBLE, SEE?
AND SINCE YOU'RE NOTHING BUT TROUBLE, CEREBUS HAS NO CHOICE. KEEP YOUR EYES CLOSED AND TRY TO LAND HEAD FIRST...
TROUBLE? THE ALBINO IS THE LEAST OF YOUR WORRIES, DESPOT!
THE GOVERNOR OF THE LEGISLATURE WAS JUST A SAMPLE...
GAH!
I'M GOING TO KILL EVERYONE WHO EVEN TRIES TO HELP YOU, AARDVARK
YOU'RE FINISHED!

SEIZING HIS ROACH-ROPE, THE DARKNIGHT DREADNOUGHT HAULS HIMSELF UP TOWARDS THE LEDGE ABOVE HIM.
≡UMPH≡ HIS FOE IS ASTOUNDED, STARING AFTER THE MOON ROACH **HELPLESSLY...**
...HOLDING A LIFE-SIZE REPLICA OF THE **MOON ROACH**'S FORMER WARD ≡UMPH≡
TWO-FISTED BUNKY THE ALBINO... IT'S A CLEVER RUSE BUT TRANSPARENT TO THE HOAX-WARY **LUNAR AVENGER**...
ALL RIGHT.
THAT **DOES** IT...
YOU'VE PUSHED CEREBUS TOO **FAR** THIS TIME, BUG...
CEREBUS IS COMING AFTER YOU, BUG... THIS TIME YOU'RE ...

NOW, SON, DON'T WORRY Y'SELF ABOUT OLD ELROD... Y'ALL JUST RUN ALONG AND HAVE FUN...
I'LL -- I SAY -- I'LL JUST CHECK OUT THE AVAILABLE HENS IN THIS L'IL OLD CHICKEN COOP AND SEE WHAT'S HATCHING...
GET IT, SON? "HENS"? "HATCHING"?
THAT'S A DOUBLE WITTY -- TRIPLE IF YOU COUNT THE "COOP."
WHAT'S THE USE? THE BUG IS RIGHT.
ALL HE HAS TO DO IS BUMP OFF EVERYONE WHO WANTS TO HELP CEREBUS ...
CEREBUS IS FINISHED.
SURELY -- AH SAY -- SURELY YOU JEST, SON.

WHY-- UNTIL YOU CAME TO IEST, IT WASN'T NOTHIN' BUT AN OLD-FASHIONED, DODDERING RELIC OF A CITY-STATE... MORIBUND, THAT IS ...
SINCE YOU ARRIVED, THE CHURCH HAS TURNED AROUND SO FAST ON THE QUESTION OF OUTSIDE INVESTMENT HIS HOLINESS AND FIVE TIERS OF HIS BUREAUCRACY HAVE WHIPLASH... PAINS IN THE NECK, THAT IS...
...ADD THAT TO THE WAY Y'ALL ALMOST SINGLE-HANDEDLY BROUGHT THE INQUISITION TO ITS KNEES...
...AND Y'ALL'VE GOT MORE PEOPLE WHO WANT TO HELP YOU THAN A NEAR-SIGHTED BANK TELLER WITH A SPILLED TILL...
HEH!-- IF THAT OLD BUG WANTS TO KILL ALL OF YOUR SUPPORTERS, HE'LL HAVE TO LINE 'EM UP AND USE A SEMI-AUTOMATIC CROSS-BOW, SON...
YOU JUST MADE ALL OF THAT UP!

WHY, NOT AT **ALL**, SON...

CEREBUS **DEAR?!**

I SAY CEREBUS DEAR?!

kLIK kLAK

I'M **BACK**, CEREBUS, DEAR ...

WHY--**I** GET IT NOW...

HUNH!

SO **THAT'S** IT!

Y'ALL GOT Y'SELF A LITTLE BLUSHIN' MAGNOLIA BLOSSOM OF Y'VERY OWN... **SWEETIE-PIE** THAT IS...

THAT'S WHY Y'ALL DIDN'T WANT ELROD AS YOUR ROOMIE...

HEH. HEH. HEH.

WHY THAT'S **ADORABLE**, SON!

THAT'S-- I SAY--THAT'S DOWNRIGHT **CUTE...**

IT'S OKAY, SON-- Y'DON'T --I SAY--Y'DON'T HAVE TO DROP THE WALL OF TSI ON ELROD THE ALBINO ...

NOSIREE.

I MANAGED ...TO...

EXCUSE ME, MA'AM WHILST AH **DISCRETELY** SLIP FROM VIEW...

AND LEAVE YOU AND Y'**DIMINUTIVE** ROMEO TO Y'COHABITATIONAL **BLISS**

KLIK-CLACK

WELL, WE ARE FULL OF SURPRISES AREN'T WE...?
I DOUBT IT, BUT GO AHEAD AND TRY...
HOW DID YOU MANAGE TO CULTIVATE THE MOST CHARISMATIC SWORDSMAN IN ESTARCION AS A FRIEND?
JUST A MINUTE!-- CEREBUS CAN EXPLAIN THIS!

FIRST OF ALL, IT ISN'T CEREBUS' FAULT... CEREBUS HAD EVERY INTENTION OF STAYING OUT OF TROUBLE BUT ALL OF A SUDDEN...

YOU'VE GOT TO BE KIDDING.

ELROD IS QUITE A CULT-FIGURE IN IEST...
EXTREMELY POPULAR WITH THE PEASANTS AND WORKERS...
SO CEREBUS DIDN'T CAUSE TROUBLE BY HAVING HIM HERE?

TROUBLE? I ONLY WISH YOU'D HAD THE GOOD SENSE TO STROLL THROUGH THE LOBBY WITH HIM...
IT WOULD'VE DONE YOUR REPUTATION A WORLD OF GOOD...
TARIM.

BUT CEREBUS DID STAY OUT OF TROUBLE ...
YES. YES, YOU DID.

YOU SAID CEREBUS COULDN'T TAKE CARE OF HIMSELF AND CEREBUS PROVED YOU WRONG!

IT MUST BE QUITE A BURDEN FOR YOU -- BEING RIGHT ALL THE TIME.
CEREBUS TOOK CARE OF EVERYTHING! EVERY-LAST-LITTLE-PROBLEM!
YOU DESERVE A MEDAL ...
YOU REALLY DO...

DARN RIGHT.
CEREBUS WOULD ALSO LIKE AN APOLOGY.

AN APOLOGY?
SO YOU TOLD THE DESK CLERK TO CANCEL MY APPOINTMENTS AND THEN CAME BACK HERE TO TWIDDLE YOUR THUMBS FOR A FEW HOURS...
BIG DEAL!
FOR YOUR INFORMATION, ASTORIA, CEREBUS WAS BUSY... FOR... EVERY...
CEREBUS?
WHAT IS IT? WHAT'S...
YOU DID TELL THE DESK CLERK TO CANCEL MY APPOINTMENTS ...
DIDN'T YOU?
CEREBUS?!

WONDERFUL!
THIS IS JUST PERFECT!
I'M AT THE LEGISLATURE TRYING TO MAKE YOU RICH AND YOU'RE UP HERE SABOTAGING ME!!
AND, OF COURSE, YOU EXPECT ME TO GO AND FIX EVERYTHING, NOW...
UNDO ALL OF YOUR DAMAGE
CLEAN UP YOUR MESS
SOLVE YOUR PROBLEMS ...
WELL, I'M TELLING YOU RIGHT NOW THAT I'M NOT GOING TO TAKE THIS FOREVER

SLAM
CEREBUS HAS A FEELING THIS MEANS HE'S NOT GOING TO GET AN APOLOGY.

LATER.

SNFX
OH.
YOU'RE BACK.
SO. HOW'D IT GO?

QUIT CLOWNING AROUND, ASTORIA...
DID YOU FIX EVERYTHING OR DIDN'T YOU?

"DEAR ASTORIA..."
"NEVER IN MY TWENTY YEARS OF DEALINGS IN THE BUSINESS COMMUNITY OF IEST HAVE I BEEN TREATED SO SHABBILY..."

"YOUR REQUEST, THEREFORE FOR AN EXTENSION ON YOUR LOAN PAYMENT IS..."
"... DENIED."
I KNOW YOU HAVEN'T GOT PATIENCE WITH ANYTHING AS MUNDANE AS A FINANCIAL TRANSACTION
SUFFICE TO SAY-- YOU'VE JUST COST US SOME MONEY ...
A GREAT DEAL OF MONEY...
FIVE-HUNDRED-CROWNS!
THAT IS-- FIVE HUNDRED CROWNS RIGHT NOW... IN A FEW DAYS, WITHOUT A MAJOR BANK TO VOUCH FOR YOU... FOR US...
...IT COULD BE AS MUCH AS A THOUSAND...
SO? WHERE ARE YOU GOING TO GET THE MONEY?

WELL, THAT'S QUITE A PROBLEM... ANY ATTEMPT TO BORROW MORE MONEY TO MEET OUR LOAN OBLIGATIONS IS GOING TO HURT OUR CREDIT RATING.
CASH FLOW IS THE KEY...
THIS WAS PRECISELY THE WORST TIME TO MAKE ONE OF OUR BANKS NERVOUS... SINCE OUR CASH-ON-HAND WAS DEPLETED BY LORD JULIUS DUMPING ALL OF HIS SEPRAN GOLD ON THE OPEN MARKET...
OH.
BY THE WAY, DO YOU STILL HAVE THAT MONEY I GAVE YOU?
THE THOUSAND CROWNS? AYE. CEREBUS HAS IT RIGHT...
...HERE!
FIVE HUNDRED WILL DO...
FOR NOW.

SLAM

EXCUSE ME, MA'AM!
YES!?
I FEEL ABOUT AS FOOLISH AS A DERMATOLOGIST WITH ZITS...
HEH HEH
AH FORGOT TO GIVE THE BOY HIS INVITATION
I-- I'LL TAKE IT.

Y'ALL BE SURE AND TELL HIM ELROD'S LOOKING FORWARD TO SEEING HIM THAR.
YES, I WILL.
SLAM

INVITATION? WHAT SORT OF INVITATION...

...WOULD...

Lord Julius presents

PETUNIACON

at the REGENCY in Iest

Concordance Holy Days

Guest of Honour

His Highness KING ELROD

of MELVINBONE

(lord julius' nominee to be the

next ranking diplomatic representative

of PALNU in IEST)

next; two days before

TWO DAYS BEFORE

DAWN. THE EARTH-PIG RETURNS FROM SEVERAL HOURS OF CONCERTEDLY DROWNING HIS SORROWS AND WALLOWING IN SELF PITY, AND SO IT IS THAT THE ANCIENT WALLS OF **THE REGENCY** REVERBERATE WITH ALL TWENTY VERSES OF "THE BARMAID AND THE WATCHDOG."

THOSE VERSES HE HAS DIFFICULTY REMEMBERING, HE REWRITES, SUBSTITUTING "ASTORIA" FOR "THE BARMAID" AND A STRING OF EXPLITIVES FOR THE REMAINDER OF THE LYRICS.

THE RANKING DIPLOMATIC REPRESENTATIVE OF PALNU...
MILADY.
DON' GIV'UM A TIP ≡HIC≡ 'STORIA!
'E ALMOS' DROPP'D CER'BUS ...
...TWICE!
JUST POUR HIM INTO THAT CHAIR OVER THERE...
AND I'LL SEE WHAT'S SALVAGEABLE.
WELL.
WE'VE HAD OURSELVES QUITE A NIGHT BY THE LOOK OF THINGS.
YEP.
WE SHER DID.
I SUPPOSE IT DOESN'T BOTHER YOU THAT YOU'RE ABOUT TO BE REPLACED AS RANKING DIPLOMATIC REPRESENTATIVE?
R'PLACED?
YES!
CER'BUS?
YES!
NOPE.
DOZEN BOTH'R CER'BUSA BIT.

PERHAPS YOU'D LIKE ANOTHER DRINK, THEN?
S'GREAT IDEA...
MAKITA DOUBLE.
IF YOU INSIST.
SLUP
HEH.
GHH
NG
WUMBA
WUMBA
WUMBA
WUMBA
WUMBA
WUMBA
P-P-POISON?
JUST A MEDICINAL COMPOUND, ACTUALLY.
IT CURES INEBRIATION BY BRINGING ON AN INSTANT HANGOVER...

I THOUGHT IF YOU WERE SOBER ENOUGH TO READ THIS INVITATION ...
WUBBA WUMBA
PLEASE -- DON'T SHOUT ...
Lord Julius presents
PETUNIACON
at the REGENCY in Iest
Concordance Holy Days
Guest of Honour
His Highness KING ELROD
of MELVINBONE
(lord julius' nominee to be the
next ranking diplomatic representative
of PALNU in IEST)
LORD JULIUS ...HOLY DAYS... ELROD... NOMINEE
SWELL.
IS THERE ANYTHING ELSE, BEFORE CEREBUS JUMPS OUT A WINDOW?
OH, FINE! KILL YOURSELF! TAKE THE EASY WAY OUT!
NNN
GO AHEAD!
LEAVE GOOD OLD ASTORIA WITH YOUR DEBTS... YOUR PROBLEMS!
OKAY! OKAY!
BUT IF YOU WANT CEREBUS ALIVE, YOU BETTER GET A DOZEN RAW EGGS, TWELVE GALLONS OF WATER AND SOME HOT TOWELS
QUICKLY.

BEFORE LONG

YOU SHOULD HAVE LET CEREBUS STAY DRUNK... CEREBUS IS FINISHED.
HARDLY, DARLING. WE'RE JUST SWITCHING TACTICS...

LORD JULIUS IS TRYING TO OUTFLANK US BY NOMINATING A MORE POPULAR FOLK-HERO TO REPLACE YOU IN IEST.
HE'S EVEN GONE SO FAR AS TO ADOPT ELROD AS HIS SON. THE BUSINESS COMMUNITY SEES IT AS A COMMITMENT FROM PALNU TO KEEP IEST SOLVENT.
IS IT?...
I DOUBT IT... MORE LIKELY LORD JULIUS IS THROWING THEM ELROD AS AN EMPTY BUT FLAMBOYANT GESTURE TO KEEP IEST BUYING FROM HIM EXCLUSIVELY...

SO HOW IS CHANGING CEREBUS' IMAGE GOING TO HELP?
WE'RE GOING TO MAKE YOU THE BUSINESSMAN'S CANDIDATE... ANNOUNCE THAT IF YOU ARE CONFIRMED AS RANKING DIPLOMATIC REPRESENTATIVE, YOU WILL USE EVERY LAST CROWN IN PALNU'S TREASURY TO SUPPORT IEST'S ECONOMY.
STARTING WITH A TRANSFER OF A HALF-MILLION CROWNS FROM LORD JULIUS' TREASURY TO THE BANK OF IEST...
CEREBUS DOESN'T GET IT...
LORD JULIUS WILL BE FORCED TO MATCH THE OFFER. IF HE DOES, WE UP IT TO ONE MILLION, ONE MILLION FIVE, TWO MILLION AND SO ON...
EVENTUALLY, HE'LL HAVE TO WITH-DRAW ELROD'S NOMINATION TO CUT HIS LOSSES AND PAY WHATEVER AMOUNT WE'VE PROMISED.
SO WHY DOESN'T THE BUSINESS COMMUNITY DEMAND THE MONEY THEMSELVES?

FOR THE SAME REASON THE LEGISLATURE WAS HESITANT TO VOTE AN INCREASE IN THE TARIFFS. THEY'RE AFRAID LORD JULIUS WILL CANCEL THEIR LINE OF CREDIT...
WILL HE?
NO ONE CANCELS A LINE OF CREDIT ANYMORE...
THEY JUST ADD ON MORE INTEREST CHARGES.
EVEN IF THE DEBT WILL NEVER GET PAID?
ESPECIALLY IF THE DEBT WILL NEVER GET PAID. IF PALNU CANCELLED IEST'S CREDIT THEY WOULD BE ADMITTING THAT THEY NEVER EXPECT TO SEE THE FOUR BILLION CROWNS IEST OWES THEM.
THEY WOULD BE WORTH FOUR BILLION CROWNS LESS THAN THEY ARE NOW... WHICH WOULD MAKE THEM A CREDIT RISK...
REQUIRING THEM TO PAY OFF ALL THE MONEY THEY OWE TO THE SEPRAN EMPIRE OR BE CRIPPLED BY THE INCREASED INTEREST RATES...
THEREBY PERMITTING THE SERAN EMPIRE TO, IN EFFECT, FORECLOSE ON PALNU...
IF THEY JUST ADD ON INTEREST CHARGES THEY CAN CLAIM IT AS FUTURE INCOME AND BORROW AGAINST IT...
THAT'S CRAZY.
ISN'T IT THOUGH?

OF COURSE THE SEPRAN EMPIRE AND LORD JULIUS BOTH REALIZE THAT FORECLOSING ON PALNU AND IEST WOULD BE A GRAVE MISTAKE...
AS THE NEW OWNERS THEY WOULD BE EXPECTED TO FIX THE ECONOMY...
TOO ORNATE.
SO THEIR NEW ANGLE IS TO NEVER SPEND MORE THAN YOU CAN PAY INTEREST ON.
TOO BUSY.
WHICH BASICALLY ALLOWS THEM TO SPEND TWENTY BILLION WHEN THEIR INCOME IS FOUR BILLION.
TOO OLD-FASHIONED.
IEST IS THE FIRST CITY TO REACH THE POINT OF NOT BEING ABLE TO AFFORD THE INTEREST ON THEIR DEBTS ...
SO WHAT DOES PALNU PLAN TO DO?
MUCH BETTER.
LORD JULIUS HAS CONVINCED IEST TO PAY ONLY THE MONEY OWED TO PALNU IN EXCHANGE FOR MORE CREDIT.
BY NOT PAYING ANY OTHER DEBT, IEST ALMOST HAS ENOUGH TAX REVENUE TO COVER THEIR INTEREST PAYMENTS.

SO WHOSE SIDE IS CEREBUS ON?
NEITHER, ACTUALLY.
YOU TOLD ME YOU WANTED TO HAVE MORE MONEY THAN ANYONE ELSE...
THERE'S GOING TO BE A LOT OF MONEY COMING INTO IEST BEFORE THE SITUATION BECOMES TRULY HOPELESS.
IF YOU'RE THE LAST ONE OUT OF THE CITY BEFORE THE COLLAPSE, THERE'S A GOOD CHANCE OF GETTING OUT WITH A KING'S RANSOM.
NO! THERE HAS TO BE SOMETHING WE CAN DO...
SOME WAY TO KEEP IEST SOLVENT...

YOU COULD DONATE ALL YOUR FUTURE EARNINGS TO THE TREASURY...
ON THE OTHER HAND, THERE'S NO POINT IN FINANCING A LOST CAUSE...

SNIP
SNIP
SNIP
THE MOST IMPORTANT THING RIGHT NOW IS TO CONVINCE THE PRIME MINISTER THAT YOU'RE A BETTER CHOICE THAN ELROD.
HOW ARE YOU GOING TO DO THAT...?
I'VE INVITED THE P.M. TO DINE WITH US THIS EVENING SO YOU CAN HAVE A NICE, LONG TALK
ABOUT WHAT...?
ABOUT YOUR COMMITMENT TO KEEP IEST SOLVENT EVEN IF IT BANKRUPTS PALNU...
SNIP
SNIP
SNIP
OH.
THAT.
IF YOU CAN CONVINCE HIM, THEN HE CAN CONVINCE HIS PARTY'S CAUCUS...
SNIP
WHO CAN THEN CONVINCE THE PARTY FAITHFUL TO VOTE FOR YOUR CONFIRMATION IN THE LEGISLATURE.
WHAT IF CEREBUS CAN'T CONVINCE HIM?
THEN WE GO STRAIGHT TO THE BUSINESS COMMUNITY WITH YOUR OFFER...
AND WE LET THEM CONVINCE HIM.
OH.

AND THIS IS GOING TO MAKE THE BUSINESS COMMUNITY LIKE CEREBUS, IS IT?
THAT'S THE MOST EXPENSIVE HAIR TONIC IN THE CITY.
YOU SHOULD HAVE USED BEAR GREASE. IT LOOKS LIKE THIS, BUT IT ALSO REPELS BLACK FLIES...
YOU'VE GOT THE JACKET MATERIAL?
YES, ASTORIA.
AND THE VEST?
YES, ASTORIA.
AND THE SHIRT?
YES, ASTORIA
AND THE MATERIAL FOR THE SASH?
YES, ASTORIA.
TELL HER WE NEED THE COMPLETE OUTFIT NO LATER THAN MID-AFTERNOON
AND GIVE HER FIFTY CROWNS, WILL YOU?
TARIM.

"THE CHURCH WILL RETREAT BEFORE HIM AND TURN INWARD, LEAVING THE ONE TRUE MESSAGE OF THE EARTH-PIG BORN..."
"FOR THIS NEW AGE WILL BE THE AGE OF THE EARTH-PIG."
STILL HERE, EH?
"HIS FOLLOWERS WILL BE FEW..."
"BUT THEIR LOYALTY SHALL ENDURE FOR ALL TIME."
SPIFFY.
NOW CEREBUS HAS A PROPHECY FOR YOU...
I AM MOST EAGER TO HEAR IT, M'LORD.
"AND IT SHALL COME TO PASS IN HIS TWENTY-EIGHTH YEAR THAT A MORON WILL BUG THE EARTH-PIG ONCE TOO OFTEN..."
"...AND FROM THAT DAY FORWARD, THE MORON SHALL TRULY HAVE TO GUM HIS FOOD AT MEAL-TIMES"

THE EVENING BEFORE

AH! THE REGENCY GARDENS "THE MOST BEAUTIFUL GARDENS IN ALL ESTARCION"
THEY SEEM TO GLOW WITH THEIR OWN LIGHT AS THE SUN FADES FROM VIEW...
I HAVE THE INCOME PROJECTIONS HERE THAT I TOLD YOU ABOUT AT DINNER...
SURELY NOT TONIGHT... THE MOON IS FULL AND THE SKY IS SO CLEAR. THE STARS WILL BE SHINING SOON.
HERE THEY ARE...
OF COURSE THE FIGURES ARE ONLY PROJECTIONS, BUT, THEY ARE BASED ON YOUR OWN GOVERNMENT'S CALCULATIONS OF INCOME...
≥SIGH≤
FOR YEAR ONE THERE'S A SUB-STANTIAL DEFICIT, GRANTED...
BUT THE REAL GAINS...
WELL, YOU CAN SEE FOR YOURSELF. STARTING IN YEAR TWO, YOU'RE GETTING A REAL GROWTH POTENTIAL ALMOST DOUBLE WHAT THE FINANCE DEPARTMENT PROJECTS IN THE FIRST QUARTER AND FIFTEEN PER CENT INCREASES FOR THE NEXT THREE...

WHAT ARE YOU TRYING TO TELL ME, ASTORIA?
YOU WILL BE PROMOTING THE ECONOMIC DESTRUCTION OF IEST IF YOU VOTE TO CONFIRM ELROD, WHEN THE LEGISLATURE RECONVENES
CEREBUS IS YOUR ONLY HOPE.
I'M AFRAID YOU'RE MISTAKEN, CHILD... MY ONLY HOPE IS TO DO WHATEVER LORD JULIUS TELLS ME TO DO.
IF YOU DON'T STOP HIM, LORD JULIUS WILL BLEED THIS CITY WHITE.
THERE'S STILL TIME.
I WISH I SHARED YOUR OPTIMISM. ALAS, I PREFER LIVING UNDER A SINGLE THUMB, PAYING AN ENDLESS SUCCESSION OF INTEREST PAYMENTS EASILY ARRANGED AND REARRANGED...
ALL LORD JULIUS DEMANDS IS TOTAL AND COMPLETE OBEDIENCE AND MORE MONEY EVERY TIME WE PAY HIM. HE'S BEING QUITE REASONABLE, REALLY...
WE'LL FIGHT YOU, THEN...
NOW. NOW.

WHAT DO YOU SUPPOSE YOU WILL ACCOMPLISH WITH SUCH FOOLISHNESS?
HMM?
OR DO YOU EVEN HAVE A GOAL?
I INTEND TO SEE TO IT, MR. PRIME MINISTER THAT CONTROL OF THE IESTAN ECONOMY REMAINS IN IEST...
IF THAT TASK REQUIRES MOVING THE REINS OF POWER FROM THE LEGISLATURE TO THE AMBASSADOR SUITE OF THE REGENCY HOTEL
THEN THAT IS WHAT I WILL DO...
YAWN
I SEE.
A THIRST FOR POWER BUT NO STOMACH FOR ELECTION.
YOU MOCK ME AT YOUR PERIL, MR. PRIME MINISTER.
I AM NOT ACCUSTOMED TO LOSING...
AT YOUR AGE NEITHER WAS I...
ONE GROWS ACCUSTOMED TO ANYTHING, ASTORIA ...
... IN TIME.
COFFEE?
YOU THINK LORD JULIUS CAN'T BE BEATEN AT HIS OWN GAME I'M TELLING YOU THAT HE CAN!...

COFFEE?
THE CUPS BETTER BE HERE WHEN I GET BACK OR I'LL HAVE YOUR LUGGAGE SEARCHED.
THE BUSINESS COMMUNITY IS WITH ME, MR. PRIME MINISTER.
EVEN LORD JULIUS CAN'T ARGUE WITH THEM...
A FINE KITCHEN STAFF SUPERVISOR YOU TURNED OUT TO BE. SELLING YOURSELF TO THE HIGHEST BIDDER ...
WHO DO YOU THINK YOU ARE? ME?
LORD JULIUS.
YOUR MOTHER AND I HAVE BEEN TERRIBLY WORRIED ABOUT YOU...
WOULD IT HAVE KILLED YOU TO SEND A POST CARD?
LISTEN--ABOUT ELROD!...
SURE! BLAME YOUR OLDER BROTHER--BUT AT LEAST HE CAME HOME WHEN AUNT SOPHIE TOOK SICK...
WE SENT YOU THE FARE... BUT, NO...
CUT THAT OUT!

DID YOU SAY SOMETHING, DEAR?
CEREBUS WAS JUST THINKING OUT LOUD...
WHY DIDN'T SHE RECOGNIZE YOU?
ASTORIA?
IF SHE WAS EVER CAUGHT NOTICING A HOTEL WAITER, SHE'D BE DE-SPOONED BY THE DAUGHTERS OF THE CIRINIST REVOLUTION.
BUT, ENOUGH ABOUT ASTORIA. THE NIGHT REEKS OF ROMANCE, THE MAD BLOOD OF YOUTH POUNDS IN MY VEINS
AT DAWN, THE FESTIVITIES COMMENCE AND THE BEER TICKETS ARE TWELVE FOR A CROWN.
LET CARE AND WORRY BE FORGOTTEN! LET JOY AND MERRY-MAKING RULE THE CITY.
CAN I PENCIL YOU IN FOR THE "GRAFT: BOON OR BLESSING" PANEL?

ONCE HE IS IN HIS NEW CLOTHES, MR. PRIME MINISTER, YOU WILL SEE WHY BUSINESSMEN EVERYWHERE WILL SOON FLOCK TO HIS SIDE ...
WHY I AM DEALING FROM A POSITION OF STRENGTH -- NOT WEAKNESS...
GAK!
A FLOCK OF BUSINESSMEN, EH?
THAT'S ABOUT AS GRISLY A PIECE OF IMAGERY AS YOU'RE EVER LIKELY TO HEAR...

HE'LL BE CHANGED IN A FEW MINUTES, MR. PRIME MINISTER I DO HOPE THIS WILL HELP TO
CLIK

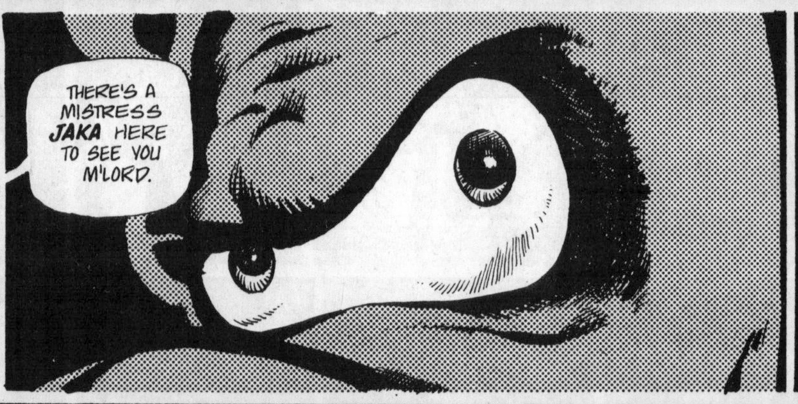

next: the night before

THE NIGHT BEFORE

YOU LOOK...
...WONDERFUL.

YES.
CEREBUS KNOWS.

THIS SUIT COST CEREBUS FIFTY CROWNS.
REAL PAPER ONES... NOT THE LOUSY GOLD CROWNS LIKE YOU HAVE IN THE LOWER CITY...

AND LOOK AT THIS...
ALMOST FOUR HUNDRED CROWNS. CEREBUS HAD A THOUSAND, BUT, HE HAD TO PAY FOR HIS SUIT, BRIBE A CAB DRIVER AND ...
...AND OTHER THINGS, TOO.

CEREBUS IS GOING TO HAVE A LOT OF MONEY SOON...
THOUSANDS ...
MILLIONS MAYBE.

I SEE.

CEREBUS GETS ALL OF HIS MEALS FOR FREE. HIS ALE, TOO.
THEY GAVE CEREBUS SEVEN ROOMS ALL TO HIMSELF...

CEREBUS HAS A BED THAT'S BIGGER THAN THE ROOM YOU LIVE IN...

I SEE.
YOU MUST BE VERY HAPPY...

WHAT? OH. YEAH. CEREBUS STARED AT A BUS-BOY UNTIL HE WET HIS PANTS. THEY'RE ALL AFRAID OF CEREBUS HERE.

ARE THEY REALLY.
PETRIFIED. CEREBUS DOESN'T EVEN HAVE TO SAY ANYTHING. ALL HE HAS TO DO IS LOOK AT THEM. LIKE...

...THIS.

CEREBUS COULD BEAT UP ANYONE IN THIS HOTEL. CEREBUS COULD TAKE THEM ON FOUR AND FIVE AT A TIME, NO SWEAT.
I SEE.
DO YOU UNDERSTAND NOW WHAT CEREBUS IS SAYING?
I'M NOT SURE THAT I DO.
NO.

CEREBUS WANTS YOU TO MOVE IN HERE WITH HIM.

WHAT ABOUT ...
ASTORIA.

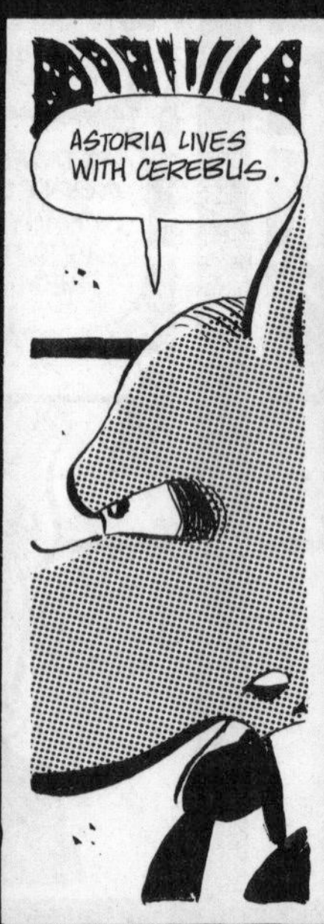
ASTORIA LIVES WITH CEREBUS.

I... KNOW.
EVERYONE KNOWS.
I MEANT-- WHAT WILL HAPPEN TO HER.

ASTORIA WILL LIVE WITH US...
SHE HAS A ROOM BEHIND A SLIDING PANEL.
THE THREE OF US.
LIVING IN YOUR SUITE...

IT'S OKAY...
SEVEN ROOMS.
THAT'S TWO EACH FOR YOU AND ASTORIA.
THREE FOR CEREBUS
...

ASTORIA IS GOING TO MAKE CEREBUS WEALTHY.
OH. AND YOU MIGHT HAVE TO DO SOME WORK.
TIDYING UP-- RUNNING ERRANDS, YOU KNOW.

OTHERWISE ASTORIA WILL ACCUSE CEREBUS OF TAKING IN A FREELOADER.

YOU MADE THE RIGHT DECISION COMING TO SEE CEREBUS...
CEREBUS WILL SEE TO IT THAT YOU NEVER HAVE TO DANCE AGAIN.

I *LIKE* DANCING.
IN GREATER IEST, DANCERS ARE CONSIDERED... WELL...
TO BE PERFECTLY **HONEST**...

IT WOULD BE BAD FOR BUSINESS IF PEOPLE KNEW CEREBUS WAS LIVING WITH A **DANCER**.

I SEE.
AND WOULD YOU STILL KILL A YAK FOR MY SUPPER...

OR WOULD THAT **ALSO** BE BAD FOR BUSINESS?

IF-YOU-REALLY WANT-A-YAK ...
CEREBUS-WILL-BUY-YOU ONE.

THANK YOU.
I'M AFRAID IT WOULDN'T BE THE SAME, SOMEHOW.

WHEN DID YOU REMEMBER ABOUT ME.
ABOUT US...

WHENEVER CEREBUS WAS...DRUNK...HE'D HAVE THESE... DREAMS.

AND, ONCE, CEREBUS SAW...

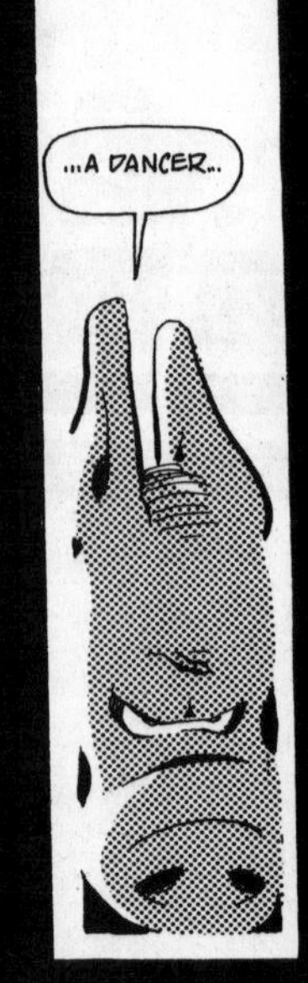
...A DANCER..

IN A TAVERN... IN...

BEDUIN.

JAKA!
YES?

WHAT'S THIS?
I--I DON'T KNOW

IEST RENEGOTIATING HER LOAN PAYMENTS.

YOU'RE CRAZY.
THE PRIME MINISTER TOLD CEREBUS THAT JOKE.

THE PRIME MINISTER.
YOU ARE MOVING UP IN THE WORLD AREN'T YOU?

THAT'S WHY CEREBUS WASN'T TOO SURPRISED WHEN YOU SHOWED UP...
ASTORIA WARNED CEREBUS IT WOULD HAPPEN.
THAT WHAT WOULD HAPPEN?
I DON'T UNDERSTAND.
FRIENDS FROM CEREBUS' PAST.
SHOWING UP ON CEREBUS' DOORSTEP.
NOW THAT CEREBUS IS SO...
SO...
...SUCCESSFUL?

ARE YOU INFERRING THAT I'M HERE FOR SOME KIND OF HANDOUT?!

NO.

CEREBUS IS IMPLYING YOU'RE HERE FOR SOME KIND OF HANDOUT...

YOU SEE, THE SPEAKER IMPLIES ...
THE LISTENER ...
I-KNOW-THE-DIFFERENCE ...

JAKA.
IT'S OKAY.
I DIDN'T COME HERE FOR CHARITY.
CEREBUS CAN AFFORD TO GIVE YOU A HANDOUT...
I CAME TO SEE YOU...
YOU DON'T BELIEVE ME, DO YOU?
I CAN TELL BY YOUR ...
JAKA!

JAKA.
CEREBUS HAS BEEN A MERCENARY -- A TAX COLLECTOR...
... A PROFESSIONAL GAMBLER...
CEREBUS MAY NOT KNOW MUCH...

...BUT CEREBUS KNOWS WHEN SOMEONE IS BROKE.

UNTIL YESTERDAY, I HAD OVER ONE HUNDRED CROWNS ON DEPOSIT IN THE BANK OF IEST...
YOUR LIFE'S SAVINGS, NO DOUBT ... AND NOW IT'S GONE?
YES.
BAD INVESTMENT?
... I'M BEGINNING TO THINK SO.
YES.

THERE ARE A LOT OF SHADY CHARACTERS IN IEST.
YOU'LL BE SAFE FROM THEM, THOUGH, LIVING HERE...
...WITH CEREBUS.
HE WASN'T A SHADY CHARACTER AT ALL. HE WAS A RESPECTED SALVAGE MERCHANT.
FROM BEDUIN...

SALVAGE MERCHANT, EH?
SO WHAT DID HE SELL YOU-- WORTHLESS STOCK IN HIS **COMPANY** OR SOMETHING?
NO...
IT WAS MORE LIKE... AN **ANTIQUE**...
UH-HUH.
I WASN'T *SURE* IT WAS **REAL** -- BUT HE LET ME PICK IT UP.
AND YOU TRUSTED YOUR ***INSTINCTS***...
YES.
AT FIRST, HE DIDN'T WANT TO SELL IT...
OF **COURSE**.
THAT'S THE OLDEST TRICK IN THE BOOK...
HE SAID IT WAS LIKE NO METAL HE HAD EVER SEEN BEFORE...
CEREBUS ONCE STAINED A JUG WITH *BERRY JUICE* AND SOLD IT AS RARE **PINK-IRON**.

AND THAT HE KNEW NOTHING ABOUT IT
EXCEPT THAT IT HAD BEEN FOUND WITH A... LARGE QUANTITY OF... GOLD COINS...
SOME OF THEM... DATING BACK... MORE THAN...
THIRTY YEARS.

YOU MUST FEEL PRETTY **FOOLISH**...
YES.

I'M AFRAID I HAVE TO **LEAVE**, NOW.
LEAVE!?
BUT...
YOU'RE BROKE! WHERE WILL YOU GO? WHAT WILL YOU DO?

I'VE TAKEN CARE OF MYSELF SINCE I WAS **TWELVE**...
I'LL MANAGE.

AT LEAST LET CEREBUS GIVE YOU SOME MONEY TO TIDE YOU OVER...
NO.
AS A MATTER OF FACT ...
I WANT TO GIVE YOU SOMETHING ...
HUH?
"IT'S IN THAT PACKAGE NEXT TO YOU..."
I'LL LEAVE IT TO YOU TO DECIDE...
...WHETHER OR NOT IT WAS A BAD INVESTMENT...

JAKA!

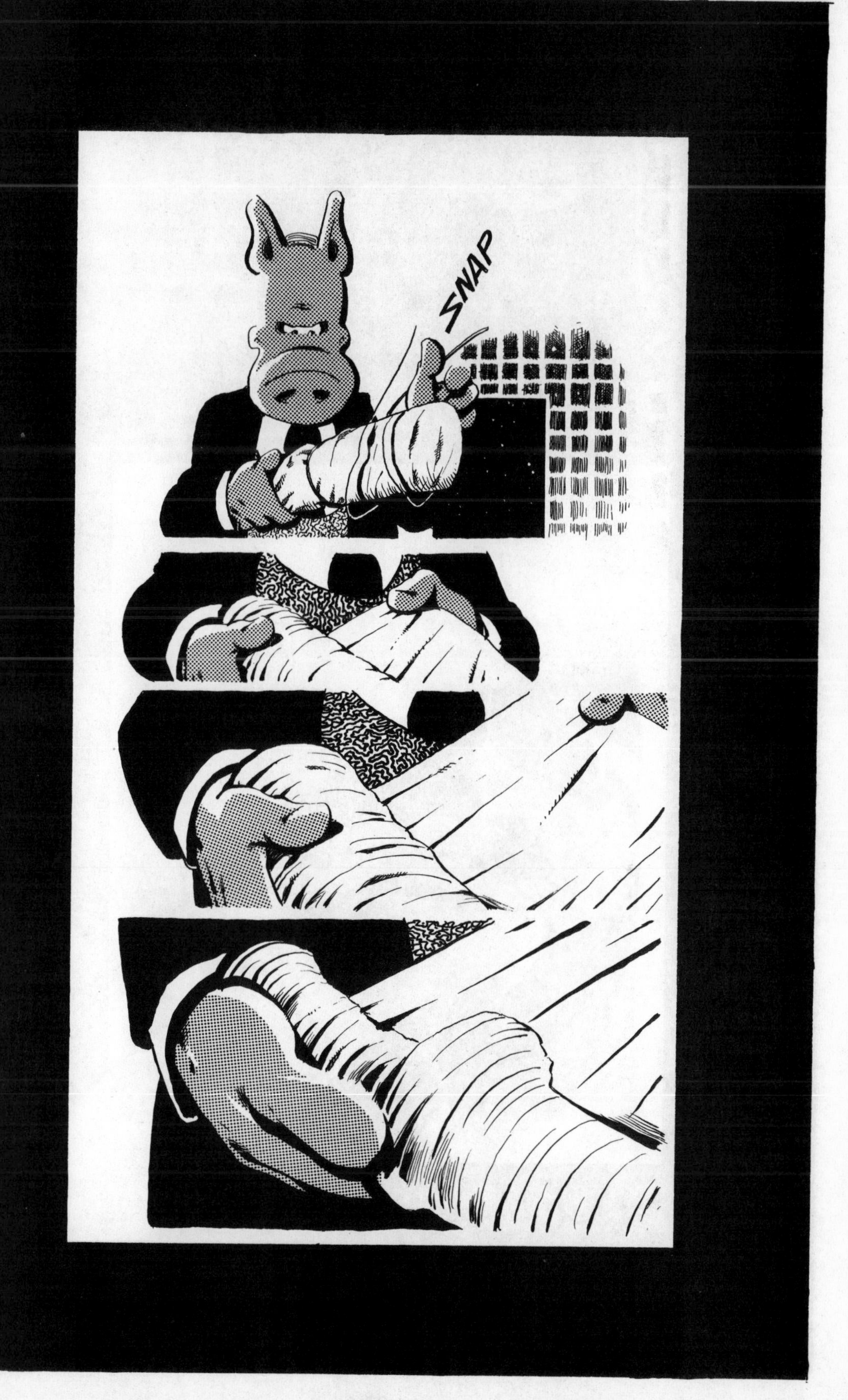
SNAP

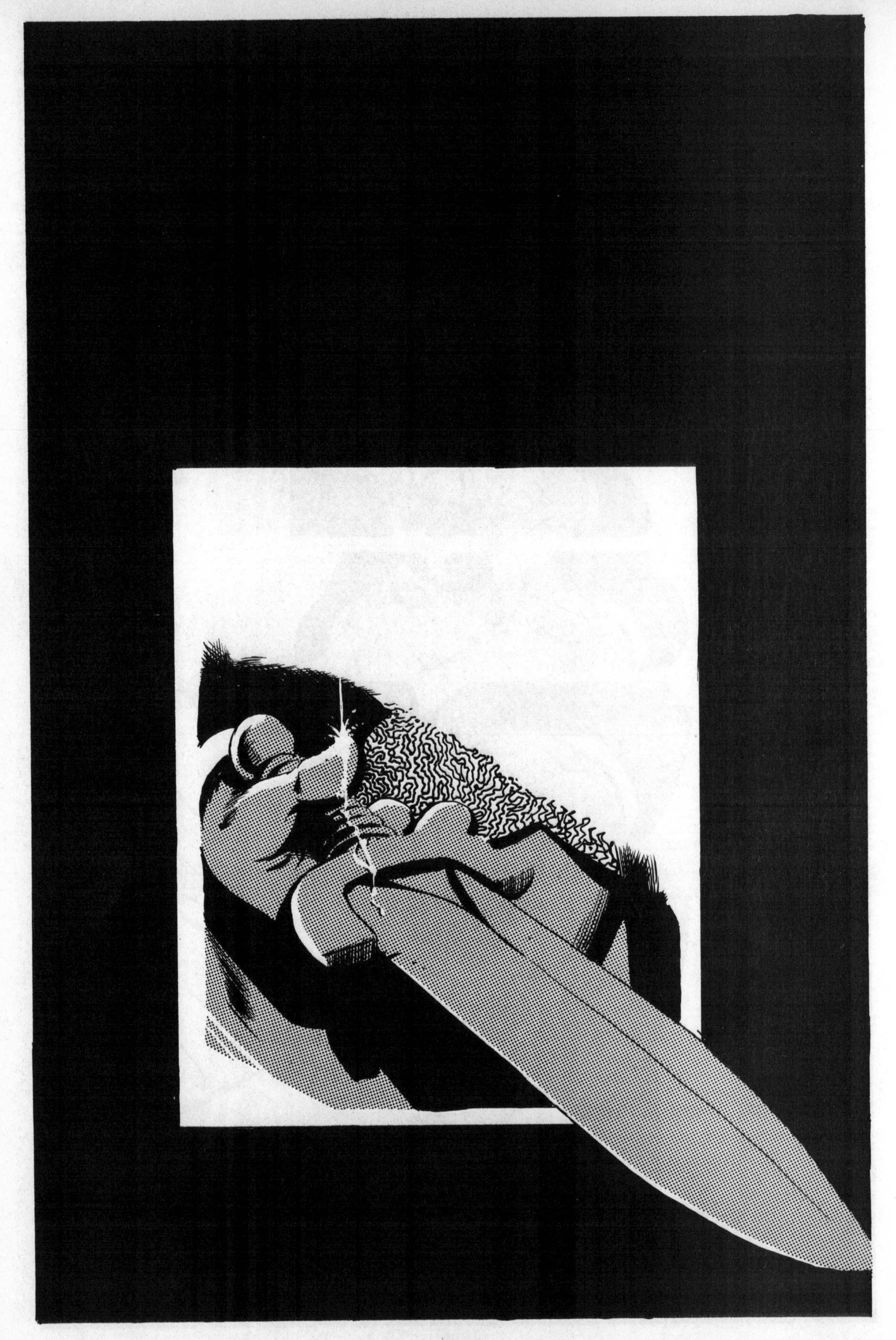

IT'S SHOWTIME!
I SUPPOSE YOU THINK YOU'RE CLEVER OR SOMETHING...

DISAPPEARING RIGHT AFTER DINNER AND LEAVING ME TO EXPLAIN IT TO THE PRIME MINISTER ...

ALL MY HARD WORK TO GET THE LEGISLATURE INTO LINE BEHIND US AND YOU THROW IT AWAY BY BEING RUDE!
YOU ARE, WITHOUT A DOUBT THE MOST UNGRATEFUL ... MISERABLE ... ILL-MANNERED...
AYE.
DON'T YOU DARE AGREE WITH ME WHEN I'M WINNING AN ARGUMENT ...

I DON'T KNOW WHY I BOTHER!
I REALLY DON'T
YOU DON'T LISTEN TO ME...
YOU DON'T LISTEN TO ANYONE!

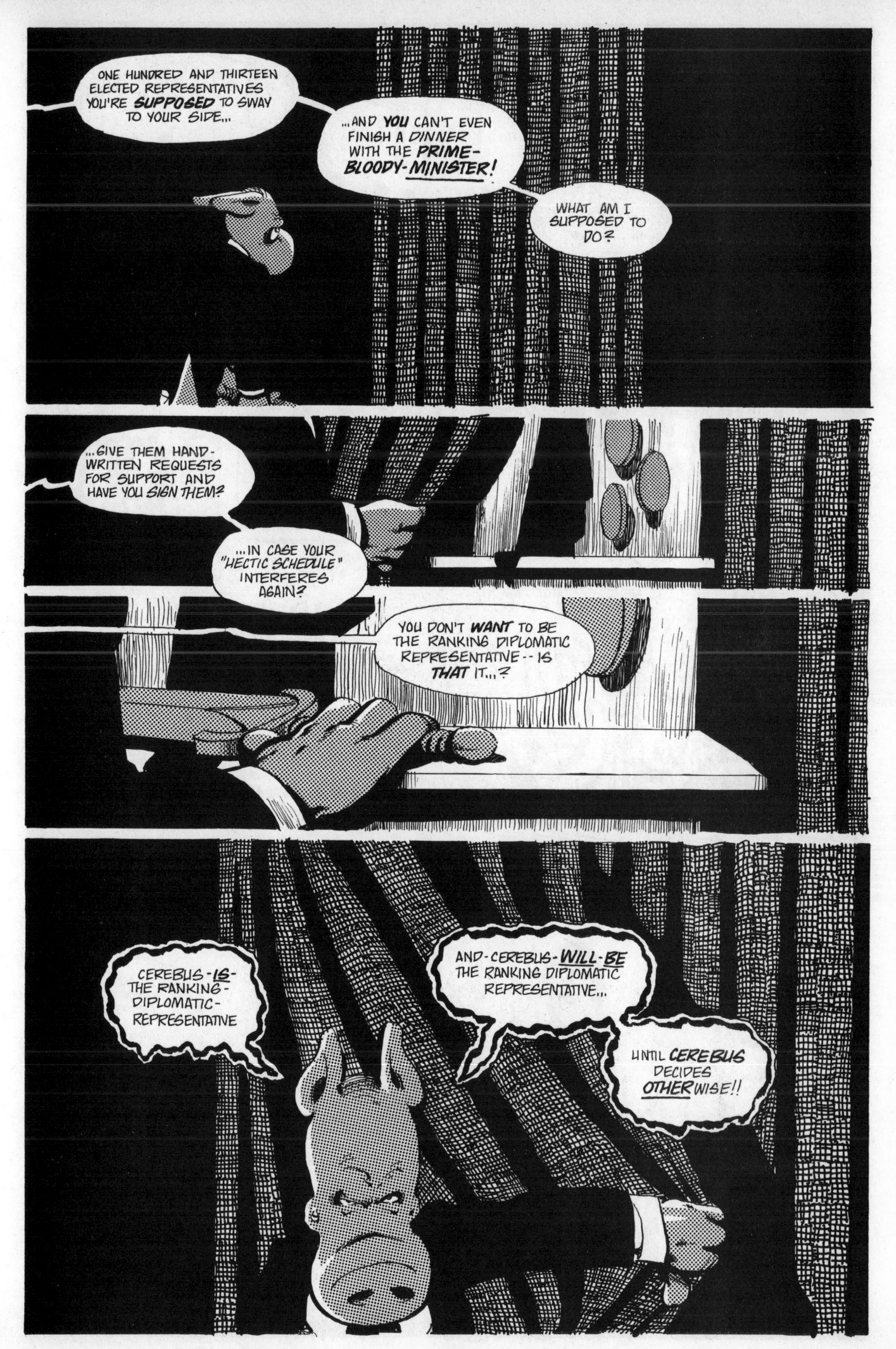
ONE HUNDRED AND THIRTEEN ELECTED REPRESENTATIVES YOU'RE SUPPOSED TO SWAY TO YOUR SIDE...
...AND YOU CAN'T EVEN FINISH A DINNER WITH THE PRIME-BLOODY-MINISTER!
WHAT AM I SUPPOSED TO DO?
...GIVE THEM HAND-WRITTEN REQUESTS FOR SUPPORT AND HAVE YOU SIGN THEM?
...IN CASE YOUR "HECTIC SCHEDULE" INTERFERES AGAIN?
YOU DON'T WANT TO BE THE RANKING DIPLOMATIC REPRESENTATIVE--IS THAT IT...?
CEREBUS-IS-THE RANKING-DIPLOMATIC-REPRESENTATIVE
AND-CEREBUS-WILL-BE THE RANKING DIPLOMATIC REPRESENTATIVE...
UNTIL CEREBUS DECIDES OTHERWISE!!

I HAVEN'T GOT TIME TO TELL YOU WHAT YOU CAN SAY AND WHAT YOU CAN'T SAY...
SO KEEP TALKING...
BUT DON'T SAY ANYTHING.
YOU MEAN WHAT LORD JULIUS DOES?
IT'S STARTING SLOW, SURE! BUT A LOT OF PEOPLE HAVE TO WORK TODAY, RIGHT?
NO, ELROD ISN'T GOING TO SHOW UNTIL AFTER LUNCH.
IS HE GOING TO BE DOING SKETCHES?
BLAKELY. BLAKELY.
I HAVEN'T GOT A BLAKELY.
YOU REMIND ME OF THE DESK CLERK.
NIACON
ELROD NOW!
TELL THEM WE NEED AT LEAST FIFTY MORE ELROD POSTERS.

YES, BUT BE DULL INSTEAD OF FLIPPANT.
THE RANKING DIPLOMATIC REPRESENTATIVE AND THE DUCHESS OF PARMOC...
RIGHT. HERE ARE YOUR BADGES AND YOUR SCHEDULE OF EVENTS.
WE'RE GOING TO PUT YOU IN THE OAK ROOM.
SORRY, WE CAN'T BE RESPONSIBLE FOR STOLEN ITEMS.
NEXT TIME, LEAVE YOUR CHILDREN IN YOUR HOTEL ROOM.

I'VE RENTED ONE OF THE LARGER ROOMS, BUT WE MIGHT STILL HAVE TOO BIG A CROWD TO HANDLE...
IF IT STARTS GETTING CRAMPED JUST ASK ONE OF THE STAFF FOR A SECURITY GUARD...
IF YOU'LL REMEMBER I WAS THE FIRST ONE TO RISE AND MOVE THAT ELROD BE GRANTED AN ENTRANCE VISA.
AND HE WAS SINCERELY GRATEFUL...
AT LEAST THAT'S WHAT HE TOLD ME AT LAST NIGHT'S PRIVATE RECEPTION.

THIS IS THE OAK ROOM...
REMEMBER KEEP TALKING-- SHAKE HANDS...
AND TRY TO LOOK...

...IMPORTANT.
YOU'D BETTER SEND FOR THE SECURITY GUARD--CEREBUS WILL NEVER MAKE IT THROUGH THOSE HORDES ALIVE.
GO IN AND SIT DOWN.
SOMEONE'S MADE A MISTAKE, --THAT'S ALL.
I'LL BE BACK SHORTLY ...

Jaka—
Cerebus would like
very, very, very much
WHAT DO YOU WANT?
I WISH ONLY TO SERVE MY LIEGE.
LOOK--
CEREBUS IS TRYING TO SAVE HIS JOB, SO ...
WHY?
HUH?

WHAT I MEAN IS-- WHY SAVE SOMETHING SO... INAPPROPRIATE?
SURELY, THERE IS SOME MORE WORTHWHILE VOCATION FOR THE EARTH-PIG BORN.
UH-HUH.
STUFF STUFF
TAKING INTO ACCOUNT THE INFERIOR BREED OF PERSON TO WHOM THE IDIOT MASSES FIND THEMSELVES DRAWN IN A FREE ELECTION
ONE CAN HARDLY SEE ANY POSITION BENEATH THAT OF PRIME MINISTER AS BEING SUFFICIENTLY AMUSING...
CAN ONE?

UH-OH.
AGAINST THAT WALL.
ONE IS SIMPLY COMPELLED TO QUESTION THE WISDOM OF STEERING THE SHIP FROM INSIDE THE ANCHOR...

PSSST.
M'LORD?
CAN WE--UH-- TALK ABOUT THIS LATER?

AH! "HE WILL ABIDE NONE WHO INTERFERE WITH HIS LIFE, HIS WAYS OR HIS MANY WIVES AND CONCUBINES..."
I QUITE UNDERSTAND.

MILADY.
WHAT'S ALL THIS?
FREE FOOD, IT SHOULD ATTRACT THE REPRESENTATIVES.
IT'S YOUR JOB TO KEEP THEM HERE.

WHO WAS THAT BY THE WAY?
HUH?
OH. NOBODY IMPORTANT. DON'T WORRY ABOUT IT.

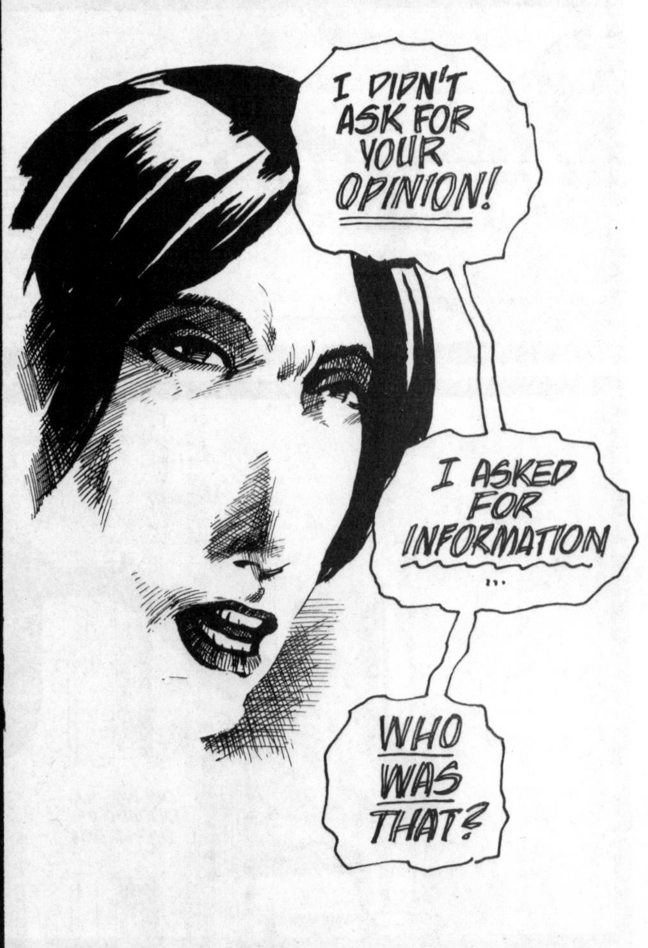
I DIDN'T ASK FOR YOUR OPINION!
I ASKED FOR INFORMATION
WHO WAS THAT?

JUST SOME NUT--THAT'S ALL!
HE SAID CEREBUS' JOB WASN'T IMPORTANT ENOUGH...
OH.

HE SAID CEREBUS SHOULD BE PRIME MINISTER...

TWELVE... SIXTEEN... TWENTY-THREE... FORTY-TWO FIFTY-ONE!
TERIM'S BLOOD...
FLIP!!
IT ISN'T CEREBUS' FAULT; CEREBUS KEEPS TELLING HIM TO TAKE A HIKE...

FIFTY-FOUR!
FLIP
FLIP
FLIP
FLIP
FIFTY-SIX!!
SIXTY-THREE!!
AND NINE UNDECIDED!!
BUT HE JUST KEEPS COMING BACK.

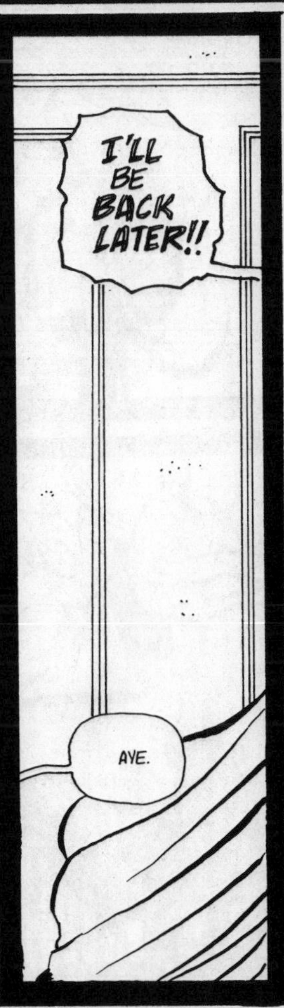
I'LL BE BACK LATER!!
AYE.

and very, very sincerely
HEY!
HEY, YOU! WIT' D'EARS!

HEY!...
DIS P'TATA SALAD IS GRATE...
WHERED'JA GET DIS STUFF ANYHOW?

IT CAME WITH THE ROOM.

CAME WIDDA ROOM?!
HEY-- DAT'S PRIDDY FUNNY...
WUDDA YOU? A COMEDIAN?
CEREBUS IS THE RANKING DIPLOMATIC ...

CARABUS?
RILLY!?
STUFF STUFF
HEY! HEY!
DIS IS YOUAH LUCKY DAY! I REPRESEN' DADOCKS!!

YOU REPRESENT WHAT?
DADOCKS!
DADOCKS!
WHERE DA BOATS COME IN-- DA DOCKS!! ...

OH.
THE DOCKS.

AT'S WHUD I SAID.
DA DOCKS.

LISSEN.
...AHHH...

WE COULD HELP EACH UDDAH, YA KNOW?
A LIDDLE ENCARAGEMENT GOES A LONG WAY...
MONEY?

I FIGYUH--TWO GRAND... IN SMALL BILLS! THAT WAY, WHEN YOUAH SHIP COMES IN ...
IT'LL MAKE IT...
IF Y'FOLLA ME?
WHAT ELSE DOES CEREBUS GET?

WHUD ELTZ?...
WHUD ELTZ?
WUDDEM I? DA GOODWILL?
I'M DOON YUH A FAVUH...

CEREBUS WILL HAVE TO THINK ABOUT IT...
FOIN!
FOIN!
LIVE ON NUTS AND BARRIES F' DA RESTA YUH LIFE!
CAN YOU BELIEVE IT?
CAN YOOU BE-E-LIEVE IT?
WO!!
BEAUTIFUL, BEAUTIFUL.
I'M HIP! I'M HIP!
NUTS AND BERRIES?
HEY! HEY!
HEY! HEY! HEY!
WOO! WOO!
WOO! WOO! WOO!

HEYYYYUH!
IT MUST BE A REAL PLEASURE TO MEET ME, HUH?
YA HA HA HA HA HA HA

I CAN'T TELL YOU HOW MUCH I'M ENJOYING YOUR POTATO SALAD ...
WOULD YOU SIGN THIS PIECE OF PAPER?
WHAT IS IT? A CHEQUE?
" A CHEQUE!"
WHAT DID I TELL YOU?
ISN'T HE A RIOT!?

WHY NO-- IT'S JUST A PIECE OF PAPER... MY WIFE MADE ME PROMISE TO GET YOUR SIGNATURE ...
YEAH?

SKRTCHA SKRTCHA
SKRTCH

ME NEXT!
ME! ME!
CAN YOU DO MINE NOW? I HAVE TO LEAVE.
CAN I HAVE A SKETCH, TOO?
ONE AT A TIME!!

HEY! HE'S SIGNING AUTOGRAPHS ... C'MON!
WHO IS HE?
I DON'T KNOW, BUT EVERYONE ELSE IS GETTING ONE.

HOW DO YOU LIKE THE REGENCY?
WHERE'S ASTORIA?
DID YOU REALLY WALK OUT ON THE PRIME MINISTER?
ARE YOU GOING TO BE HERE TOMORROW?
ARE YOU RICH?
YEAH-- AND WHAT ABOUT THE GRAND INQUISITOR?
DID YOU REALLY TELL HIM TO JUMP OFF A BRIDGE?
WHAT'S ELROD REALLY LIKE?
DID HE REALLY RIP THE DOOR OFF ITS HINGES TO HELP YOU ESCAPE FROM SERREA?

FINE.
ELSEWHERE.
AYE.
AYE.
NOT YET.
NO.
ELROD.
DEFINITELY NOT.
Cerebus

I'LL TELL YOU WHAT I'D LIKE TO KNOW, M'LORD.
I'D LIKE TO KNOW WHAT IT'S LIKE...
...LIVING WITH LORD JULIUS' EX-WIFE...
SNAP
TSK TSK. HAVE ONE OF MINE...
AYE.
AS LONG AS IT'S SMEARED ANYWAY, BE A GOOD CHAP AND TURN IT INTO A TREE, HMM?

SO? WHAT IS IT LIKE?
CEREBUS CAN'T TALK RIGHT NOW ...
CEREBUS IS SKETCHING A TREE!
SKETCHING?
DID HE SAY... SKETCHING?
I THINK HE DID...
ANYONE HAVE SOME PAPER WITH THEM?

COULD YOU MAKE THE TOP BRANCH A LITTLE LONGER?
NO SWEAT.
MARVELOUS DETAIL...
LEAVES? WHEN DID HE START DOING LEAVES?
MINE WAS THE FIRST
HE SAID HE MIGHT BE DOING ROCKS TOMORROW...
REALLY!
SAY!
WHAT DO ELROD'S SKETCHES LOOK LIKE?
WHY--
I DON'T THINK I'VE SEEN ONE...
HAVE YOU?
NO, BUT I'VE HEARD RUMOURS THAT THEY'RE QUITE SOMETHING
HE PROBABLY DOES A LOUSY TREE.

FINALLY

Cerebus: When the representatives are called for a vote return to the suite and STAY THERE! Don't talk to anyone! Astoria
NOW?
ONE MORE BRANCH.
AALMOOST...

DONE!
THANKS

HEY! CEREBUS KNOWS YOU--YOU'RE THAT ARTIST AND COLLECTOR...
...CHAP. *
FWUMP
* CEREBUS No. 25
YOU KNOW WHAT THOSE ARE?...
I'LL TELL YOU WHAT THOSE ARE ...
YOU!

ONE HUNDRED AND THIRTEEN FULLY-RENDERED SKETCHES -- GIFTS FROM LORD JULIUS TO THE ART-STARVED REPRESENTATIVES...
LANDSCAPES! PETS! BUILDINGS! BRIDGES! SUNSETS! SUNRISES!
YOU NAME IT AND I DREW IT-- HIDING THE WORDS "VOTE FOR ELROD" IN EACH BACKGROUND.
FIFTY-FIVE HUNDRED CROWNS I WAS SUPPOSED TO GET...
ENOUGH TO PAY TWO YEARS RENT ON MY CASTLE UP NORTH...
NOW--
THANKS TO YOU--
EVERYONE WANTS AN ORIGINAL ELROD SKETCH INSTEAD.
ESPECIALLY LORD JULIUS SINCE IT DOESN'T COST HIM ANYTHING...

HERE!
HAVE AN ELROD "BUNNY"

HAVE A DOZEN!
HAVE A HUNDRED!
HE-CAN-DO-ONE-EVERY-FIVE-DAMN-SECONDS!
BUNNIES.

RAZAFRAZZIN' "BUNNIES"
RAZAFRAZZIN' "TREES"
RAZAFRAZZIN' POLITICIANS...
CUTE.

HAVE TO FIGURE OUT HOW TO SKETCH POTATO SALAD...
OR CEREBUS IS FINISHED! FINISHED! FINISHED!
JAKA.
YES.
I CAME BACK...
...TO ASK YOU A QUESTION.
JAKA...

AREN'T YOU DRESSED YET?!

CEREBUS!
UNH!

PETUNIACON

'SOKAY!
'SOKAY.
CER'BUS WAS JUST RESTING HIS EYES!
I SHOULD'VE KNOWN! I CAN'T LEAVE YOU ALONE FOR A SECOND...
WE'RE ALREADY LATE!
HURRY UP! HURRY UP!

...DAY TWO

COME ON! YOU CAN FINISH DRESSING ON THE WAY.
JUST WHEN CEREBUS WAS GETTING THE HANG OF SKETCHING POTATO SALAD...

TRY NOT TO BE SO ABRASIVE TODAY...
THE REPRESENTATIVE FOR THE DOCKS SAID YOU WERE VERY RUDE TO HIM...
IT WOULDN'T KILL YOU TO BE NICE ONCE IN A WHILE...

HEY! HEY! THERE HE IS!
WOO WOO
HEY! HEY!
WE WERE WONDERING WHERE HE WAS!
AND HERE HE IS NOW!
HEY! HEY! HEY!

ARE YOU GOING TO DO ROCKS TODAY LIKE YOU SAID?!

CEREBUS DOESN'T KNOW, YET...
WHEN WILL YOU KNOW?
LATER.
AFTER LUNCH?
MAYBE.
FOR SURE BY DINNER TIME?
PROBABLY.
WHAT KIND OF ROCKS?
PLAIN ROCKS?
CEREBUS DOESN'T KNOW.
WHEN WILL YOU KNOW?

TARIM.
WHAT'S WITH THE BANDAGES?
WE WERE CHOSEN BY ELROD TO HELP WITH HIS SWORDS-MANSHIP EXHIBITION.

EVEN WITH A WOODEN SWORD HIS RIGHT ARM WAS A BLUR...
SLASH!
SLASH!
UNERRING ACCURACY
SLASH!
SLASH!
EVERY MOVE A STROKE OF BRILLIANCE.

I SHOULD KNOW...
I WAS THREE-TIME CHAMPION AT THE SEMINARY...

WOW.

DO YOU WANT TO COME WITH US TO SEE ELROD'S KEYNOTE ADDRESS?
NO... CEREBUS JUST HAD A NAP A WHILE AGO ...
WHAT?
NOTHING.

M'LORD--I'VE BEEN LOOKING FOR YOU EVERYWHERE ...
YOU'RE SUPPOSED TO BE ON A PANEL...
"GRAFT--BOON OR BLESSING?"

NO, M'LORD... "US AND THEM: ERADICATING THEM"
YOU MIGHT BE IN TIME FOR THE QUESTION AND ANSWER PERIOD
WHAT ABOUT ELROD'S KEYNOTE ADDRESS?
IT WAS RE-SCHEDULED TO YESTERDAY...

HERE WE ARE...
YOU CAN GO RIGHT IN...
AND MAY I SAY, ON BEHALF OF THE HOTEL STAFF HOW HAPPY WE HAVE BEEN TO SERVE YOU, AND THAT WE HOPE YOU WILL BE HAPPY WHEREVER YOU GO, WHEN THE VOTE...THAT IS... WHEN ELROD...
WHEN ELROD DOES WHAT?
ER--NOTHING M'LORD...
NO PROBLEM. ELROD'S BEEN DOING THAT SINCE HE WAS BORN...

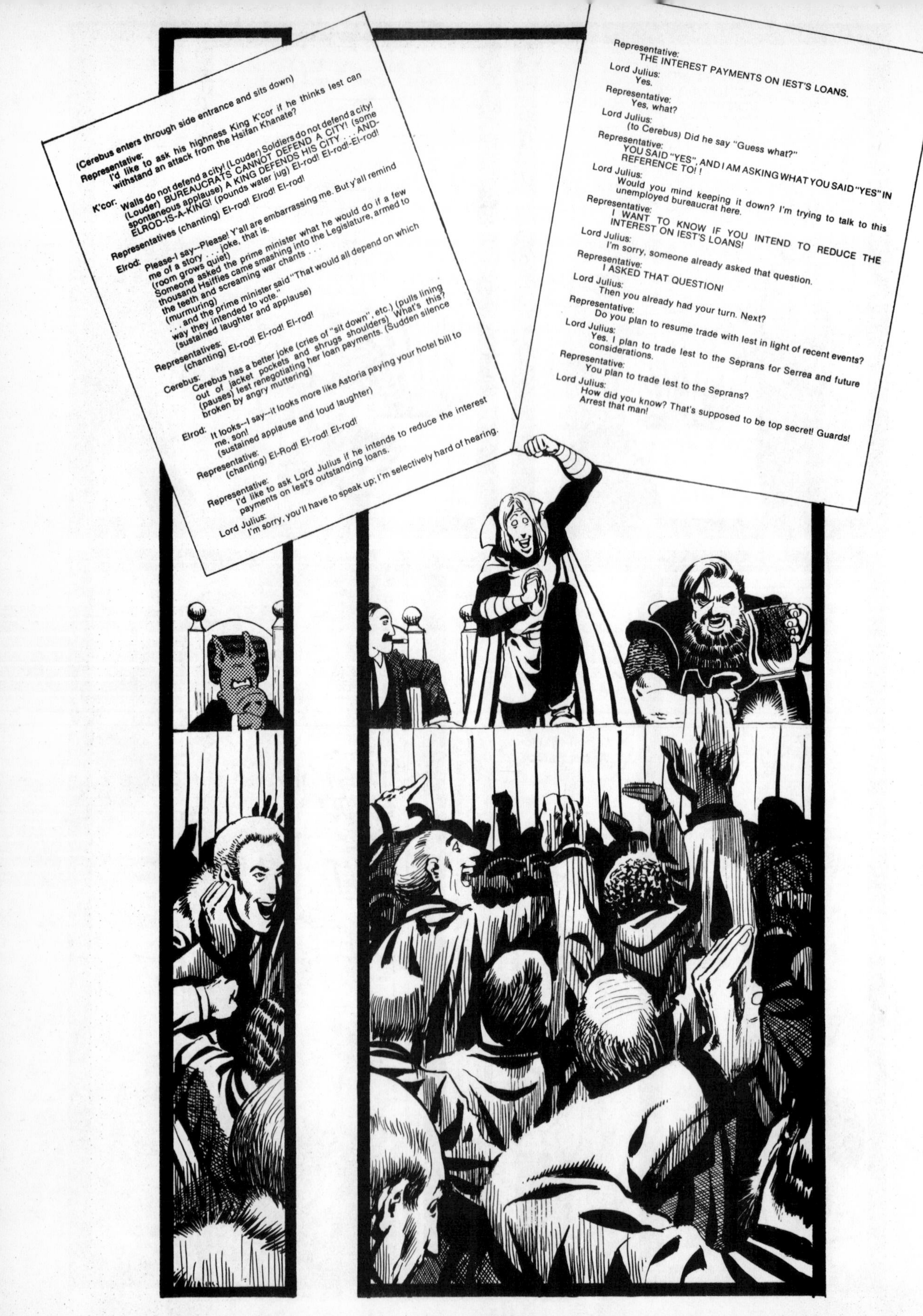

(Cerebus enters through side entrance and sits down)

Representative:
I'd like to ask his highness King K'cor if he thinks Iest can withstand an attack from the Hsifan Khanate?

K'cor:
Walls do not defend a city! (Louder) Soldiers do not defend a city! (Louder) BUREAUCRATS CANNOT DEFEND A CITY! (some spontaneous applause) A KING DEFENDS HIS CITY . . . AND-ELROD-IS-A-KING! (pounds water jug) El-rod! El-rod!-El-rod!

Representatives (chanting) El-rod! Elrod! El-rod!

Elrod:
Please-I say--Please! Y'all are embarrassing me. But y'all remind me of a story . . . joke, that is.
(room grows quiet)
Someone asked the prime minister what he would do if a few thousand Hsiffies came smashing into the Legislature, armed to the teeth and screaming war chants . . .
(murmuring)
. . . and the prime minister said "That would all depend on which way they intended to vote."
(sustained laughter and applause)

Representatives:
(chanting) El-rod! El-rod! El-rod!

Cerebus:
Cerebus has a better joke (cries of "sit down", etc.) (pulls lining out of jacket pockets and shrugs shoulders) What's this? (pauses) Iest renegotiating her loan payments. (Sudden silence broken by angry muttering)

Elrod:
It looks--I say--it looks more like Astoria paying your hotel bill to me, son!
(sustained applause and loud laughter)

Representative:
(chanting) El-Rod! El-rod! El-rod!

Representative:
I'd like to ask Lord Julius if he intends to reduce the interest payments on Iest's outstanding loans.

Lord Julius:
I'm sorry, you'll have to speak up; I'm selectively hard of hearing.

Representative:
THE INTEREST PAYMENTS ON IEST'S LOANS.

Lord Julius:
Yes.

Representative:
Yes, what?

Lord Julius:
(to Cerebus) Did he say "Guess what?"

Representative:
YOU SAID "YES", AND I AM ASKING WHAT YOU SAID "YES" IN REFERENCE TO! !

Lord Julius:
Would you mind keeping it down? I'm trying to talk to this unemployed bureaucrat here.

Representative:
I WANT TO KNOW IF YOU INTEND TO REDUCE THE INTEREST ON IEST'S LOANS!

Lord Julius:
I'm sorry, someone already asked that question.

Representative:
I ASKED THAT QUESTION!

Lord Julius:
Then you already had your turn. Next?

Representative:
Do you plan to resume trade with Iest in light of recent events?

Lord Julius:
Yes. I plan to trade Iest to the Seprans for Serrea and future considerations.

Representative:
You plan to trade Iest to the Seprans?

Lord Julius:
How did you know? That's supposed to be top secret! Guards! Arrest that man!

Representative:
Lord Julius! I PROTEST!

Lord Julius:
In that case let him go and have him repeat the question.

Representative:
DO-YOU-INTEND-TO-TRADE-THIS-CITY-TO-THE-SEPRANS?!

Lord Julius:
Oh, THAT's what you said. . . I thought you wanted me to offer YOU a deal.

Representative:
I would never trade my city for another.

Lord Julius:
That's why I threw in the future considerations. Next?

Representative:
Taking into account the fact that King Elrod has never been defeated in combat, I'd like to ask His Highness why he never attacked the Hsifan Khanate while he was living in Lower Felda.

Elrod:
Well, son--I look at it this way. It takes a strong man to walk away from a fight
(applause)

Elrod:
And it takes an even stronger man to win that fight.
(more applause)

Elrod:
And it takes an even stronger man to win that fight, walk away and then come back and win it again!!
(applause)

Elrod:
And . . . uh . . . so on. Etcetera, that is.

K'cor:
(pounding water jug) Etcet-RA! Etcet-RA! Etcet-RA!

Representative:
(chanting) Etcet-RA! Etcet-RA! Etcet-RA!

Representative:
I'd like to ask each of the distinguished panelists if they will tell us to what do they attribute their success.

Cerebus:
Walking into the right hotel. (scattered chuckling)

Lord Julius:
I attribute my success to ambition, determination, guts, integrity, fairness, honesty and having enough money to buy people with those qualities.

Elrod:
(chuckles) Why, I suppose it sounds corny, but I guess clean living, royal blood, and the mightiest sword arm in all Estarcion is what makes me the unqualified success I am today. (Cerebus makes choking noises, drowned out by chants of El-rod, El-rod, El-rod and much more applause and stamping)

K'cor:
I am successful because I am the only person in my city who is not heavily addicted to powerful narcotics.

Lord Julius:
Are you sure you aren't from Palnu?

Representative:
Lord Julius, do you intend to reduce lest's interest payments? Please answer yes or no.

Lord Julius:
Gee, we just ran out of time. Why don't you drop by the hospitality room and if I'm not there, we can talk about it.

(Lord Julius and Elrod exit quickly).

transcript concluded.

relay by courier to His Holiness.

WHAT--I SAY--
WHAT A CANDIDATE!
WHAT STYLE!
WHAT POISE!
HE'LL THRASH
THOSE HSIFFIES.
WHY, I FEEL SAFER THAN A GAME-BIRD WITH A CROSSBOW!
DISMEMBER, THAT IS...
EL-ROD! EL-ROD!

'SCUSE ME, SON--
WOULD YOU MIND PUTTING MORE LEAVES ON IT...?
IT LOOKS BARER THAN THE PRIME MINISTER'S BANK ACCOUNT...
EL-ROD EL-ROD
OUR PROBLEMS ARE SOLVED...
CURED, THAT IS.
WE'VE--I SAY--
WE'VE FOUND A LEADER!
EL-ROD! EL-ROD!
CEREBUS WILL START SKETCHING ROCKS ONLY WHEN THIS ROOM IS QUIET!
SILENT, THAT IS!!

WHAT'S-- I SAY-- WHAT'S...
SHHHHHHHH!
DID--I SAY-- DID SOMEONE DIE?
HE'S SKETCHING ROCKS, BUT HE'LL STOP IF WE AREN'T QUIET...
SH.
M'LORD... I'VE COME TO...
SHHHH!
M'LORD.. I'VE COME TO TELL YOU THAT THEY'RE READY FOR YOU ON THE NEXT PANEL.
THE NEXT-- I SAY-- THE NEXT PANEL?
IS ELROD ON IT?
WHY-- YES.
WAHOO!
OUTA MY WAY!
I'M GOING TO BE AT THE FRONT THIS TIME!

K'cor:
In my city there is only one kind of graft. You do exactly what I want you to do and you will be rewarded with narcotics and food and be permitted to live.
Lord Julius:
You'd have to go a long way to find a better offer than that.
Elrod:
Personally, I feel . . . I say . . . I feel that the average man in the street . . . or legislature . . . needs more than that. (some applause)
Lord Julius:
Like what?
Elrod:
Like guaranteed pension for five or more years of government services. (applause and cheers)
Elrod:
Like reduced taxes for government employees. (applause and cheers)
Lord Julius:
The average man in the street sounds a little expensive. Do you have anything in "below average"?
Elrod:
How . . . I say . . . how about the kid in the bunny suit? (laughter and applause)
K'cor:
Any citizen of a city should be grateful his worthless life is spared by his Benevolent Sovereign. Grant him any more than that and he becomes soft! Flabby! (nervous coughs in the audience)
Lord Julius:
Baskin! Make a note to offer this man whatever he wants to become Ranking Diplomatic Representative to Eshnosopur.
Baskin:
Yes, Lord Julius.
Lord Julius:
Now that all the spies from Eshnosopur have had coronaries, we'll take some questions from the audience.
Representative:
I'd like to ask Mister Baskin what life is like in the government of Palnu. (long pause)
Lord Julius:
Baskin!
Baskin:
Lord Julius?
Lord Julius:
The nice man asked you a question.
Baskin:
Who?! Me?
Lord Julius:
The "mister" part threw him for a minute.
Baskin:
Life in the government of Palnu?
Lord Julius:
You can leave out the part about you-know-what.
Baskin:
You-know-what?
Lord Julius:
The you-know-what we were discussing you-know-where when you-know-who walked in.
Baskin:
Oh. Well, aside from that, it's very nice.
Lord Julius:
The dream of Truth in Government marches on. Next?
Representative:
Is graft really necessary? Perhaps all of the panelists would address this issue. How necessary is graft?
Cerebus:
Graft is as necessary as throwing up when you drink too much.
Lord Julius:
He really knows how to turn a phrase, doesn't he?
Elrod:
I think I know what the boy is driving at . . . implying that is. We don't LIKE graft, but sometimes . . . I say . . . sometimes you have to grease the wheels.
Lord Julius:
Or they squeak too much.
K'cor:
In my city when wheels squeak too much, we hit them with a hammer until they stop.
Lord Julius:
On second thought, pencil him in as chief negotiator for the Public Sevice contract negotiations.

Baskin:
I think graft is necessary for government officials who are unhappy with their position unlike government officials like me who like their position and don't want anything else.

Lord Julius:
Make a note to cancel your cut in salary.

Baskin:
Yes, Lord Julius. Thank you, Lord Julius.

Lord Julius:
Next question?

Representative:
What I want to know is why nobody pays graft to Dadocks (sp?). Don't anybody worry about their ships meeting with small accidents?

Lord Julius:
What do you have in mind?

Representative:
Well, just as an example, for instance, those five merchant ships from Palnu in the harbour right now. What if they was to, all of a sudden, sink, like.

Lord Julius:
You think that's possible?

Representative:
Well, I ain't no shipbuilder, but if a crew of dockworkers don't right away go out and fix the holes that are about to appear below the water-line, I would say it's not only possible, but, ah, inevitable.

Lord Julius:
How much do you suppose this crew of dock workers would need to fix these possibly inevitable holes?

Representative:
They is awfully big holes.

Lord Julius:
How about two hundred crowns?

Representative:
They would have to, as well, be thoroughly tarred.

Lord Julius:
I know exactly how they feel. Three hundred?

Representative:
Yes, that would about cover it.

Lord Julius:
Pleasure doing business with you.

Representative:
Likewise, I'm sure.

Lord Julius:
Next Question.

Representative:
I would like to know if Lord Julius intends to insure that his ships pass safely through my riding of Harbourgate West by financing inspection of the Honourable Member's repair of the inevitable holes mentioned earlier.

Lord Julius:
Perhaps K'cor, my temporary Minister for Naval Blackmail would like to answer that question.

K'cor:
The ships will pass safely after a free inspection and you will be permitted to live the rest of your life with your spine intact.

Lord Julius:
Fair enough?

Representative:
Yes, Quite fair. Thank you.

Lord Julius:
Next question.

Representative:
I would like to know if Lord Julius intends to reduce the interest on Iest's outstanding loans.

Lord Julius:
In answer to your question, Elrod will be doing free sketches in the hospitality room as soon as we get there. Last one there gets a sketch of a rotten egg. (mass confusion as Lord Julius and Elrod, surrounded by the representatives, make their way to the rear of the hall)

transcript copy to Her Worship Cirin of Upper Felda.

transcript copy to Astoria, Duchess of Parmoc, Ambassador Suite.

M'LORD?
M'LORD.. I JUST WANTED TO TELL YOU HOW UNFAIR I THINK IT IS THAT AN AC-COMPLISHED PALNAN CABINET MINISTER WHO RISKED HIS LIFE TO SAVE US ALL FROM THE GRAND INQUISITOR ...
...SHOULD END UP WITH NO ALLIES IN THE LEGISLATURE WHILE THAT... THAT...THUG WITH NAUGHT TO RECOMMEND HIM BUT AN ABILITY TO MURDER OTHER THUGS ...
...SHOULD END UP WITH SO MANY...
... SHOULD HAVE THE ENTIRE LEGISLATURE ...
...WELL.
I JUST DON'T THINK IT'S FAIR.
I THOUGHT YOU SHOULD KNOW.
GOODBYE, M'LORD.

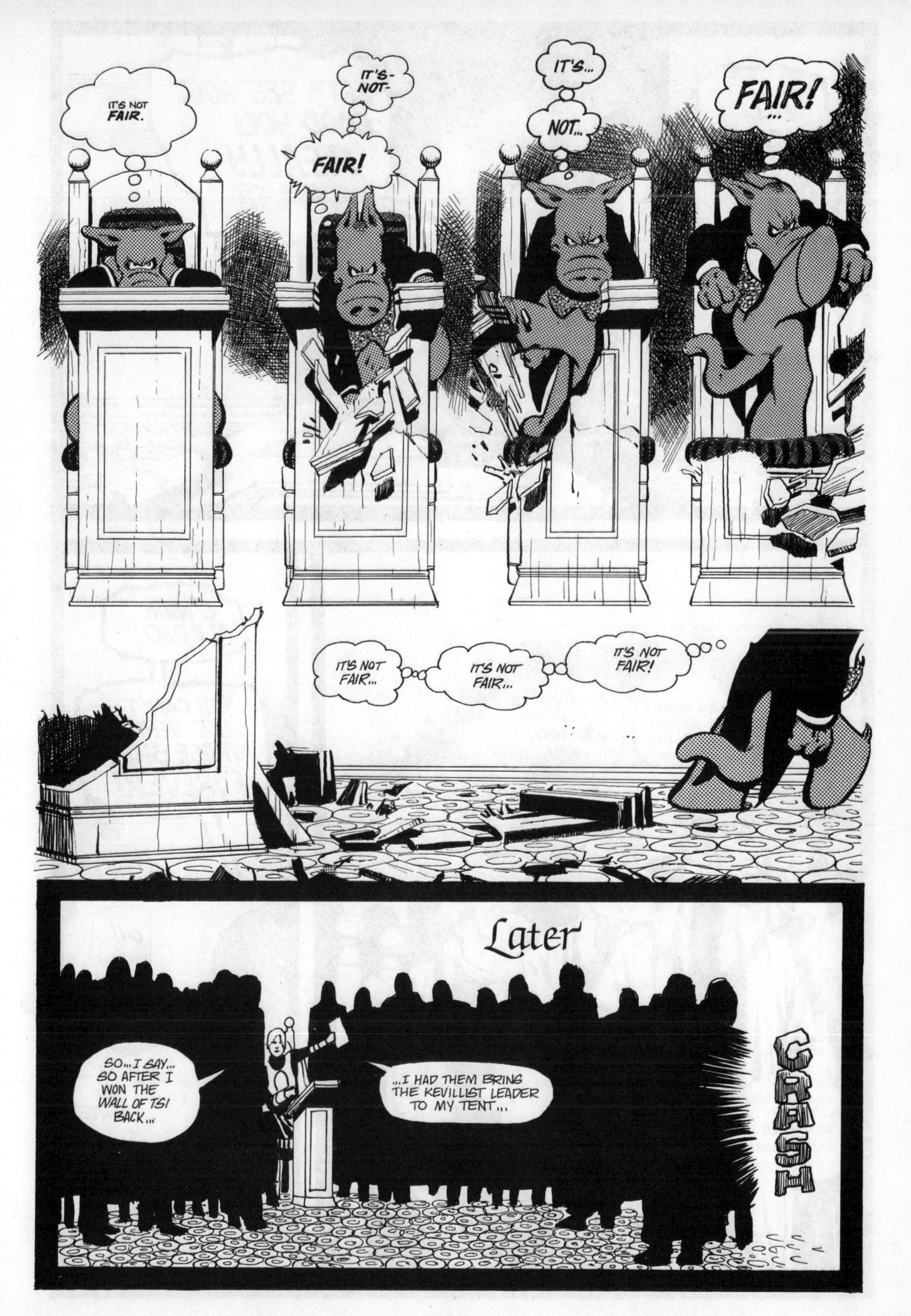
IT'S NOT FAIR.
IT'S- NOT-
FAIR!
IT'S...
NOT...
FAIR! ...
IT'S NOT FAIR...
IT'S NOT FAIR...
IT'S NOT FAIR!
Later
SO... I SAY... SO AFTER I WON THE WALL OF TSI BACK...
...I HAD THEM BRING THE KEVILLIST LEADER TO MY TENT...
CRASH

ALL RIGHT ALBINO! ...
LET'S SEE HOW GOOD YOU REALLY ARE!!
OF ALL-- I SAY--OF ALL THE UNMITIGATED GALL! ...
REALLY!
HE MUST BE INSANE-- CRAZY, THAT IS...
OR DESPERATE TO KEEP HIS JOB, MORE LIKELY...
HIS HIGHNESS WILL CUT HIM TO RIBBONS...
HE LOOKS LIKE SOME SORT OF RUFFIAN... SAVAGE, THAT IS...
UH-OH.
C'MON ALBINO!!
YOU CAN'T HIDE BEHIND THOSE SHEEP FOREVER!
SHEEP?
OH!
THE NERVE!

YOU'LL PAY FOR THAT REMARK, BARBARIAN.
EL-ROD EL-ROD
BUT-- IT'S NOT A FAIR FIGHT-- HE'S SHORTER THAN ME--I, THAT IS!
WE'LL SEE WHO IS HIDING FROM WHOM!
NONSENSE!
HE ISSUED THE CHALLENGE.
SEERSUCKER II, YOUR HIGHNESS.

EL-ROD
EL-ROD EL-

CEREBUS!!
OH NO.
GET OUT HERE THIS INSTANT!

BOOO!! COWARD! COW-ARD!! BOOOOOOO! WHAT'S
CEREBUS WILL BE BACK IN A MINUTE, ALBINO
TAK
...I SAY... TAKE YOUR TIME, SON...

I THOUGHT I TOLD YOU NOT TO MAKE ANY WAVES...
YOU TOLD CEREBUS NOT TO SAY ANYTHING...
CEREBUS ISN'T GOING TO SAY A WORD...
CEREBUS IS JUST GOING TO CUT ELROD INTO LITTLE-ALBINO-CHUNKS!
YOU'LL RUIN EVERYTHING.
CEREBUS IS FINISHED AS RANKING DIPLOMATIC REPRESENTATIVE ANYWAY
POINT ONE:
THE GOVERNMENT WILL COLLAPSE WITHIN DAYS DUE TO GROSS ECONOMIC MISMANAGE-MENT...
IF IEST WANTS A SWORDS-MAN FOR THE JOB, CEREBUS WILL SHOW THEM A REAL ONE...
HOW ABSOLUTELY STIRRING.
YOU'LL UNDOUBTEDLY BE LYNCHED.
POINT TWO: I HAVE A COALITION OF DISAFFECTED GOVERNMENT MEMBERS AND HIGH PROFILE MEMBERS OF THE OPPOSITION WHO WANT YOU TO FORM A NEW PARTY AND RUN FOR PRIME MINISTER...
CEREBUS DOESN'T CARE ABOUT...

PRIME MINISTER?
YES.
CEREBUS DOESN'T WANT TO BE PRIME MINISTER! ...
CEREBUS WANTS TO TURN ELROD INTO ALBINO CUTLETS!
CHOK

THE PRIME MINISTER'S SALARY IS **FIFTY THOUSAND CROWNS** A YEAR...
CEREBUS DOESN'T WANT TO **HEAR** ABOUT IT!
CEREBUS IS GOING TO SHOW **EVERYONE** THAT ELROD IS NOTHING BUT A...
IT INCLUDES A SUMMER HOME IN THE HILLS, PRIVATE GAME PRESERVE, A WINTER HOUSE IN THE CITY WITH SIXTY ROOMS OVERLOOKING THE FELD RIVER...

LISTEN!...
CEREBUS IS GOING TO **KILL THAT ALBINO ... IT DOESN'T MATTER WHAT YOU...**

EVERY MANNER OF RARE AND EXOTIC FOODSTUFF--SPICES, CURED AND SMOKED MEATS, **CHOCOLATE...**

LISTEN!...
OKAY! OKAY!
WHAT DOES CEREBUS HAVE TO DO? ...

THE FINEST COLLECTION OF WINES, SPIRITS AND LIQUEURS ON THE CONTINENT...

GO BACK IN AND ADMIT THAT ELROD IS A BETTER SWORDSMAN THAN YOU.
FORGET IT!!
CEREBUS WILL JUST HAVE TO GET LYNCHED!
THE PRIME MINISTER ALSO EXERCISES ABSOLUTE CONTROL OVER THREE THOUSAND BUREAUCRATS, AN ARMY OF FIFTY THOUSAND MERCENARIES...
... A LEGISLATIVE STAFF OF TWO HUNDRED...
...AND A PERSONAL ENTOURAGE OF ONE HUNDRED SERVANTS, SECRETARIES AIDES AND CABINET MINISTERS
ABSOLUTE...
...CONTROL.
OKAY! OKAY!

WELL? WHAT ARE...
CEREBUS WILL BE BACK IN A MINUTE!!
"TWO BOTTLES OF BOREALAN WHISKEY"
AYE.
"FOUR FOOT LENGTH OF CHAIN STUDDED WITH THREE-INCH SPIKES"
AYE
"FIFTY POUND SACK OF FLOUR"
AYE.
"RESERVATION -- CORNER TABLE FOR ONE -- "RAM'S LORD'S TAVERN." "
"TAXI TO BE READY AT EAST ENTRANCE IN A HALF-HOUR."
ANYTHING ELSE, M'LORD?
CHARGE IT ALL TO ASTORIA'S ACCOUNT...

THE NEXT PRIME MINISTER OF IEST, COMPORTING HIMSELF LIKE A COMMON THUG IN SOME SQUALID TAVERN...
HONESTLY!
IF I HADN'T SENT SOMEONE TO GET YOU, I CAN JUST IMAGINE WHAT PEOPLE WOULD BE SAYING...
HURRY UP!
WE'RE LATE!
GOOD MORNING, ASTORIA.
MR. BLAKELY!
PETUNIACON
AND THE CANDIDATE HIMSELF...
HOW FORTUITOUS.
WE HAVE SO MUCH TO DISCUSS.
DAY THREE

BUT, HE'S SUPPOSED TO...
I SHOULDN'T THINK IT NECESSARY TO REMIND YOU, ASTORIA, THAT I COULD ALWAYS RUN FOR PRIME MINISTER, **MYSELF**...
BUT...
BUT...
NOW, BE A GOOD GIRL AND RUN ALONG...
AH! THE AMBASSADOR SUITE...
"THE REGENCY'S FIFTH FLOOR COAL-MINE"
"BE A GOOD GIRL..."
"AND RUN ALONG!?!"
The Ambassador Suite

YOU COULD RUN FOR PRIME MINISTER?
AGAINST CEREBUS?
MM.
AND I WOULD WIN. DECISIVELY.
YOU NEEDN'T WORRY, THOUGH.
EVER SINCE YOU DROPPED THAT STONE SCULPTURE ON THE GRAND INQUISITOR
OUR ENTIRE WAY OF LIFE HAS BEEN CHANGED...
BLACK TOWER DYNASTY. LOVELY PIECE.
I DON'T WANT TO WIN.
I HAVE NO DESIRE TO PRESIDE OVER THE RAPID DECLINE AND FALL OF THE CITY-STATE...
MY LOYALTY IS TO HIS HOLINESS AND THE CHURCH OF TARIM.
THOUGH IT WOULD SEEM THEY ARE GONE FOREVER ...ALL THE HIGH PRIESTS AND CHURCH OFFICIALS SEALED UP IN THE SACRED CATHEDRAL...
EVERY DAY, ANOTHER PROPHECY IS FULFILLED.
OUR LEADERS ARE IN DISREPUTE.
OUR LEGIONS ARE DIMINISHED BY TWO THIRDS.
OUR DEBTS GROW UNCHECKED ...
THE CHURCH DESTROYS ITSELF.
AND IT IS LEFT TO ME TO EITHER BE THE NEXT PRIME MINISTER OR CHOOSE THE NEXT PRIME MINISTER...

WHICH BRINGS US TO YOU... AND WETHER OR NOT YOU ARE SUITABLE FOR THE ...
SORRY TO INTERRUPT.
MIND IF I USE YOUR BATHTUB? MINE STILL HAS A RING AROUND IT FROM THE BLACK SUN PUNCH ELROD MADE IN IT LAST NIGHT
THROUGH THERE...
TARIM'S MERCY! THAT WAS... HE... WAS IT NOT?
LORD JULIUS? AYE.
WHAT ABOUT IT?
YOU WOULDN'T HAPPEN TO HAVE SOAP WOULD YOU?
TOP SHELF.
BUT I THOUGHT... THAT IS ...
WHEN HE ADOPTED ELROD... NOMINATED HIM...
I MEAN, WHY IS HE BEING FRIENDLY?
HE SHOULD CONSIDER YOU AN ENEMY ...
YOU'RE TRYING TO MAKE SENSE... SO FAR AS CEREBUS KNOWS ...
LORD JULIUS HAS NEVER MADE SENSE.

HMMM.
YOU'RE LIVING WITH LORD JULIUS EX-WIFE AND LORD JULIUS COMES IN TO BATHE...
EVEN THOUGH HE AND ASTORIA ARE OSTENSIBLY BITTER ENEMIES
THAT DOESN'T MAKE SENSE.
LIKE CEREBUS SAID...
PERHAPS
HMM
PERHAPS... LORD JULIUS AND ASTORIA ARE NOT THE ENEMIES THEY APPEAR TO BE...
YES.
PERHAPS THEY ARE ALLIES.

LORD JULIUS KNOWS HIS POPULARITY IS DECLINING ...
BECAUSE HE REFUSES TO REDUCE IEST'S INTEREST PAYMENTS...
SO HE HAS ASTORIA PROMOTE YOU BEHIND CLOSED DOORS...
AND EVERYONE VOTES AGAINST LORD JULIUS BY VOTING FOR YOU
I HAVE AN URGENT MESSAGE FOR...
THROUGH THERE...
A CLEVER PLOY, TO BE SURE! ...

I WISH TO FURTHER EMPHASIZE HOW REPREHENSIBLE I FIND THE GROUND-SWELL OF SUPPORT FOR CEREBUS' CANDIDACY AND...
IXNAY ON THE ICTATION-DAY WHILE THE ORON-MAY IS ISTENING-LAY...
TOO LATE!
I'VE HEARD ENOUGH!
YOU CAN FORGET THIS CHARADE OF CRITICISM, LORD JULIUS.
I KNOW NOW, THAT CEREBUS IS YOUR CHOICE FOR PRIME MINISTER...
CHARADE? HOW DARE YOU INFER AND OR IMPLY SUCH A THING?
I WAS SIMPLY ANSWERING THIS LETTER FROM ONE OF CEREBUS' MANY DUPES...
AND YOU JUST HAPPENED TO OVERHEAR!
THAT PAGE, SIR, IS BLANK!
YOU IDIOT! I TOLD YOU TO WRITE A FAKE LETTER--
NOT FAKE WRITING A LETTER...
LORD JULIUS?

I TOLD YOU TO WRITE A...
FORGET IT.
I BARELY GOT IT RIGHT THE FIRST TIME...
SO YOU ADMIT THAT THE LETTER IS A FAKE!
THAT MEANS ...
uh...
TAKE YOUR TIME-- IT'LL COME TO YOU...
IT MEANS THAT YOU WERE TRYING TO MAKE ME BELIEVE THAT CEREBUS IS YOUR CHOICE FOR PRIME MINISTER
WHEN IN REALITY...
uh
DON'T LOSE IT, NOW, KID, YOU'RE HALF-WAY HOME.
WHEN IN REALITY HE IS NOT YOUR CHOICE AT ALL!
YOU DON'T WANT HIM TO BE ELECTED...
JUST GOES TO SHOW THAT YOU SHOULDN'T TRY FOOLING SOME-ONE WHO GREW UP IN A MONASTERY IN THE KOTA MOUNTAINS
INDEED IT DOES, MY DEAR LORD JULIUS.

COME ALONG, BASKIN, I SHOULD HAVE KNOWN BETTER THAN TO TRY AND RESHAPE A PERFECT SOCIETY.
TAXI!
REMARKABLE.
AN ALLIANCE WITH HIS EX-WIFE SO NO ONE WOULD BE SUSPICIOUS AND...
BUT WHY WOULD ASTORIA CAMPAIGN FOR YOU-- IF SHE AND LORD JULIUS DON'T WANT...
PARDON, M'LORD-- DID ANYONE ORDER A TAXI?
WHY, LORD JULIUS DID, BUT HE'S ALREADY...
SMASH
STAND WHAR YER AT, FANCY BOYS!!
DIRTY FLEAGLE McGREW AN' HIS BABY BROTHER DIRTY DREW HAVE DONE BUSTED OUT!!

OH NO
SEE HERE!
WHAT IS THE MEANING OF THIS...?
MAH BROTHER AN' I ARE RIGHT PEEVED, YER SNOBBISHNESS OVER US BEIN' LOCKED UP UNJUSTLY-LIKE...
FER A KIDNAPPIN' WE DIDN'T DO NOTHIN BUT SPECTATE AT...AN' FER WHICH WE EARNED...
THE GRAND TOTAL OF ONE DAM DUCK STATCHOO! AN' I, FER ONE...
...AM NOT PARTIAL T'SERVIN' THE REST O' MY FORTY-FOUR-YEAR, NINE-MONTH SIX-WEEK-'N'-EIGHT DAY STRETCH...
DO YOU KNOW WHAT THIS CREATURE IS BABBLING ABOUT?
UH,
UH.

THE MEMORIES COME FLOODING BACK LIKE A TORRENT OF WHITE WATER ; ONCE AGAIN HE SEES THE RED CLAW ONLIU TENEMENT OWNERS GLOATING AS THEY SAW THROUGH HIS PARENT'S SEMI-DETATCHED DWELLING...
SEES AGAIN, A SMALL BOY VOWING TO HAVE REVENGE! REVENGE! REVENGE!!

THOUGH IT MEANS SACRIFICING HIS CIVILIAN IDENTITY
DIRTY DREW! LOOKY THAR!
HE'S A' TAKIN' HIS SHIRT OFF...!
AN' LOOKIT WHUT HE'S A-W'ARIN' UNDERNEATH ...

THE LIGHTNING SWIFT TRANSFORMATION IS MADE AS BLAKE JOCKLEY, TAXI DRIVER, VANISHES...
TO BE REPLACED BY...
NOW HE'S TAKIN' HIS PANTS OFF!
HE AIN'T JUST A FANCY BOY...
HE'S A FUNNY BOY...

THE MERELY MAGNIFICENT MOON ROACH!
COVER YER VALUABLES, DIRTY DREW-- HE LOOKS LAK THE MEANEST DAM FUNNY BOY AH EVER SEEN! ...
GOTCHA, DIRTY FLEAGLE

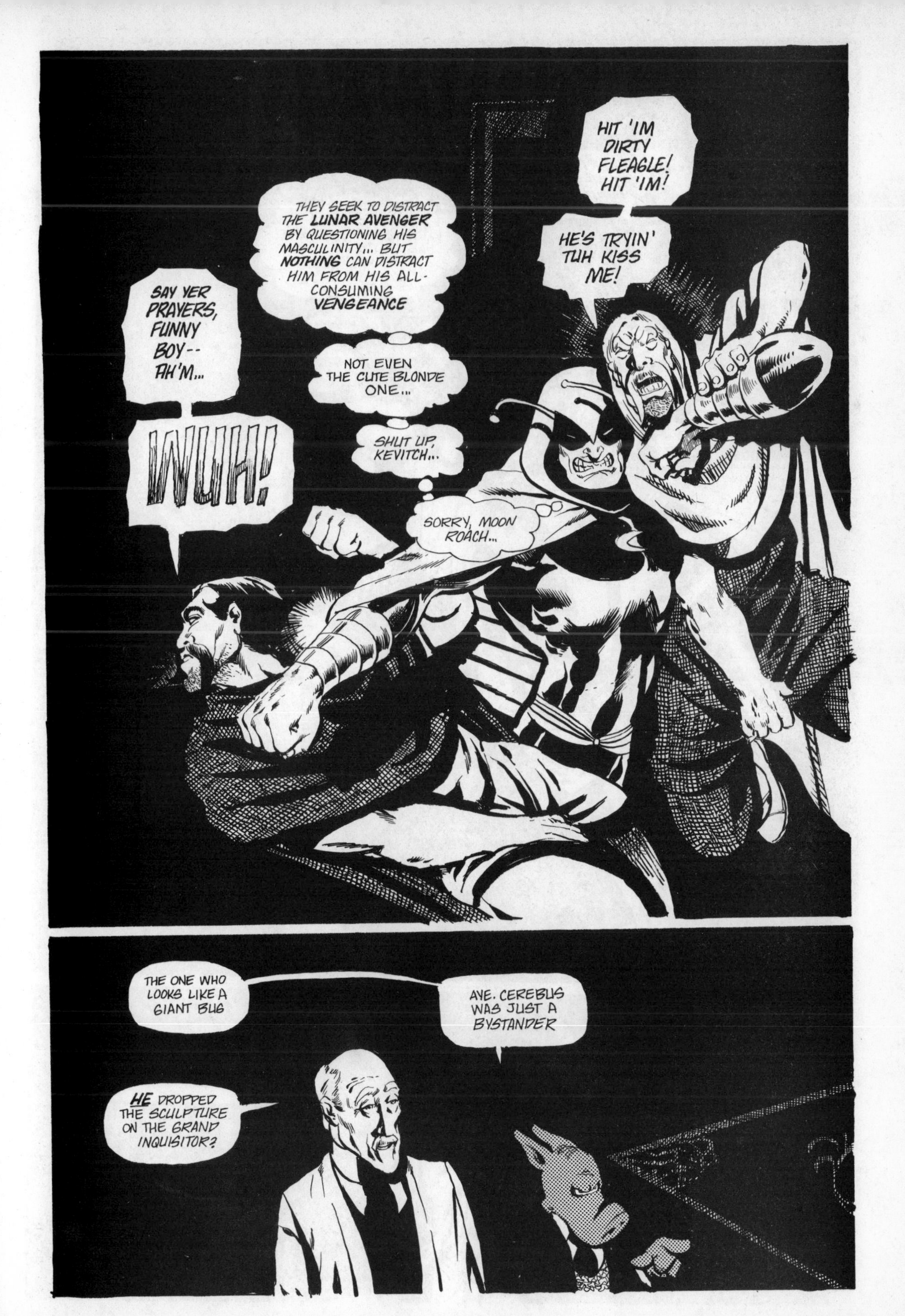
HIT 'IM DIRTY FLEAGLE! HIT 'IM!
HE'S TRYIN' TUH KISS ME!
THEY SEEK TO DISTRACT THE LUNAR AVENGER BY QUESTIONING HIS MASCULINITY... BUT NOTHING CAN DISTRACT HIM FROM HIS ALL-CONSUMING VENGEANCE
SAY YER PRAYERS, FUNNY BOY-- AH'M...
NOT EVEN THE CUTE BLONDE ONE...
SHUT UP, KEVITCH...
WUH!
SORRY, MOON ROACH...
THE ONE WHO LOOKS LIKE A GIANT BUG
AYE. CEREBUS WAS JUST A BYSTANDER
HE DROPPED THE SCULPTURE ON THE GRAND INQUISITOR?

HIT 'IM, DIRTY DREW! AH GOT HIS EYES A-COVERED...!
HSSS! THE ONLIU EXPLOITERS OF THE POOR FAIL TO RECKON WITH MY REMARKABLE ROACH SENSE...
PING
PING
PING
PING!
BUT, IF WHAT YOU SAY IS TRUE -- THAT THE LARGE INSECT CHAP USED TO BE ASTORIA'S BOY-FRIEND AND THAT HE DROPPED THE STONE SCULPTURE ON THE GRAND INQUISITOR...
...THEN THE ASTORIA AND LORD JULIUS ALLIANCE DOESN'T MAKE SENSE!
BECAUSE THE GRAND INQUISITOR WAS THE ONE WHO ADVOCATED EXCLUSIVE TRADE WITH PALNU...
LIKE CEREBUS SAID...

THE MOON ROACH STANDS POISED ABOVE THE STILL FORMS OF HIS FALLEN FOES! ONCE MORE, THE TYRANNY OF ECONOMIC ENSLAVEMENT HAS BEEN TOPPLED...
BY THE PURE-BRED STRENGTH AND BRUTE FORCE OF A GOOD SOLID RIGHT TO THE JAW!
"THE WEED OF MONEY BEARS BITTER INTEREST RATES" HE HISSES QUIETLY.
"THE MOON ROACH KNOWS! HSSSSSSS!"
YOU'RE QUITE SURE HE IS ASTORIA'S OLD BOYFRIEND? --I MEAN...
HE DOESN'T SEEM TO BE HER...TYPE SOMEHOW...
EXCUSE CEREBUS A MINUTE...

BUG!
BUG!!
MAD FINANCIERS! SELLING ORPHANS TO MEET THEIR STOCK MARGINS!!
WHERE?
WHERE?
LOWER FELDA!!
"TO LOWER FELDA" HE CRIES!
LEAPING INTO SPACE, HE SEIZES HIS SILKEN CORD
AND IS ONCE MORE
...
WHAM!!

HOTEL SECURITY, M'LORD.
THAT PILE OF DIRTY LAUNDRY ON THE CARPET CONTAINS TWO CONVICTED FELONS.
ABRUPTLY THE MOON ROACH REMEMBERS THAT HE HAD ARRIVED IN HIS CIVILIAN IDENTITY AND THAT THERE WAS NO SILKEN CORD OUTSIDE THE WINDOW
SLIPPING INTO UNCONSCIOUSNESS, HE BARELY

And so, after the McGrews have been removed ...
YOU SEE, IT'S NOT THAT WE DON'T THINK YOU'RE A GOOD ENOUGH ADMINISTRATOR
OR THAT WE IN ANY WAY DOUBT YOUR CREDENTIALS ...
BOREALAN, EIGHTH CENTURY.
NO?
NOT AT ALL...
IT'S JUST THAT WE WILL BE FACING MANY... CHALLENGES IN THE NEXT FEW MONTHS...
WE ARE GOING TO NEED A CHAMPION AS PRIME MINISTER -- A CHAMPION OF THE PEOPLE
DYED BURLAP...
A WARRIOR -- STRONG! SELF-CONFIDENT
HOW LIKE THE REGENCY.
SOMEONE LIKE ELROD.
OR PERHAPS EVEN ELROD HIMSELF.
THERE ARE THOSE WHO SUSPECT THAT THAT IS WHAT LORD JULIUS HAD IN MIND FROM THE VERY...
PARDON-- AH SAY--PARDON ME F'BARGING IN, SON...
BUT LORD JULIUS SUGGESTED I SHOULD COME UP AN' OFFER MY CONDOLENCES...
IT'S--I SAY IT'S OFFICIALLY TIME T'SHAKE HANDS
AHM THE NEW RANKING DIPLOMATIC REPRESENTATIVE

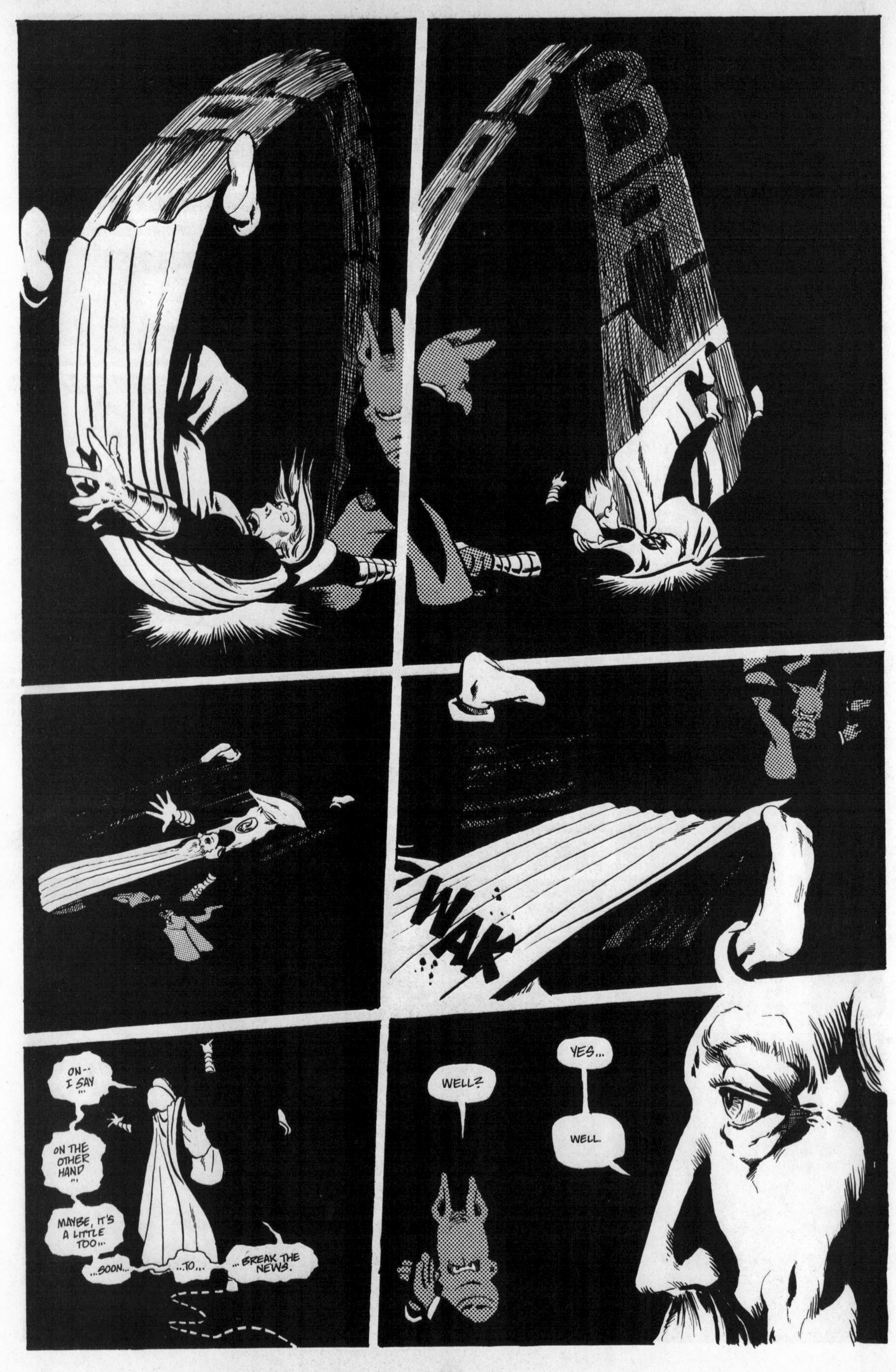
WAK
ON-- I SAY ...
ON THE OTHER HAND ...
MAYBE, IT'S A LITTLE TOO...
...SOON...
...TO...
...BREAK THE NEWS.
WELL?
YES...
WELL.

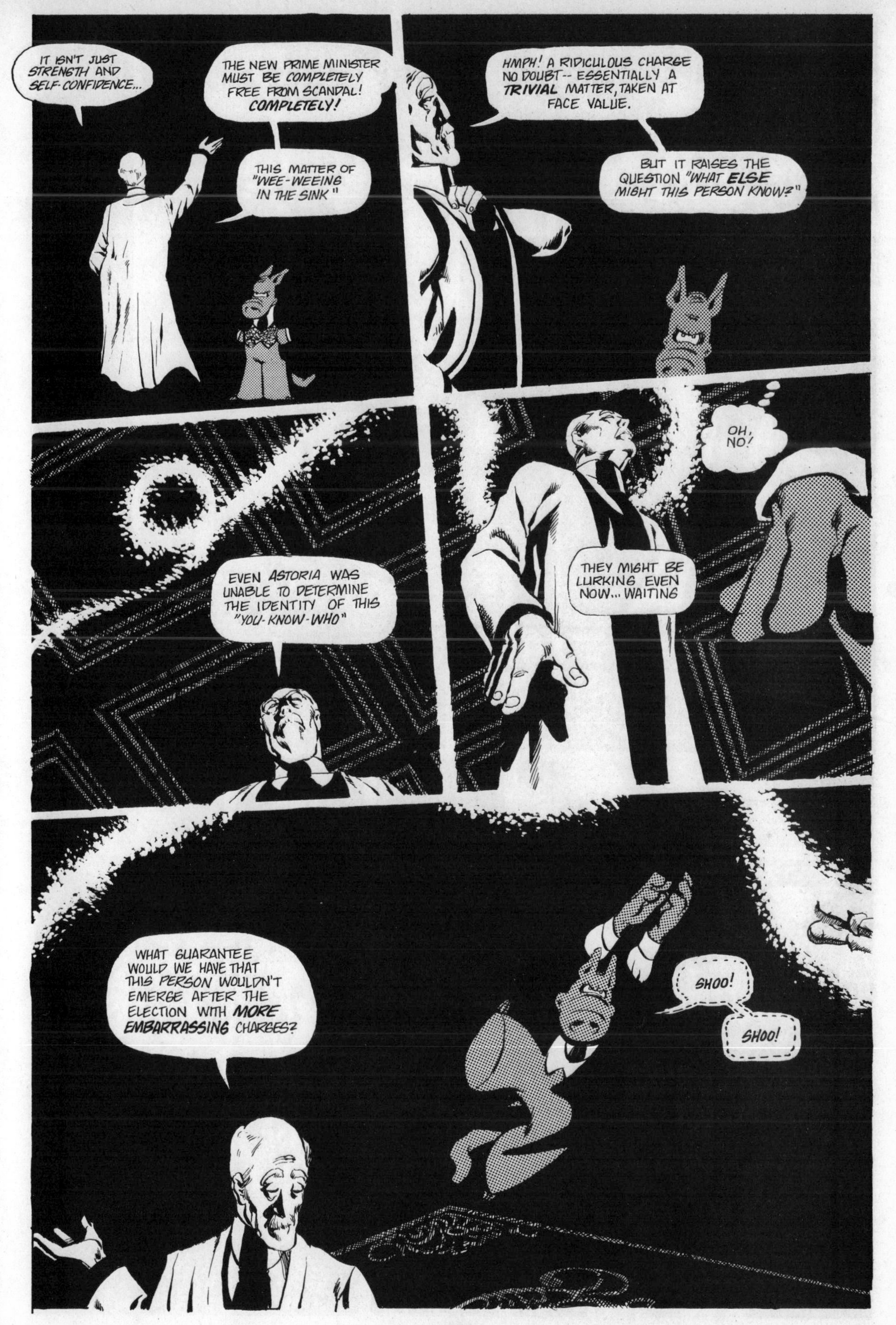
IT ISN'T JUST STRENGTH AND SELF-CONFIDENCE...
THE NEW PRIME MINISTER MUST BE COMPLETELY FREE FROM SCANDAL! COMPLETELY!
THIS MATTER OF "WEE-WEEING IN THE SINK"
HMPH! A RIDICULOUS CHARGE NO DOUBT-- ESSENTIALLY A TRIVIAL MATTER, TAKEN AT FACE VALUE.
BUT IT RAISES THE QUESTION "WHAT ELSE MIGHT THIS PERSON KNOW?"
EVEN ASTORIA WAS UNABLE TO DETERMINE THE IDENTITY OF THIS "YOU-KNOW-WHO"
OH, NO!
THEY MIGHT BE LURKING EVEN NOW... WAITING
WHAT GUARANTEE WOULD WE HAVE THAT THIS PERSON WOULDN'T EMERGE AFTER THE ELECTION WITH MORE EMBARRASSING CHARGES?
SHOO!
SHOO!

THEN IT'S OKAY, MR. BLAKELY!
'CAUSE I'M THE ONE WHO WROTE IT--BUT I DID IT WHEN I WAS MAD AND NOW I'M NOT!!
GAH!
SO YOU CAN SUPPORT CEREBUS!
ELF.

AN AARDVARK PRIME MINISTER!! AN AARDVARK PRIME MINISTER!!
YAY! WE HAVEN'T HAD AN AARDVARK PRIME MINISTER SINCE...

SINCE...
HEY!
THAT'S RIGHT!

ELF.

THAT WAS BEFORE THERE WERE PRIME MINISTERS!!
YAHH!

ELF!

HUH?

OH.

NO
NO
IT WAS VERY NICE MEETING YOU...
BUT I THINK I HAVE TO BE GOING, NOW.

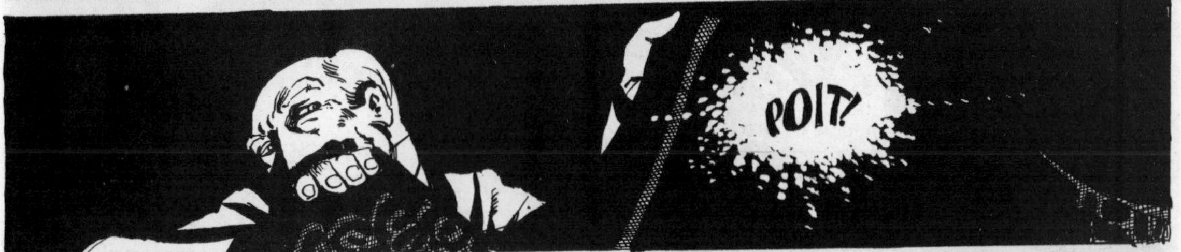
POIT!

THAT WAS...
HER!
SHE! I MEAN...

THE
REGENCY
POIT!
ELF.

THE
REGENCY

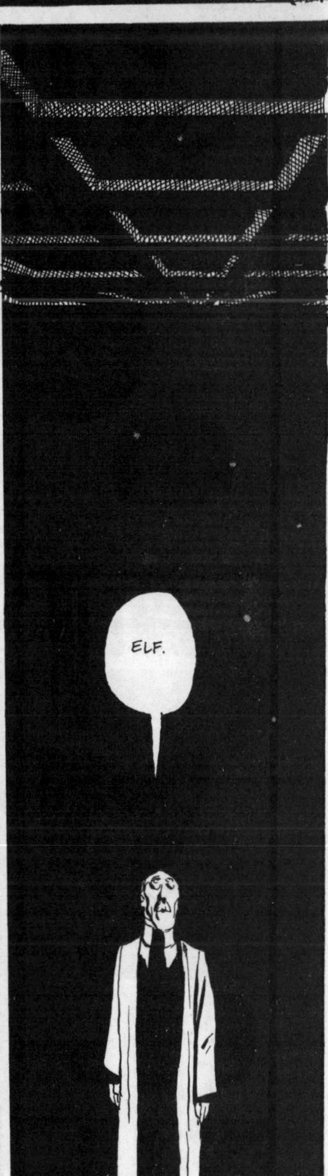
ELF.

NEXT: CAMPAIGN

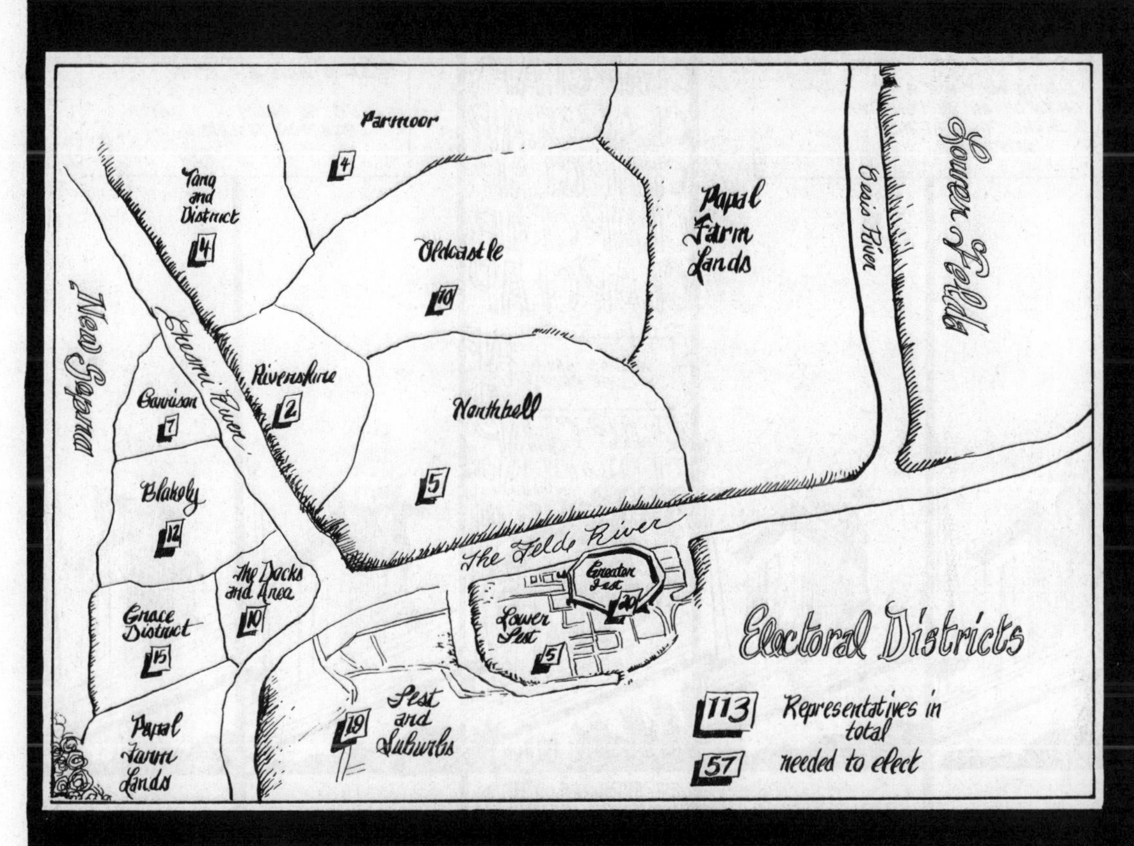

CAMPAIGN

" OF COURSE THE DOCKS, AND IT'S NEIGHBORING TOWNS OF B'ORN GRACE AND DUNHAM, WERE CRUCIAL TO THE PLANS OF ASTORIA'S NEWLY FORMED THEOCRATS. SHE HAD INTENDED TO TAKE 'THE DOCKS AND AREA' AND 'IEST AND SUBURBS'. COMBINED WITH HER SUPPORT FROM LORD BLAKELY'S HOME DISTRICT AND THE GUARANTEE OF ALL TWENTY SEATS IN GREATER IEST, SHE EXPECTED CEREBUS WOULD LEAD A MAJORITY GOVERNMENT "

FROM "THE TRUE H'STORY OF THE 1413 ELECTION" BY SUENTEUS PO.

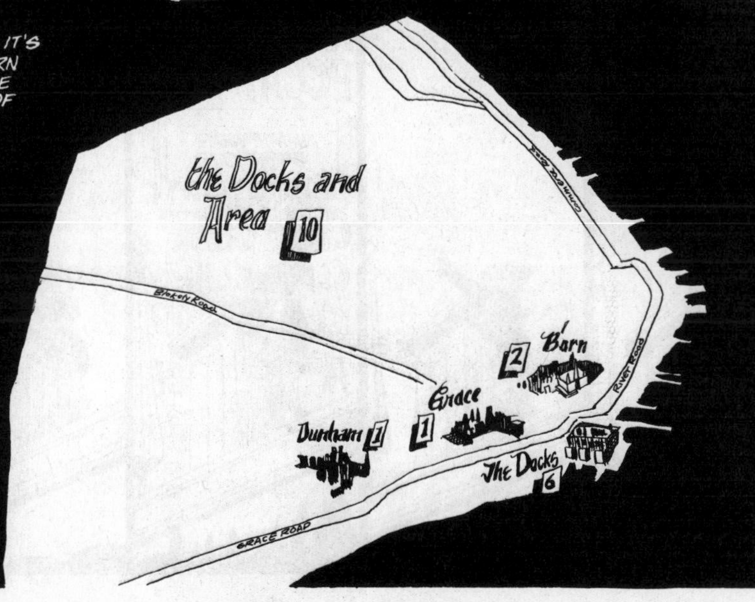

SO WHAY'S ASTARIA, ANYHOW? WHUDDA WE? HSIFFIES? HE DON'T BRING 'IS HATSHAT CHICK WIDDEM WHEN HE COMES TO DADOCKS, HANH?
I GOTTA WAIT F'R'M T' SHOW UP AN' HE DON'EVEN BRING DA FEATCHUH ATTRACTION...
CLAPCLAPCLAPCLAP CLAPCLAPCLAPCLAP CLAPCLAPCLAPCLAP
WHUDEE SAY? WHUDEE SAY?
CLAP CLAP CLAP CLAP
HE SEZ WE GOTTA CUT GAVEMENT SPENDING.
'EY!-- I'M AWL F'DAT! HE CAN CUT OFF DOSE STOOPID EARS WALL 'E'S AT IT.
'E'S SO SHOAT -- I GOTTA GRANDSON TALLER'N 'IM.
AH, SHADDAP, Y'SELF! HANH? NOT YOU -- DA DOPEY GUY TWO ROWS OVAH ..."SHADDAP" 'E SEZ! LIKE I DIDN'T PAY MY TWO CROWNS T'SEE DIS CARABUS CHARACTUH...
CLAPCLAPCLAPCLAP CLAPCLAPCLAPCLAP
WHAAT? WHAT? WHUDEE SAY?
CLAPCLAP CLAPCLAP
'E' SEZ WE GOTTA TELL LOAHD JULIUS T'TAKE A HOIK.
'EY! I'M AWL F'DAT! ASK 'IM IF HE'S GOT ANY MORE EX-WOIVES F'ME WHEN Y'DO...
WOO! WOO!

GIT BACK, YUH HERO-WORSHIPIN' VARMINT-LOVER AFORE AH DIS-LOCATE YER POINTY HEAD!!
IT WAS TRUE. ASTORIA NEEDED THE MOON ROACH NOW MORE THAN EVER--" BUT WHAT OF MY NEEDS" HE MUSES TO HIMSELF...
BAF
THIS PART HERE.
LEAVE IT OUT?
EAT FOOT YUH LILY-LIVER'D FLAG-WAVIN' FANCY BOY!!
WUMP
THE ADVANCE SHEET FROM IEST AND SUBURBS LOOKS VERY GOOD.
DOWN! DOWN!
OUCHIE!! LEGGO YUH CRAZY OLD BROAD!!
YES, YES, FINE.
DID YOU PRACTICE YOUR SPEECH FOR THE MERCHANTS' ASSOCIATION?
HE PUTS HIS ARM AROUND HIS CHICK TO SHOW HER HE ISN'T SORE AT HER
MMM.
WHEN TH' NEXT BATCH O'CAMPAIGN FUNDS ARRIVE, C'N WE RENT ONE MORE CARRIAGE
SO'S WE AIN'T AS CRAMPED, YER FEMALENESS?
WE'LL SEE.

AND SO, I GIVE YOUSE DA NEXT PROIME MINISTUH OF IEST -- CARABUS DA AWDVAWK...
AHA! SABOTAGEE!
I COME BEFORE YOU TODAY TO PROMISE THAT THERE WILL
TELL 'IM T'BE CAREFUL WHAR HE STANDS
THERE'S A TRAP DOOR ...
UNDER
SEEMS TUH BE SOME KINDA...
LEVER.
UH-OH

MILADY
M'LOAHD
WALCOME TUH DUNHAM MANOR.
IT'S WORKING.
SO FAR NO ONE SUSPECTS THAT ASTORIA IS REALLY THE MOON ROACH'S CHICK...
CEREBUS -- THIS IS LORD DUNHAM...
HI! H'WAH YUH?
FOIN.
GUD! GRATE!
JUST IN CASE YOUSE AW HUNGRY, I HAD D'KITCHEN STAFF PREPARE SUM...
FOOD!
I'M TERRIBLY SORRY.
'EY! AT'S OKAY. I GOT T'REE BADYGAWDS O' MY OWN.
MUNCH
MUNCH
GOBBLE
SLURP
GLUP
CHOMP
SMAK

WAL, F'ONE THING --I AM ONLY ONE GUY--DERE ARE T'REE UDDAH GUYS WHO WOULD NEED TA BE PUHSUADED...
YAH KNOW
THEN PERSUADE THEM, LORD DUNHAM...
I WOULD, F'RINSTANCE
...HAF TA OFFUH DEM SOMET'IN'
BETWEEN MR. BLAKELY AND MYSELF, WE HAVE THIRTY-TWO SEATS GUARANTEED.
MY TWENTY BEING IN GREATER IEST...
I NEED TWENTY-FIVE SEATS MORE... FOR A MAJORITY GOVERNMENT...
THE DOCKS USUALLY VOTES AS DIRECTED BY ITS MORE...
AFFLUENT CITIZENS
I COULD USE TEN MORE SEATS...
OFFER THEM A CHANCE TO SAVE A GREAT DEAL OF MONEY.
HANH?
ONE...
ANY DISTRICT THAT VOTES FOR US GETS GOVERNMENT INVESTMENT
TWO...
ANY DISTRICT THAT VOTES AGAINST US GETS THEIR IMPORT TAXES TRIPLED...
IS DAT A THREAT?
NO, LORD DUNHAM.
IT'S AN OFFER.
I SUGGEST YOU GRAB IT BEFORE SOMEONE BEATS YOU TO IT.

UPPER FELDA IS PREPARING FOR A MAJOR OFFENSIVE IN THE SPRING... LOWER FELDA INTENDS TO HAVE IT'S TROOPS ON THE BORDER BEFORE THE FIRST SNOW...
IF YOU WERE TO INVADE AT MID-WINTER; PRESS EAST AS FAR AS BEDUIN
A WINTER CAMPAIGN?
AYE.
ONCE YOU'VE SEIZED THE FARMLANDS IN THE WESTERN PROVINCES.
YOU CAN STARVE THEM INTO SUING FOR PEACE.
THE POPULACE WILL BE DE-MORALIZED...
THEN YOU GIVE BACK THE FARM LAND.
IN EXCHANGE FOR THEIR FINEST HEAVY CAVALRY
AND GENERAL LE CHAMP'S SERVICES.
THEN, AIDED BY THE SOUTHERN CITY-STATES, YOU STRIKE INTO THE SEPRAN EMPIRE
QUICKLY.
THE EMPIRE IS LOSING THE BLOOD WARS.
THEY'RE WEAK.
VIRTUALLY INDEFENSIBLE BY THEIR REMAINING FORCES.
WHEN YOU TAKE SERREA, YOU DECLARE YOUR-SELF EMPEROR AND RE-INTRODUCE MANDATORY MILITARY SERVICE
THAT WILL GIVE YOU AT LEAST FIVE TIMES THE MANPOWER NEEDED TO ANNEX ENOTHAS AND DEHRSION,
YOU USE THEIR NAVAL FORCES TO BLOCKADE ESHNOSOPUR'S SHIPPING ROUTES TO PALNU AND...
CEREBUS!
COME ALONG NOW
IT'S TIME FOR BED.

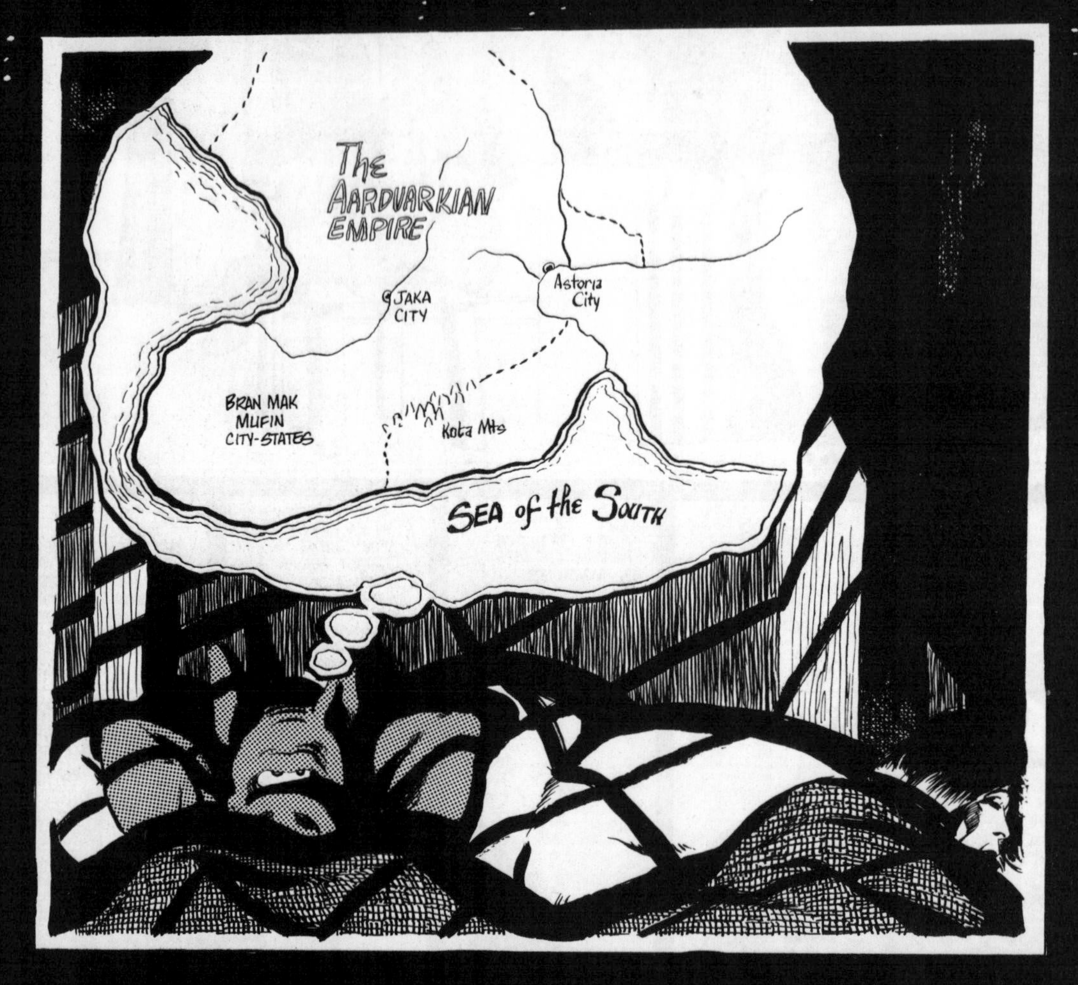
The Aardvarkian Empire
Jaka City
Astoria City
Bran Mak Mufin City-States
Kota Mts
Sea of the South

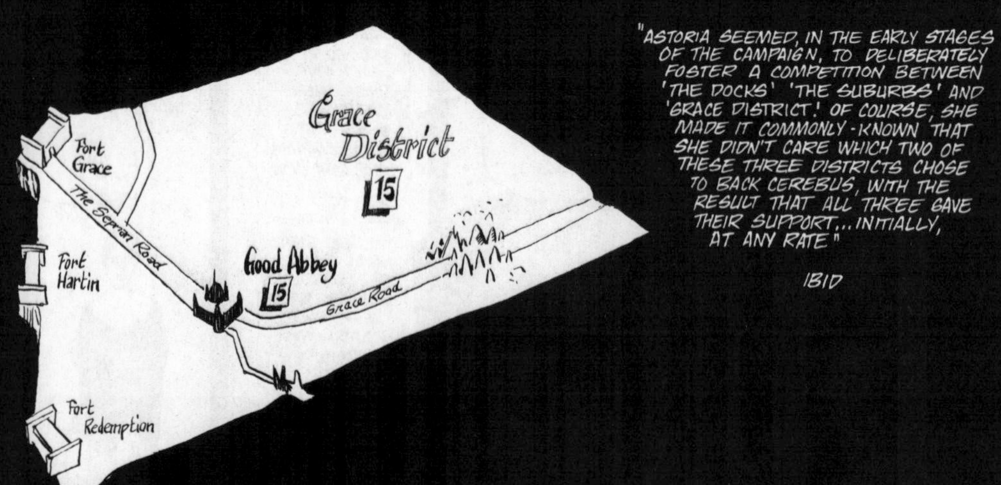
Grace District
15
Fort Grace
The Sepran Road
Fort Hartin
Good Abbey
15
Grace Road
Fort Redemption
"ASTORIA SEEMED, IN THE EARLY STAGES OF THE CAMPAIGN, TO DELIBERATELY FOSTER A COMPETITION BETWEEN 'THE DOCKS' 'THE SUBURBS' AND 'GRACE DISTRICT.' OF COURSE, SHE MADE IT COMMONLY-KNOWN THAT SHE DIDN'T CARE WHICH TWO OF THESE THREE DISTRICTS CHOSE TO BACK CEREBUS, WITH THE RESULT THAT ALL THREE GAVE THEIR SUPPORT... INITIALLY, AT ANY RATE"
IBID

"THERE IS A SOME-WHAT GARBLED ACCOUNT IN ASTORIA'S JOURNAL, OF THE FIRST VISIT TO GRACE DISTRICT. SHE MENTIONS A DRIVING RAINSTORM..."

"ONE SURMISES FROM THE ACCOUNT THAT THERE WAS SOME DAMAGE DONE IN SOME WAY TO ONE OF THE WHEELS OF THE CARRIAGE, ATTRIBUTED BY ASTORIA TO INCOMPETENCE ON THE PART OF THEIR DRIVER. EVIDENTLY THIS PROVOKED A HEATED EXCHANGE. IT IS AT THIS POINT THAT SHE MENTIONS THE MYSTERIOUS ARTEMIS STRONG FOR THE FIRST TIME."

"HER ACCOUNT OF THE EPISODE CONCLUDES WITH THE NOTATION 'ARTEMIS PROVIDED US WITH A SUBSTITUTE WHEEL.' A CURIOUS REFERENCE, SINCE A SPARE WHEEL IS NOT LISTED AS BEING AMONG ARTEMIS STRONG'S PERSONAL EFFECTS IN THE CAMPAIGN MANIFEST."

"IT IS WIDELY-BELIEVED THAT ASTORIA WAS A DEDICATED CIRINIST AT THE TIME OF THE ELECTION -- IN POINT OF FACT, EVIDENCE ON THIS MATTER IS DECIDEDLY AMBIGUOUS. THERE IS ALMOST NO MENTION OF HER FIRST VISIT TO THE ABBESS AT GOODABBEY IN HER JOURNAL. "THE ABBESS IS UNABLE TO AID US." DETRACTORS CITE THIS AS EVIDENCE OF A CRUMBLING CONSPIRACY... DEFENDERS, AS ASTORIA'S DOCUMENTED RENUNCIATION OF THE CIRINISTS."
I'M SORRY WE'RE SO LATE...
WE HAD SOME TROUBLE ON THE ROAD...
THE CANDIDATE ONLY! THE ABBESS WAS MOST SPECIFIC...
BUT -- I'M SURE SHE
THE CANDIDATE ONLY!!
PLEASE ASK HER THEN IF I MIGHT BE GRANTED SPECIAL...
KLIK

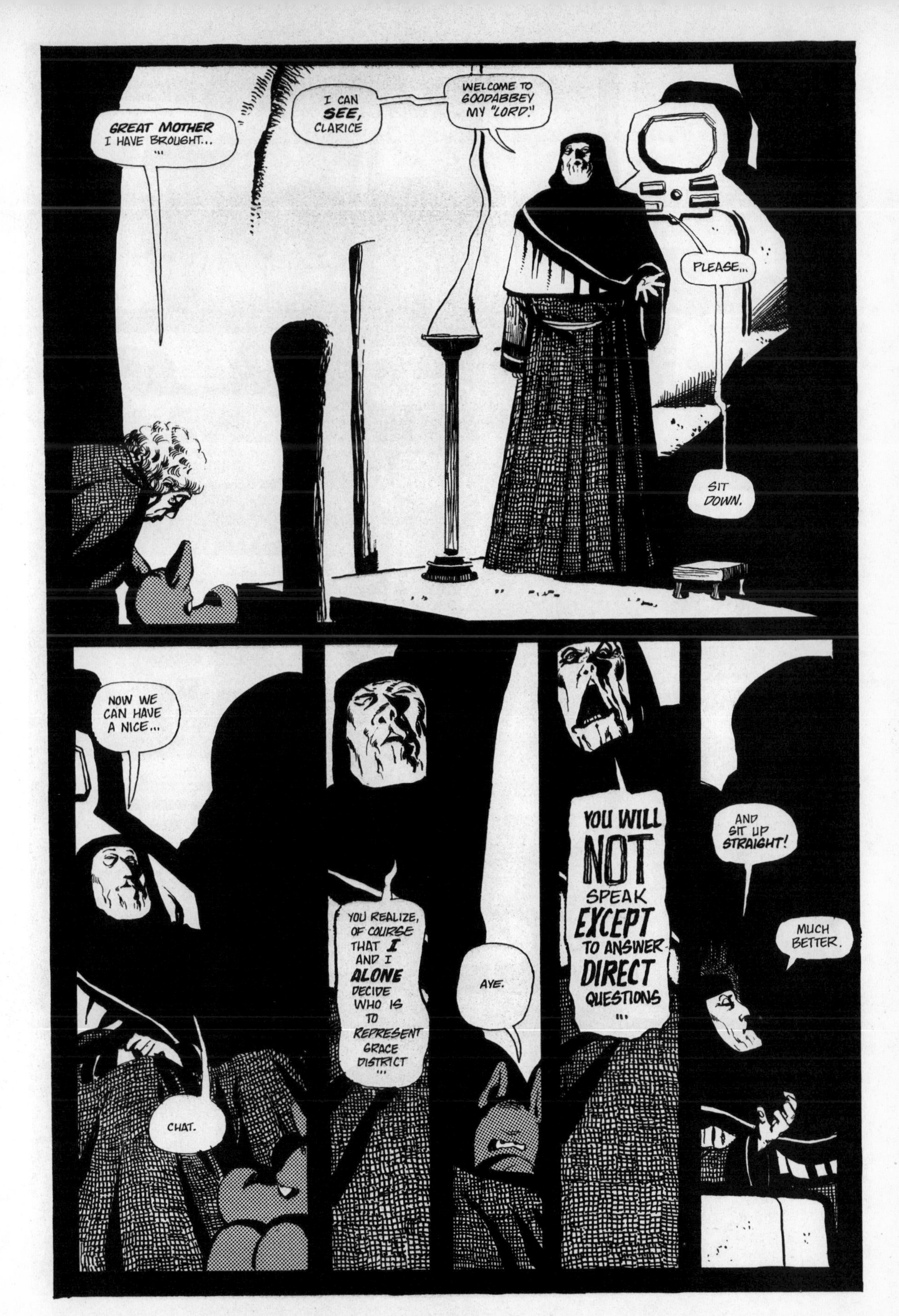
GREAT MOTHER I HAVE BROUGHT...
...
I CAN SEE, CLARICE
WELCOME TO GOODABBEY MY "LORD."
PLEASE...
SIT DOWN.
NOW WE CAN HAVE A NICE...
CHAT.
YOU REALIZE, OF COURSE THAT I AND I ALONE DECIDE WHO IS TO REPRESENT GRACE DISTRICT ...
AYE.
YOU WILL NOT SPEAK EXCEPT TO ANSWER DIRECT QUESTIONS ...
AND SIT UP STRAIGHT!
MUCH BETTER.

THIS SHOULDN'T PROVE TOO DIFFICULT FOR YOU...
LORD JULIUS' GOAT WAS IN AND OUT IN A MATTER OF MINUTES
EYES CLOSED.
THAT'S IT
I WANT YOU TO ANSWER EACH QUESTION WITH A NAME...
ONE NAME ONLY.
DO EXACTLY AS I SAY
PLEASE DO NOT PAUSE TO THINK.
NOW.
WHOM WOULD YOU CHOOSE IF YOU HAD TO CHOOSE SOMEONE TO REPLACE YOU AS YOUR PARTY'S CANDIDATE?
WE ARE CONCENTRATING NOW
CONCENTRATE ...
ASTORIA
VERY GOOD. VERY WELL DONE.
CONCENTRATING. CONCENTRATING.
WHOM WOULD YOU MOST TRUST TO MAKE MILITARY DECISIONS?
BRAN MACMUFIN.
YES. YES.
YOU'RE DOING SPLENDIDLY.
WHOM DO YOU LOVE MORE -- YOUR MOTHER OR YOUR FATHER?
UNH?
CEREBUS uh...
NEVER MIND.

ASTORIA MUST GO...
DISMISS HER, AND ALL FIFTEEN REPRESENTATIVES ARE YOURS
YOU MAY GO NOW.
FSSSS
SO?
SHE'LL BACK CEREBUS
IF CEREBUS DISMISSES YOU.
WHAT ARE YOU DOING?
MAKING A NOTE IN MY JOURNAL.
FER THE LAST DAMN TIME
AH DIDN'T SWIPE YER LAST DAMN DRIED A-PRICOT
WAL, SUMBUDDY DID!
AN AH AIMS TUH FIND OUT WHO!

"HAVING VISITED BOTH THE DOCKS AND GRACE DISTRICT, THEY NOW RE-CROSSED THE FELD RIVER TO THE TOWN OF HARBOURSIDE WHERE CEREBUS WAS TO ADDRESS THE SUBURBAN MERCHANTS' GUILD WHILE ASTORIA CONFERRED WITH THE GUILD EXECUTIVE."
Oldham
6
Harbourside
6
Nelson
6
East
Chapel
1
West and Suburbs
19
"WE WILL ABIDE NO GRAFT, TOLERATE NO INJUSTICE, CONDONE NO... NO..."
...OUTSIDE MANIPULATION
"OUTSIDE MANIPULATION"

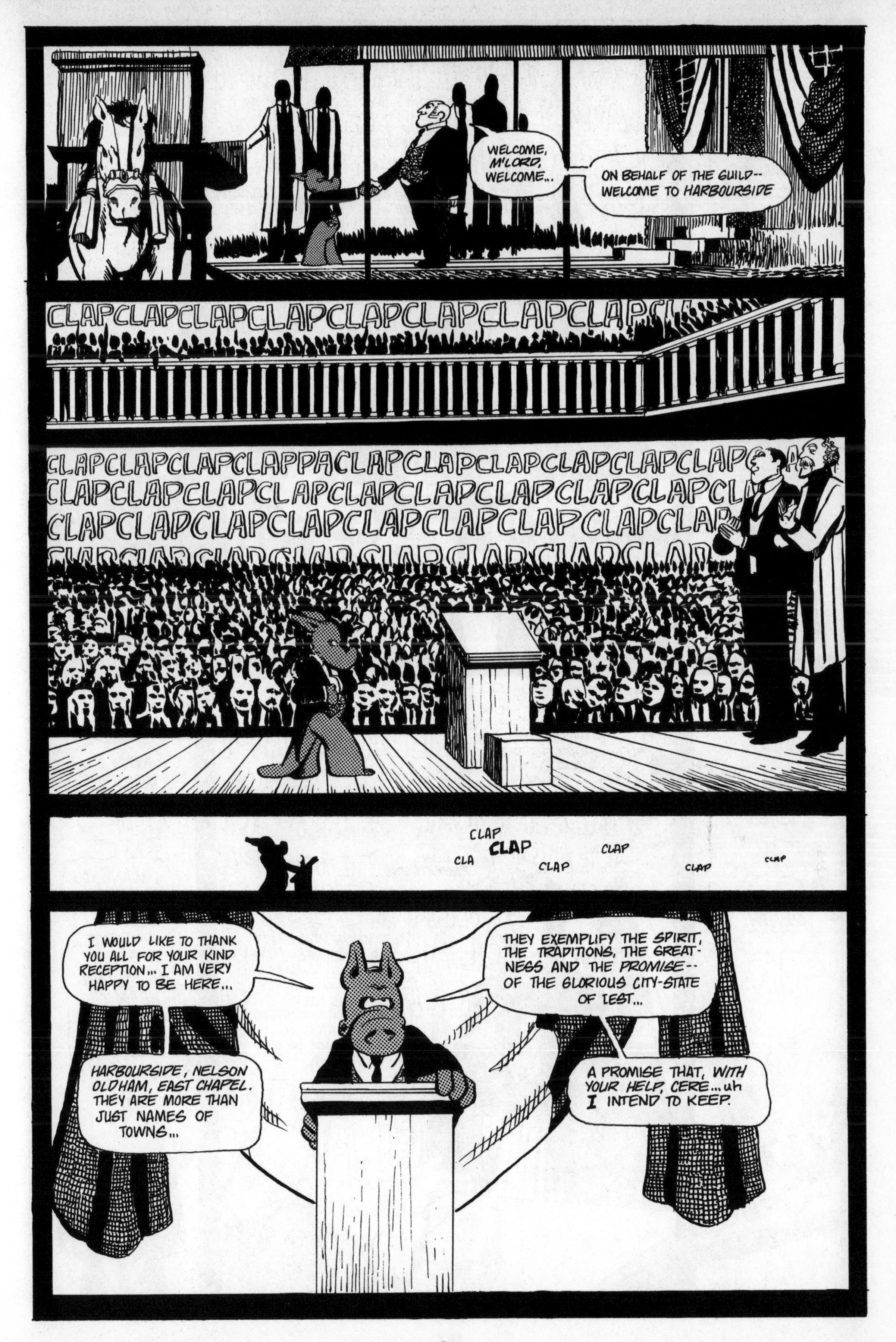

WELCOME, M'LORD, WELCOME...
ON BEHALF OF THE GUILD-- WELCOME TO HARBOURSIDE
CLAPCLAPCLAPCLAPCLAPCLAPCLAPCLAP
CLAPCLAPCLAPCLAPPACLAPCLAPCLAPCLAPCLAPCLAP
CLAPCLAPCLAPCLAPCLAPCLAPCLAPCLAPCL
CLAPCLAPCLAPCLAPCLAPCLAPCLAPCLAP
CLAP
CLAP
CLA
CLAP
CLAP
CLAP
CLAP
I WOULD LIKE TO THANK YOU ALL FOR YOUR KIND RECEPTION... I AM VERY HAPPY TO BE HERE...
HARBOURSIDE, NELSON OLDHAM, EAST CHAPEL. THEY ARE MORE THAN JUST NAMES OF TOWNS...
THEY EXEMPLIFY THE SPIRIT, THE TRADITIONS, THE GREAT-NESS AND THE PROMISE-- OF THE GLORIOUS CITY-STATE OF IEST...
A PROMISE THAT, WITH YOUR HELP, CERE...uh I INTEND TO KEEP.

WE WILL ABIDE NO GRAFT...
TOLERATE NO INJUSTICE
CONDONE NO OUTSIDE INTERFERENCE
CLAPCLAPCLAPCLAPC
SO, THAT'S THE PROPOSITION I'VE OUTLINED TO ALL THREE DISTRICTS
SUPPORT IN EXCHANGE FOR FUTURE INVESTMENT GUARANTEES.
AND TO LORD JULIUS WE SAY
IEST FOR IESTANS!
WHAT HAPPENS IF ALL THREE WANT TO JOIN YOU?
THEN YOU CAN ALL START BIDDING.
IN GOLD.
LOWER INTEREST RATES
OR DEATH!
EVEN AS THEY SPEAK, EACH OF THE EXECUTIVES IS WONDERING IF ASTORIA IS THE MOON ROACH'S CHICK...
I HONESTLY DON'T WANT TO VOTE IN A GOAT FOR PRIME MINISTER
HOW ENCOURAGING.
AT THE SAME TIME, AT LEAST I KNOW WHAT A GOAT IS...
YOU TELL ME THAT'S AN AARDVARK AND I HAVE TO TAKE YOUR WORD FOR IT...
NOW I WANT YOU TO STAND UP--
I WANT YOU TO SAY IT WITH ME!
TO SAY IT SO HE CAN HEAR IT AT THE REGENCY

LOWER INTEREST RATES OR DEATH!

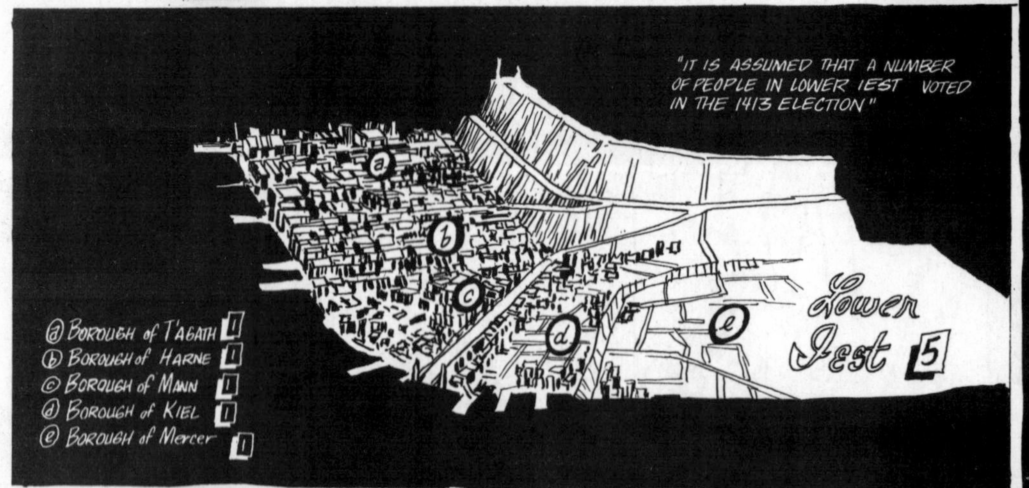
"IT IS ASSUMED THAT A NUMBER OF PEOPLE IN LOWER IEST VOTED IN THE 1413 ELECTION"
Lower Iest 5
ⓐ BOROUGH of T'AGATH 1
ⓑ BOROUGH of HARNE 1
ⓒ BOROUGH of MANN 1
ⓓ BOROUGH of KIEL 1
ⓔ BOROUGH of Mercer 1

CEREBUS IS GOING TO SWEEP **EVERY** DISTRICT!!

CEREBUS CAN FEEL IT WHENEVER THEY APPLAUD -- THE WHOLE CITY IS GOING TO VOTE FOR ME
I CAN SEE IT NOW
CEREBUS! THE MOST BELOVED PRIME MINISTER IN IEST'S HISTORY!
MOVE YOUR STUPID FOOT, ARTEMIS ...

YOU!
BOY!
COME ALONG AND SHAKE MY HAND -- ONE DAY YOU CAN TELL YOUR GRANDCHILDREN!
WHY?

WHY?! BECAUSE I'M...

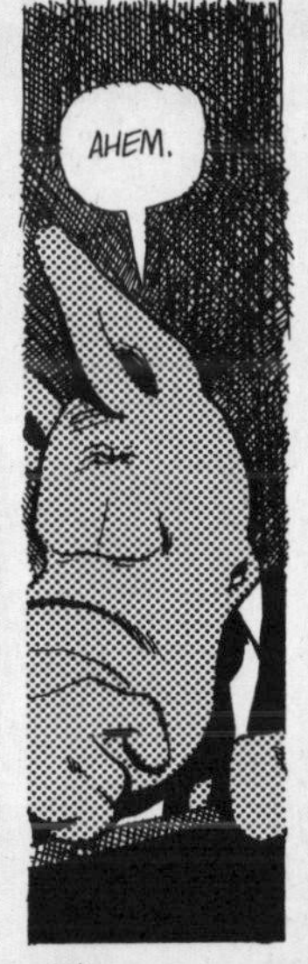
AHEM.

BECAUSE I'M GOING TO BE THE MOST BELOVED PRIME MINISTER IN IEST'S HISTORY

THE PRIME MINISTER?
YOU MUS' BE DAFT!

LOOK.
KID.
CEREBUS IS GOING TO BE THE NEXT PRIME MINISTER.
END OF DISCUSSION
COR.
Y'REALLY ARE--AIN'T YUH?

THAT'S RIGHT!
NOW, BE A GOOD LAD...
QUICKLY NOW BEFORE IT'S TOO LATE.

A LITTLE FASTER.
YOU'RE ALMOST HERE.

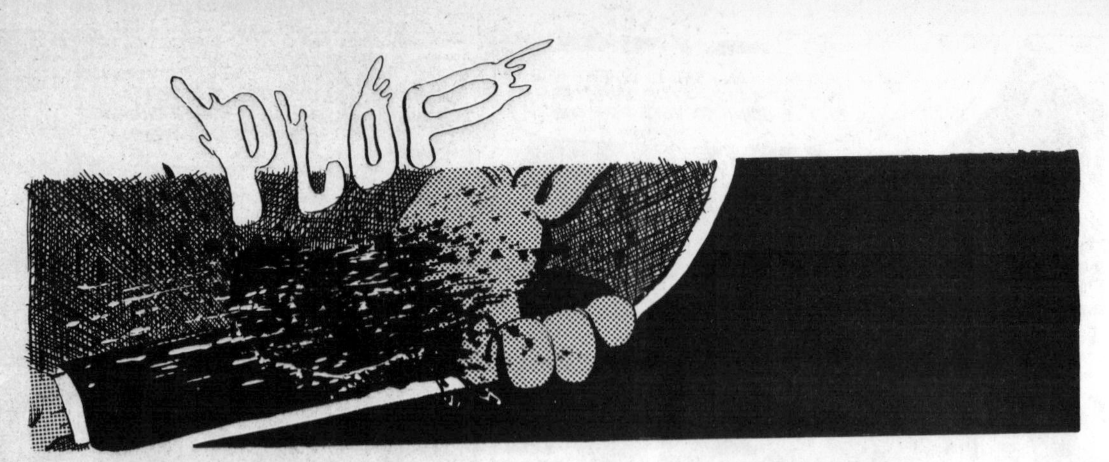
PLOP

LET GO, ASTORIA!
CEREBUS IS GOING TO BREAK ALL FOUR OF HIS LITTLE URCHIN LIMBS!!
SIT STILL DAMN YOU YOU'RE GETTING MUD ON EVERYTHING
LET GO...
NICE THROW, TOM.
THE MOON ROACH CONTEMPLATES THE WIDE SMEAR OF MUD ON HIS BRAND-NEW-TIGHTS!!
WHUT'S GOIN' ON? WHUT HAPPENED
SOMEONE WILL PAY! HSSSS.
I THINK IT CAME FROM OVER YONDER ON TH' GRASSY KNOLL!!
E'S RIGHT Y'KNOW.
I CAN'T WAIT T'TELL MY GRANDCHILDREN.

GOAT

the abbess: Welcome to Good Abbey "Lord" Julius . . . I would

Lord Julius: Would you mind lending a hand. I think he swallowed twenty pounds of ball bearings at the last stop.

the abbess: Blessed Mother of us All! A goat! A real goat.

Lord Julius: Yes Ma'am. Finest example of pure-bred one-hundred per-cent goat this side of the Kota mountains - if you don't include my uncle Seymour.

the abbess: Am I being led to understand, that this is your candidate for prime minister?

Lord Julius: My father used to say "Son, you can lead an abbess to understand, but you can't make her think."

the abbess: I am not interested in your father.

Lord Julius: Neither was my mother. Which makes me something of a mystery, doesn't it?

the abbess: Well . . . I . . .

Lord Julius: You're right. Let's cut out all this smart talk and get right to the dumb talk. The goat is willing to cut lest's interest payments in half.

the abbess: Why - that's wonderful!

Lord Julius: What's so wonderful about it? He wants to keep the other half for himself. Half for him, half for me, and you're the little abbess that cries down the lane.

the abbess: I'm afraid I don't understand.

Lord Julius: Exactly my point. A goat walks in off the street and drains your treasury down to it's I.O.U.'s. A fine way to run a city-state. You'd better wake up and smell the goats or it's burlap soup for us all.

the abbess: Burlap soup?

Lord Julius: No thanks, I had lunch on the way over.

the abbess: That's quite enough! I want you to sit down.

Lord Julius:	You win. How's this?
the abbess:	I meant on the chair, not on me!
Lord Julius:	Oh what's the use? I'm tired of pretending. Tired of the lies - the deceptions.
the abbess:	Why - what do you mean?

Lord Julius:	You're mine! All mine!
the abbess:	Lord Julius!
Lord Julius:	Your lips, your eyes, your one nostril that's bigger than the other.
the abbess:	Lord Julius! Stop that this instant!
Lord Julius:	Don't fight it - it's bigger than both of us. In your case that verges on the incredible.
the abbess:	You're insane!
Lord Julius:	Mad with passion! I want to nibble your warts.
the abbess:	Lord Julius! Stop! Your goat is eating my habit.
Lord Julius:	I'll say.
the abbess:	Lord Julius!
Lord Julius:	Well I'll be. My goat really **is** eating your habit.
the abbess:	LEAVE! NOW! BOTH OF YOU!
Lord Julius:	Don't say a word. I want to remember you this way - The firelight dancing on your mustache hairs.
the abbess:	OUT! OUT!

transcript copy to Her worship Cirin of Upper Felda.
Astoria Duchess of Parmoc

transcript copy to the Abbess of Good Abbey burned as requested.

SO CEREBUS STEPS THROUGH THE CURTAINS
AND SUDDENLY A THOUSAND MEN --LAWYERS, BUSINESS LEADERS, WEALTHY MERCHANTS
REALLY IMPORTANT PEOPLE
WHAT COLOUR WERE THEY?
WHAT COLOUR WERE THEY?
THE CURTAINS, SILLY.

THEY WEREN'T DYED BURLAP OR ANYTHING YUCCHY LIKE THAT, WERE THEY?
HONESTLY-- THERE ARE DAYS WHEN I GET SO SICK OF DYED BURLAP, I COULD JUST ABOUT...
FORGET IT.
YOU'RE OBVIOUSLY NOT INTERESTED IN CEREBUS' CAMPAIGN.

OH, BUT I AM! I AM! REALLY!
REALLY!
I JUST ASKED ABOUT THE CURTAINS BECAUSE
OOOOH!
I'M SORRY I'M SORRY
TELL ME ABOUT YOUR CAMPAIGN
PLEASE PLEASE PLEASE PLEASE
PLEEEEEASE...
SO CEREBUS STEPS THROUGH THE CURTAINS AND SUDDENLY ALMOST TWO THOUSAND MEN LEAP TO THEIR FEET ...
MILLIONAIRES, CHURCH OFFICIALS, IMPORTANT REPRESENTATIVES, BANKERS
AND ALL AT ONCE...
KNOCK KNOCK

HEROES
WHAT IS IT BUG!? WHAT?
STAND UP STRAIGHT! YOU LOOK LIKE LORD JULIUS' PERSONAL ACCOUNTANT ... HUH?
The Times
AARDVARK TRAILS GOAT IN DOCKS, SUBURBS

YOU MEAN CEREBUS IS LOSING TO THAT DUMB ANIMAL...
WHO KNOWS
WHO CARES
WHAT'S THE MATTER BUG? DID SOMEBODY SAW THROUGH YOUR ORPHANS AGAIN?

ASTORIA DOESN'T LOVE....M...ME
SHE
L...LOVES
YOU!

IT'S NOT FAIR! I'M TALLER AND STRONGER! I'M MORE SENSITIVE! MORE HEROIC!
THE PIECE OF PAPER, BUG-- WHERE'D YOU ...?

SUDDENLY, REALIZING WHAT A FOOL HE'S MAKING OF HIMSELF, THE MOON ROACH STRAIGHTENS UP!
HIS EYES NARROW TO THIN SLITS OF ICY CONTEMPT.
"TO BE HONEST," HE HISSES...

I DON'T CARE, KEVITCH! I DON'T! I DON'T! JUST LEAVE ME ALONE--ALL OF YOU!! I WANT TO DIE! DIE!! DIE!!

KNOCK KNOCK

THAT'S HER!
SHE
I'D KNOW HER KNOCK ANYWHERE
OH NO!
THINK! THINK!
EXCUSE ME, BUG.

I'LL SET A TRAP!
NO!
I'LL HIDE!
NO NO!
HAVE TO SHOW HER THE MOON ROACH CAN'T BE HURT.

ABRUPTLY, THE MOON ROACH LEAPS INTO A NEARBY CHAIR AND STRIKES A CASUAL POSE...
HO-HUM. DID YOU HEAR A KNOCK JUST THEN?

WHOEVER IT IS, TELL THEM THEY CAN'T STAY BECAUSE I HAVE EIGHT CHICKS COMING OVER IN A WHILE TO PLAY SPIN-THE-BOTTLE AND I DON'T WANT THE JOINT TOO CROWDED, OKAY?

YOU CAN'T STAY BECAUSE HE'S GOT EIGHT CHICKS COMING OVER IN A WHILE TO PLAY SPIN-THE-BOTTLE AND HE ...
AH HEARD! AH HEARD!
OF ALL TH' DOUBLE-DEALIN' TWO-FACED SELFY-CENTERED

"BOOTSIE" MAKES ASTORIA LOOK LIKE FIVE MILES OF BAD ROAD...
BUT WHOEVER-YOU-ARE-THAT-JUST-CAME-IN DON'T TELL ASTORIA I SAID SO...
IT MIGHT HURT HER FEELINGS

YOU JEST WAIT 'N' SEE IF'N AH EVER TAKE YUH WITH ME TUH MAGGIE'S CATHOUSE AGIN!
OH NO

AH DON' NEED HIM T'GIT NO THIRTY PER CENT DISCOUNT... NOSIREE! IT WUZ ME THET WON TH' ENDOORANCE RALLY -- NOT THET NO-ACCOUNT FUNNY BOY BUG...
SO WHAT DOES ASTORIA WANT CEREBUS FOR.
DANGED IF'N AH KNOW! SHE SEZ FETCH 'N' AH FETCH...

WHAAH! FIRST I LOSE ASTORIA ...
AND NOW MY THIRTY PER CENT DISCOUNT AT MAGGIE'S

D'WAY I LOOG AT IT-- WHUD'S DA DIFFRENCE?
NOBUDDY IN DADOCKS C'N READ... 'NCLOOD'N' ME.
WE'RE TALKING ABOUT AN EFFECTIVE LITERACY RATE OF LESS-THAN-ONE -PERCENT...!
I MEAN, EVEN ASSUMING THAT LORD JULIUS IS BEHIND IT...
LORD JULIUS IS BEHIND IT AND YOU ARE REACTING JUST THE WAY HE EXPECTS YOU TO
LORD JULIUS DOESN'T MAKE ILL-CONSIDERED MOVES...
I SAY WE SHOULD PRINT A PAPER JUST LIKE HIS SAYING "GOAT TRAILS CEREBUS"
WE CAN'T GIVE HIM ANY ADVANTAGE WITH ANY OF THE VOTERS
GIVEM D'LESS THAN ONE PUH CENT...
CONSIDERING HIS COSTS, HE DESERVES THEIR SUPPORT
IT'S PROBABLY MORE LIKE TEN PERCENT IN THE UPPER CITY.
TEN PER CENT STILL ISN'T GOING TO COST US THE ELECTION UP HERE
HOW CAN WE BE SURE?
WHO'S GONNA PAY F'DIS PAPUH, ANYHOW?
WE HAVE MONEY
"WE"? YOU TALKIN' ABOWT "YOUAH WE" MUNNY OR "MY-WE" MUNNY?
LOOK, IF YOU'RE GOING TO GET CHEAP ABOUT IT
CHEAP? I DON' WANNA SPEND THOUSANDS O' CROWNS ON A PAPUH I CAN'T READ
THAT AIN'T CHEAP--THAT'S SMART!
LOOK! FIND OUT WHAT IT COSTS TO ENGRAVE AND PRINT THAT PAPER
ADD UP HOW MUCH MONEY WE HAVE AND THEN MAKE A DAMN DECISION
THE AMOUNT OF TIME THE BUNCH OF YOU SPEND SITTING AROUND JABBERING
WHAT ARE YOU GRINNING ABOUT?
NOTHING. NOTHING AT ALL, M'LORD.

NEW ONE?
MM.
SEZ "AS--
AS-TOR-EYE"
"AS-TOR-EYE"
NEW ONE?
MM.
"AS-TOR-EYE-UH
RE-REJEK-
RE-JEK-TID"
"BOY"
OY NOW! OY NOW! I WOZ JOOST RESTIN'
"RE-JEK-TID... BOY..."
SIR
CUR
KUR-RYE-
SIR-RYE
"ASTORIA REJECTED BY CIRINISTS"
"'OY'M WINNING' SEZ GOWT."
FLAMIN' SMARTASS KIDS'LL BE THE RUIN O' THIS CITY.
IT'S TH' TRUTH.

GLUP. GLUP.
AN' SO I ENNEDUP IN'ER ROOM WITH BLOOD POUREEN OUTTA ME'N' SHE SEZ, "OOOH" SHE SEZ
"YER HURD," SHE SEZ

THANGS. THANG YOO.

DAM STRADE I'M HURD!
WOODEN YOO BEEZ
GLUP GLUP GLUPPA

HERE--YOO'AVE TH'REST...
AS FER MEE!...
I GOT THINGS T'GO AN' PLACES T'DO!...
SO!!

IT'SUP-UP AN' AWWOOOOOOOO

WHFM

I TELL YOU, IF HE DOESN'T START SHOWING A LITTLE MORE ENTHUSIASM, I'M GOING TO QUIT...
NOW, ASTORIA.
I EVEN EXPLAINED TO HIM HOW BADLY WE NEED THE NINETEEN REPRESENTATIVES
I'M BEGINNING TO THINK HE WANTS TO LOSE JUST TO SPITE ME.
OH, I DON'T KNOW. DO YOU THINK HE WANTS TO LOSE, FILGATE?
HE NEEDS DADOCKS MOAH DEN DADOCKS NEEDS HIM. DAT'S ALL I KNOW.
'AT'S 'ER... THE ONE INNA BACK.
AS-TOR-EYE-UH?
HE EITHER WANTS TO LOSE OR HE FIGURES THAT SOMEHOW...
AM I? AM I REALLY?
... HE CAN CONJURE THE FIFTEEN SEATS HE NEEDS OUT OF THIN AIR.
THEKESA, DEAR -- STOP STARING AT MR. McGREW. YOU'RE MAKING HIM NERVOUS...

CEREBUS TOLD YOU FROM THE BEGINNING HE WAS GOING TO WIN.
YOU HAVEN'T WON JUST YET, GREAT CEREBUS.
IT'S JUST A MATTER OF TIME...
VERY LITTLE TIME.
AH THINK HE'S RIGHT YER MUFIN-SHIP.
THE MOON ROACH SILENTLY DISAGREES. THE AARDVARK HAD MADE IT THIS FAR ON SHEER DUMB LUCK.
KEVITCH CONCURS WITH THAT.
I SUSPECT YOU'RE TRYING TO CONVINCE ME BY CONVINCING YOURSELF.
YOU DON'T KNOW CEREBUS VERY WELL, THEN.
PERHAPS I KNOW YOU BETTER THAN YOU THINK I DO.
IN OR OUT?
IN.
HA-HA! A PAIR O' PRIESTESSES!
HE DID HAVE THE OTHER ONE!

WHEN CEREBUS IS ELECTED, YOU WILL HAVE A VERY GOOD JOB, NO?
WAL, AH 'SPECT SO, MISS
SAY! IZNIT A MITE TOO DRAFTY IN HYAR
WITH YER DRESS UN-BUTTONED CLEAR DOWN
TUH*
YER*
THERESA!
YES M'LADY?
FIND THE CANDIDATE AND TELL HIM IT'S TIME FOR HIM TO GIVE HIS SPEECH
YES, M'LADY
PLEASE, YER LENIENCY, AH DINT ASK 'ER TUH...
OF COURSE YOU DIDN'T
SHE'S A MERE CHILD
WHOOEE. FER A MINNIT THAR AH THOUGHT YUH WUZ...
GONNA
GONNA*
WHY ME? WHY, ALL TH' DANG TIME, IS IT ME?

WUD'S IT SAY? HANH?
BACK, FOUL SUBURBANITE
GIVE ME A SECOND TO GET IT OPEN.
EAT DELEGATE, YUH SOCIAL-CLIMBIN' WAHOO!
HEY!
SO LONG AS HER POSITION IS THAT OF ADVISOR ONLY, AND ONLY OF SUB-CABINET RANK
SHE HAS NO OBJECTIONS
I THOUGHT I SMELLED MONEY WHEN I WOKE UP T'DAY.
GIT THOSE FINGERS BACK BEHIND THET RAILIN' AFORE AH SNAP'EM OFF AT TH' SHOULDER!
THE ABBESS ACKNOWLEDGES RECEIPT OF YOUR LETTER AND, AS REGARDS YOUR COUNTER-OFFER OF RETAINING ASTORIA ...
THE FIFTEEN REPRESENTATIVES ARE YOURS ...
CONGATULATIONS, "MR. PRIME MINISTER"

WE CAN'T THANK YOU ENOUGH. THAT WAS QUITE A STIRRING SPEECH
NOT AT ALL, WE'RE JUST DELIGHTED, WHENEVER WE HAVE A CHANCE TO SEE THE HEART-LAND OF THIS GREAT CITY-STATE.
HOW KIND.

IT WILL ONLY BE THROUGH THE COMBINED EFFORTS OF ALL THESE GRASS-ROOTS COMMUNITIES THAT WE WILL BE ABLE TO GET THIS CITY-STATE MOVING AGAIN.
WE MUST ALL SHARE IN THE TASK OF RESTORING CONFIDENCE AND PROSPERITY

GOODBYE FOR NOW.

PRIEST.
DID ANYONE GET THE NAME OF THAT CATTLE TROUGH?
OLDHAM.
ASTORIA SEZ "TH' CANDIDATE" NEEDS THAR SIX SEATS
ASTORIA ALSO SAYS "THE CANDIDATE" NEEDS HER
WHICH SHOWS HOW MUCH SHE KNOWS.

GUESS WHAT
GUESS WHAT
GUESS WHAT
GUESS WHAT
ELF. CEREBUS HAS BEEN TRAVELLING SINCE LAST NIGHT. NO RIDDLES, OKAY?
ASTORIA TOLD ARTEMIS TO FIND IT FOR HER!
OKAY. ONE RIDDLE
WHAT THE HECK ARE YOU TALKING ABOUT?
LISTEN
LISTEN
LISTEN
LISTEN
LISTEN!

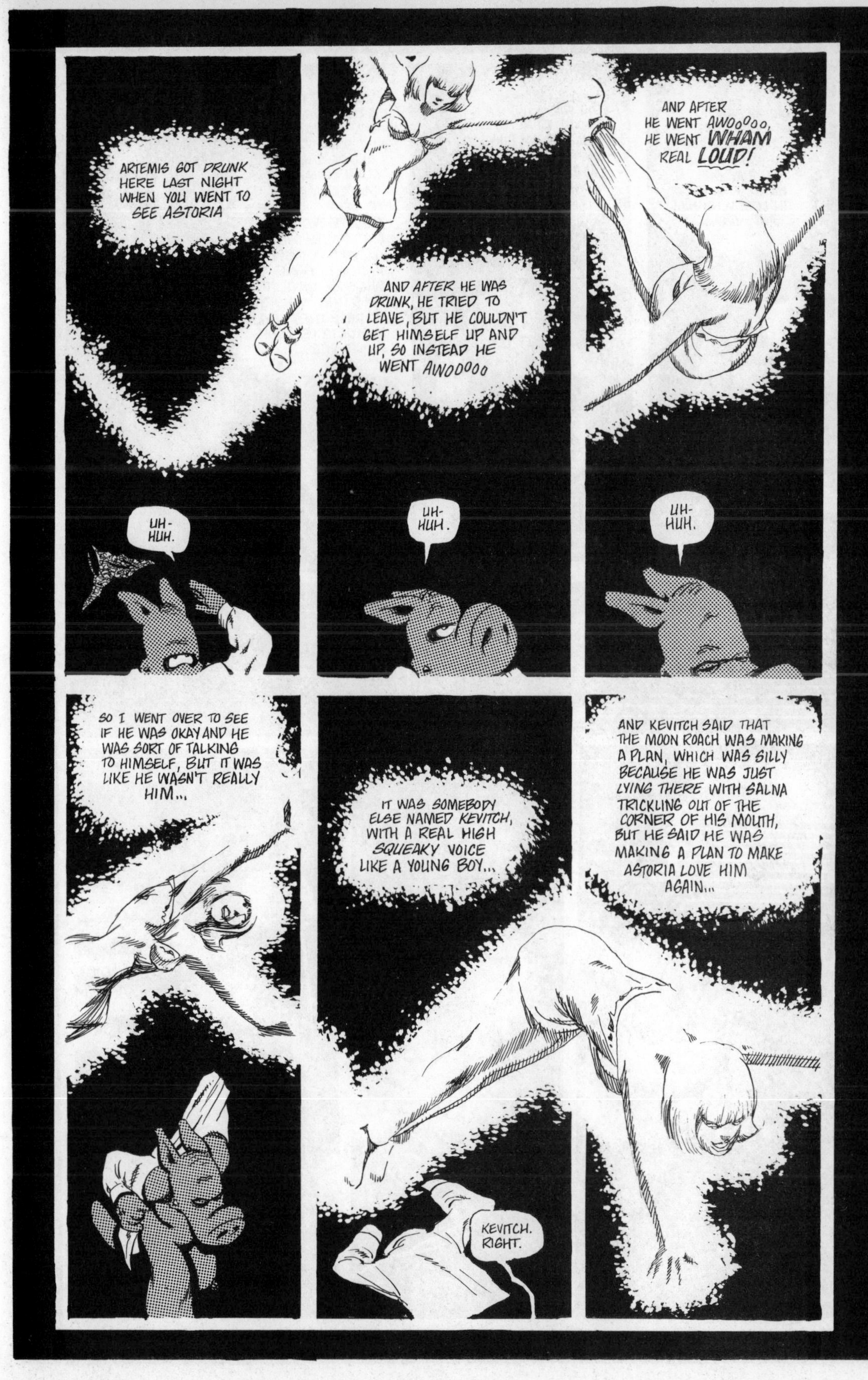
ARTEMIS GOT DRUNK HERE LAST NIGHT WHEN YOU WENT TO SEE ASTORIA
AND AFTER HE WAS DRUNK, HE TRIED TO LEAVE, BUT HE COULDN'T GET HIMSELF UP AND UP, SO INSTEAD HE WENT AWOOOOO
AND AFTER HE WENT AWOOOOO, HE WENT WHAM REAL LOUD!
UH-HUH.
UH-HUH.
UH-HUH.
SO I WENT OVER TO SEE IF HE WAS OKAY AND HE WAS SORT OF TALKING TO HIMSELF, BUT IT WAS LIKE HE WASN'T REALLY HIM...
IT WAS SOMEBODY ELSE NAMED KEVITCH, WITH A REAL HIGH SQUEAKY VOICE LIKE A YOUNG BOY...
AND KEVITCH SAID THAT THE MOON ROACH WAS MAKING A PLAN, WHICH WAS SILLY BECAUSE HE WAS JUST LYING THERE WITH SALNA TRICKLING OUT OF THE CORNER OF HIS MOUTH, BUT HE SAID HE WAS MAKING A PLAN TO MAKE ASTORIA LOVE HIM AGAIN...
KEVITCH. RIGHT.

AND HE SAID IF HE COULD JUST FIND THE ANTIQUE SHE WAS LOOKING FOR THAT SHE WOULD FALL BACK IN LOVE WITH HIM AND... AND...
AND WHAT?

WELL, HE WENT ON FOR A WHILE ABOUT WHAT SHE WOULD DO TO HIM UNDER THE COVERS WHEN SHE LOVED HIM AGAIN...
OKAY.
SKIP THAT PART.

AND THEN HE STARTED DESCRIBING HOW HE WOULD JUST HAVE TO FIND ALL OF THE RED CLAW CRIMINAL MASTERMIND EXPLOITERS OF THE DISADVANTAGED AND MAKE THEM ALL EAT A FEW KNUCKLE SAND-WICHES UNTIL THEY TOLD HIM WHERE TO FIND THE ANTIQUE ASTORIA IS LOOK-ING FOR...
UH-HUH.

AND THAT'S WHEN HE SAID IT...
PHOOOOF
SAID WHAT?

HE SAID HE DIDN'T EVEN KNOW WHAT AN ALBATROSS LOOKS LIKE!

FSSSSS

THE DUCK STATUE.
YES!
YES!
YES!
YES!

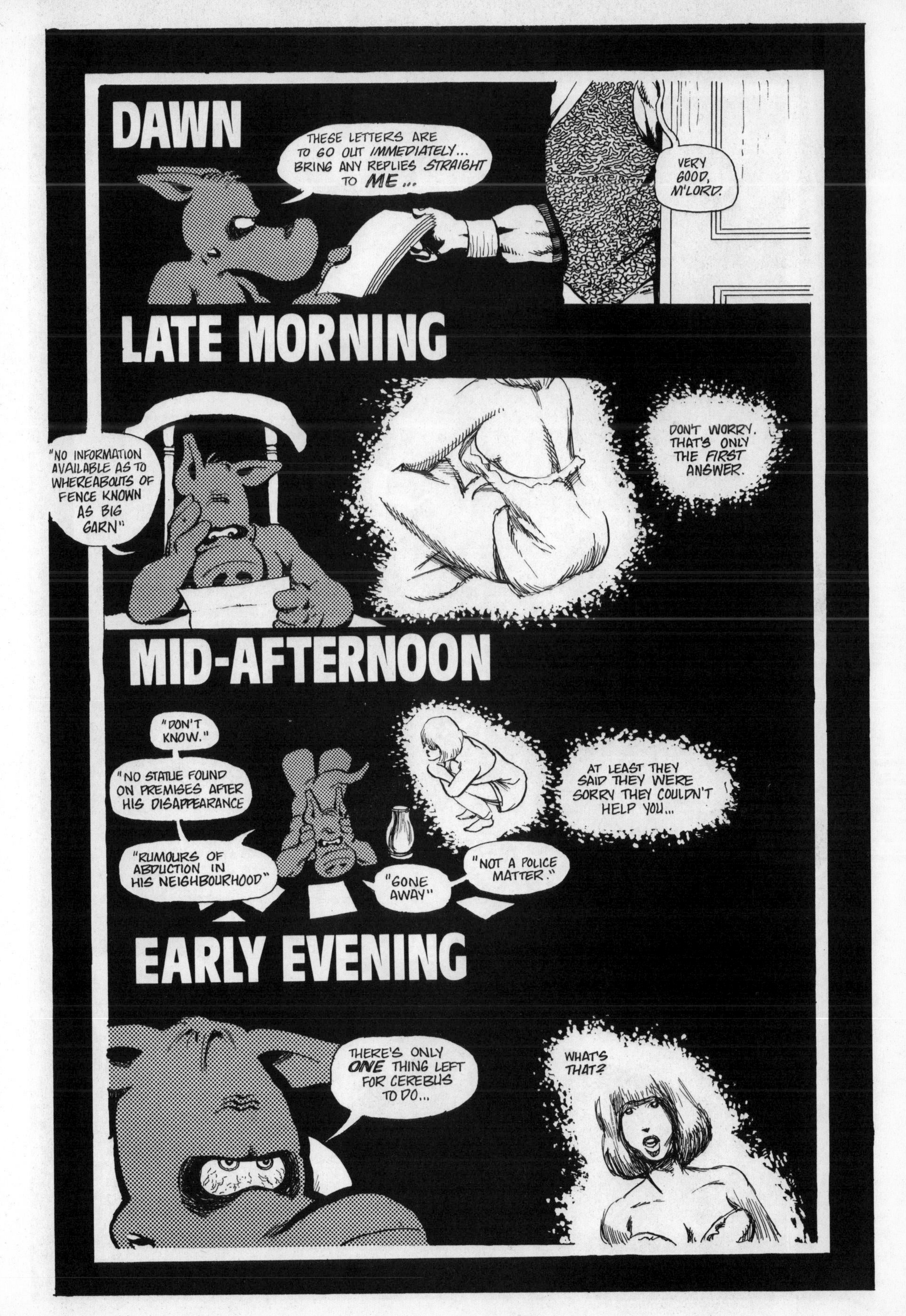
DAWN
THESE LETTERS ARE TO GO OUT IMMEDIATELY... BRING ANY REPLIES STRAIGHT TO ME...
VERY GOOD, M'LORD.
LATE MORNING
"NO INFORMATION AVAILABLE AS TO WHEREABOUTS OF FENCE KNOWN AS BIG GARN"
DON'T WORRY. THAT'S ONLY THE FIRST ANSWER.
MID-AFTERNOON
"DON'T KNOW."
"NO STATUE FOUND ON PREMISES AFTER HIS DISAPPEARANCE
"RUMOURS OF ABDUCTION IN HIS NEIGHBOURHOOD"
"GONE AWAY"
"NOT A POLICE MATTER."
AT LEAST THEY SAID THEY WERE SORRY THEY COULDN'T HELP YOU...
EARLY EVENING
THERE'S ONLY ONE THING LEFT FOR CEREBUS TO DO...
WHAT'S THAT?

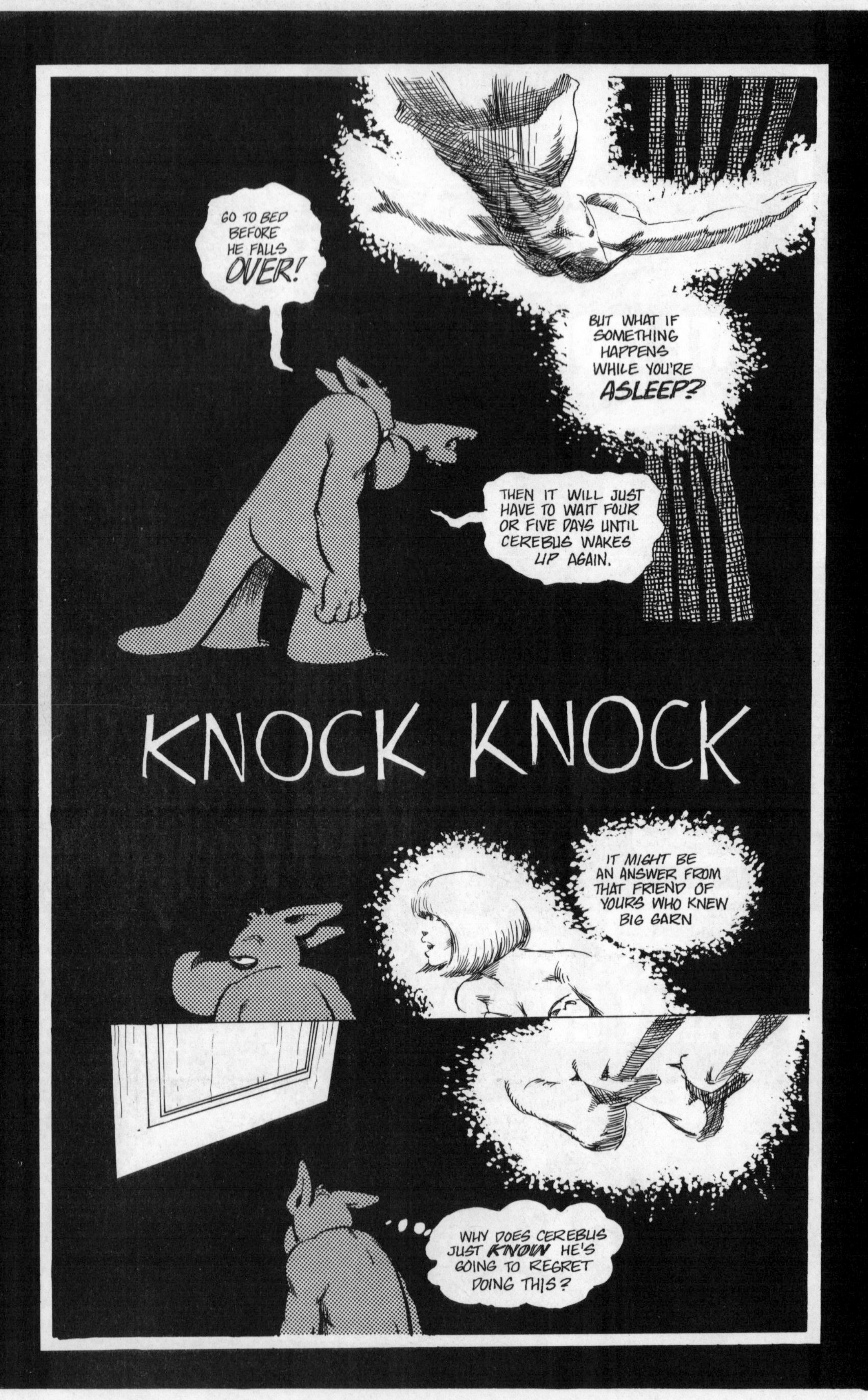
GO TO BED BEFORE HE FALLS OVER!
BUT WHAT IF SOMETHING HAPPENS WHILE YOU'RE ASLEEP?
THEN IT WILL JUST HAVE TO WAIT FOUR OR FIVE DAYS UNTIL CEREBUS WAKES UP AGAIN.
KNOCK KNOCK
IT MIGHT BE AN ANSWER FROM THAT FRIEND OF YOURS WHO KNEW BIG GARN
WHY DOES CEREBUS JUST KNOW HE'S GOING TO REGRET DOING THIS?

WORD JUST CAME THROUGH THAT SOMEHOW LORD JULIUS GOT A BILL PASSED BEFORE THE LEGISLATURE WAS DISSOLVED FOR THE ELECTION WHICH REDUCES THE NUMBER OF SEATS IN GREATER IEST TO EIGHT FROM TWENTY WHICH MEANS ASTORIA NOW FIGURES YOU HAVE TWENTY-NINE SEATS GUARANTEED WHEN IN FACT WITH SUPPORT YOU HAVE FROM GRACE DISTRICT YOU NOW HAVE FORTY-FIVE SEATS GUARANTEED SIX SEATS SHORT OF A MAJORITY GOVERNMENT SO WE HAVE NO OTHER CHOICE THAN TO HEAD NORTH AND TRY TO DRUM UP SUPPORT IN THE FARMING COMMUNITIES ASTORIA WANTS YOU DOWNSTAIRS IN FIVE MINUTES, BUT I CAN'T WAIT AROUND BECAUSE I HAVE FOUR MORE PEOPLE TO NOTIFY AND ASTORIA SAYS WE'R LATE AL-READY BEASTLY SHORT NOTICE I KNOW AND I AM AWFULLY SORRY HAVE TO GO NOW BYE
OH DEAR.
NO.
PLEASE.

NO.
PLEASE.
I FEEL JUST TERRIBLE ABOUT THIS-- KEEPING YOU UP ALL DAY.
NO
PLEASE
YOU WANT TO BE THE FIRST AARDVARK PRIME MINISTER OF IEST DON'T YOU.
NO
PLEASE.
STRAIGHTEN YOUR FINGERS AND PUSH THEM THROUGH THE ...
THA-AT'S IT.

Cerebus the Aardvark

UNLESS ONE UNDERSTANDS THE SEQUENCE OF EVENTS, IN CONTEXT, WHICH LED TO THE ELECTION, IT BECOMES DIFFICULT TO APPRECIATE THE PROFOUND CHAOS THE CITY-STATE OF IEST LIVED THROUGH IN THOSE TUMULTUOUS DAYS. THE LEGISLATURE HAD NEVER BEEN INTENDED AS A GOVERNING BODY. THE CHURCH OF TARIM INSTITUTED IT WHEN IT BECAME APPARENT (SOME HUNDRED YEARS EARLIER) THAT A DISPROPORTIONATE AMOUNT OF HIS HOLINESS' TIME WAS BEING SPENT ADJUDICATING ECONOMIC MATTERS. HIS SOLUTION WAS TO ALLOW EACH DISTRICT OF THE CITY-STATE, IN PROPORTION TO THEIR CONTRIBUTION TO THE ECONOMY, TO SEND REPRESENTATIVES TO DEBATE AND FORM ECONOMIC POLICY FOR THE MOTHER CHURCH. THESE REPRESENTATIVES WERE APPOINTED BY THE LOCAL CHURCHES AND THEN ELECTED BY THE LOCAL PEOPLE TO SERVE EITHER AS CONSERVATIVE OR LIBERTINE ECONOMISTS IN IEST. IT WAS STRICTLY A MATTER OF EVOLUTION WHICH LED TO PRIME MINISTER GATSON'S CORRUPT REGIME; THE BORROWING OF MILLIONS OF CROWNS; THE INTER-CONNECTED HOUSE OF CARDS THAT WAS IEST'S INTERNATIONAL TRADE BALANCES; ALL DISCRETELY HIDDEN FROM PAPAL AUTHORITY AND OVERVIEW BY SEVERAL TONS OF OBFUSCATING PAPERWORK. IT WAS HIS SENSE OF SOMETHING BEING HORRIBLY AMISS AND HIS INABILITY TO DISCOVER JUST WHAT IT WAS WHICH LED HIS HOLINESS TO INSTITUTE AN INQUISITION INTO CORRUPTION IN THE LEGISLATURE. AND IT WAS THE APPOINTED GRAND INQUISITOR WHO, AFTER A SERIES OF MEETINGS WITH THE PRIME MINISTER, DECIDED THAT THE SOURCE OF THE PROBLEM WAS DEMONS INHABITING MANY MEMBERS OF THE BUSINESS COMMUNITY. UNDOUBTEDLY, HE HAD BEEN OFFERED AND HAD ACCEPTED A BRIBE TO LEAVE THE PRIME MINISTER ALONE AND HAD ACCEPTED AN OBVIOUS SOLUTION BY INSTITUTING A REIGN OF TERROR. IT IS GENERALLY OVERLOOKED THAT ALL OF THE WEALTHY MERCHANTS AND TRADERS WHO WERE BROKEN ON THE RACK WERE "STRIPPED OF THEIR WORLDLY GOODS" (TO QUOTE THE EDICT). THESE WORLDLY GOODS WERE THEN SPLIT THREE WAYS -- ONE SHARE FOR THE PRIME MINISTER, ONE FOR THE GRAND INQUISITOR AND ONE FOR THE PAPAL VAULTS WHERE IT COULD BE USED AS SOLID EVIDENCE THAT THE INQUISITION WAS HAVING A POSITIVE EFFECT ON IEST'S ECONOMY. THIS CONTINUED UNTIL THE GRAND INQUISITOR DEMANDED AND RECEIVED (FROM A VERY RELIEVED PONTIFF) THE TITLE OF EARTH-BORN MESSENGER, WHICH TECHNICALLY PLACED HIM ABOVE THE PONTIFF IN THE RELIGIOUS (THOUGH NOT THE POLITICAL) INFRASTRUCTURE OF THE CHURCH. THE POSITION, HOWEVER WAS A DANGEROUS ONE TO HOLD, BECAUSE IT FIGURED IN NO LESS THAN FIFTY SACRED TEXTS. THE GRAND INQUISITOR BECAME THE FOCUS OF AN IMMENSE CHARISMATIC CULT WITHIN THE CHURCH. IF HE SNEEZED, IT MEANT THIS; IF HE SPILLED A GLASS OF WATER, IT MEANT THAT. WHEN HE WAS ASSASSINATED, IT WAS THIS CULT WHICH PERSUADED HIS HOLINESS THAT THE APOCALYPSE WAS AT HAND AND WHICH CONVINCED HIM TO INITIATE THE "EXODUS INWARD" PREDICTED SEVERAL HUNDRED YEARS BEFORE WHICH REQUIRED THE CHURCH TO "SEAL ITS DOORS AGAINST THE HORROR" AND TO SEVER ALL CONNECTION WITH THE OUTSIDE WORLD. ALL OF THE TRIPE WRITTEN ABOUT IRRESISTIBLE POLITICAL FORCES AT WORK AND LORD JULIUS' MASTER PLAN IS SO MUCH ROMANTIC HOGWASH. WHEN THE CHURCH SEALED ITSELF UP IN THE SACRED CATHEDRAL, IEST BECAME A BODY WITHOUT A HEAD AND NATURALLY TURNED TO THE COMING ELECTION AS THE ONLY MEANS OF RESTORING SOME MANNER OF GOVERNING AUTHORITY...

FROM "THE TRUE HISTORY OF THE 1413 ELECTION" BY SUENTEUS PO

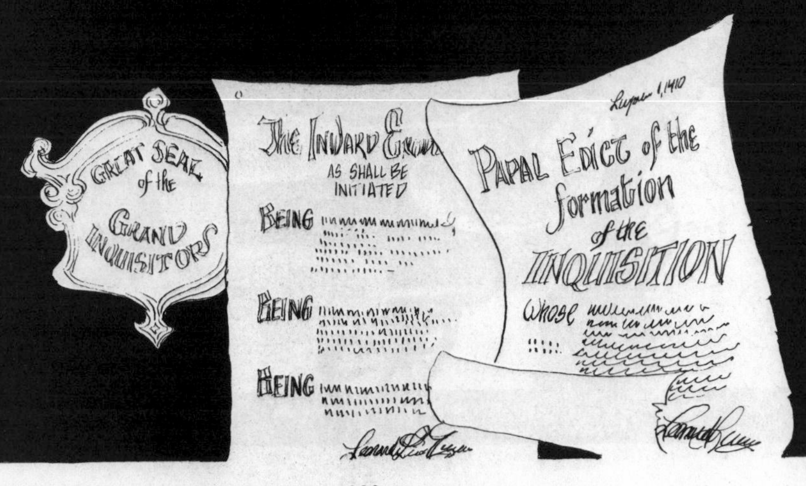

Northbell
Storm'send Manor
5
5
Shireway
North Road
The Oldcastle Road
Feld River Road
I WANT YOU TO GO OVER TO THAT FARMER'S OLD HOVEL AND ASK FOR CLEAR AND SPECIFIC INSTRUCTIONS TO STORM'SEND MANOR AND I DON'T WANT YOU TO COME BACK UNTIL YOU HAVE THEM. UNDERSTAND?
YES, M'UM...
I'M GONNA FREEZE T'DEAT' OUT HE' AN' MY NO-GOOD COUSIN IS GONNA ROB ME MUDDAH BLOIND. I NOW IT.
I'M SARRY, MA.
HONESTLY-- THE DRIVERS YOU GET THESE DAYS ARE SO INCOMPETENT...
WE PROBABLY PASSED STORM'S-END MANOR AN HOUR AGO...
DID YOU ASK?
WELL? WHAT DID HE SAY?
YES, M'UM.
IT SEEMS THE OLD HOVEL IS STORM'SEND MANOR, MU'UM.

CAMPAIGN'S END

I'LL TELL YOU THE SAME THING I TOLD THE PAINTED-UP-FELLER...
I HASN'T VOTED MYSELF FER A P'LITICAL PARTY AN' I DON'T AIM T'START NOW-- AS FER THE FOLKS AROUND THESE PARTS...
SCRAPE SCRAPE
AH LET THE WAY THEY VOTE DECIDE WHO GITS OUR FIVE REPRESENTATIVES
OR PORTION THEREOF
YOU MISSED SOME BY THE HEEL...
BUT DON'T YOU SEE THE BENEFIT FOR NORTHBELL IN HAVING REPRESENTATION IN THE WINNING PARTY?
WAL, MA'AM, THE ONLY TIME WE VOTED WITH THE WINNERS, WE HAD RUST ON THE CROPS ...
AND A DRY SPELL THET LASTED EIGHT WEEK.
BUT--THAT WAS ONLY A COINCIDENCE, SURELY...
MEBBE SO...
BUT AROUND THESE PARTS, WE TRY T'MAKE SURE OUR COINCIDENCES ONLY COINCIDE ONCE.
KNOCK WOOD.
TAP TAP

THE IMPLICATIONS WERE CLEAR ONCE THE BATTLE-LINES HAD BEEN DRAWN BETWEEN ASTORIA'S THEOCRATS AND LORD JULIUS' DEVOTIONALISTS THAT THE PRIMARY ISSUE WAS FOREIGN OWNERSHIP OF THE CITY-STATE OF IEST. THOSE WHO FELT THAT IEST'S FATE WAS ALREADY INEXTRICABLY BOUND TO THAT OF PALNU (AND, CONSEQUENTLY, TO THAT OF ITS CHARISMATIC LEADER) WERE QUITE PREPARED TO ELECT A GOAT TO THE OFFICE OF PRIME MINISTER, WITH THE UNDERSTANDING THAT THE NEXT STEP (ANNEXATION, MILITARY INVASION, ETC.) WOULD BE UP TO LORD JULIUS. IT IS A SIGN OF THE NEAR-COMPLETE COLLAPSE OF THE IESTAN ECONOMY THAT SO MANY PEOPLE EMBRACED THIS SOLUTION. THOSE WHO ADVOCATED IESTAN SOVEREIGNTY ALLIED THEMSELVES WITH ASTORIA AND CEREBUS, THE ONLY TWO INDIVIDUALS KNOWN TO HAVE LEFT LORD JULIUS' INNER CIRCLE. IT MUST BE ADDED THAT THERE WAS A SIGNIFICANT PERCENTAGE OF THE IESTAN POPULATION WHO FELT ASTORIA AND LORD JULIUS WERE STILL ALLIED AND THAT THEIR DIVORCE WAS A TRICK TO ELIMINATE SUSPICION OF THIS FACT.

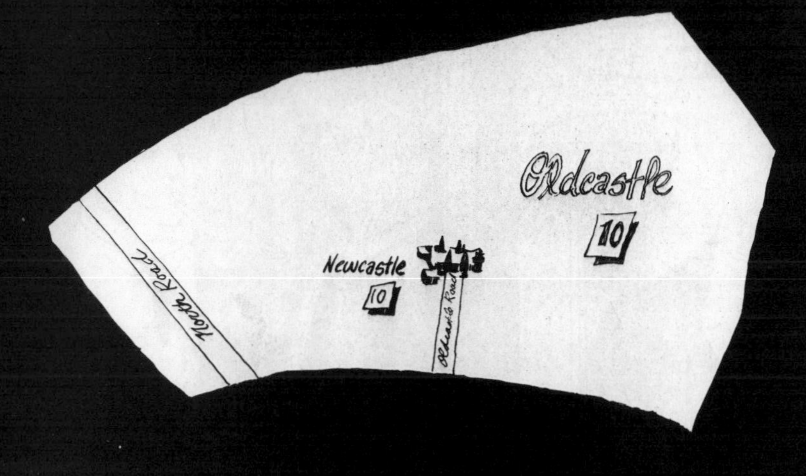

IT TOOK FIVE YEARS, BUT I TOLD YUH I'D COME UP HE'E SUM DAY.
FILGATE! C'MON IN. GOOD T'SEE YUH. GOOD T'SEE YUH.
SWELL PLACE Y'GOT HE'E.
YAH. YAH. SWELL PLACE.
BUT IT'S NOT LIKE THE OLD NEIGHBUHOOD Y'KNOW WHAT I MEAN?
YAH.
I MEAN-- THE OLD NEIGHBUHOOD WAS TOUGH Y'KNOW?
YAH?
ARE YOU KIDDIN'-- I'M TALKIN' TOUGH HE'E. I USED T'HAVE T'WEAR A HELMET, THREE LAYERS OF MAIL AND A BUCKLUH...
AN' THAT WUZ JUST T'GO T'TH' TOILET.
TOUGH. TOUGH NEIGHBUHOOD.
THE OLD NEIGHBUHOOD THEY'D DRAW AN' QUARTUH Y'AT TH' PRE-TRIAL HEARING
...T'SAVE TIME.

AND THE COPS WERE TOUGH.
TOUGH COPS.
YOU KIDDIN'? THEY DIDN'T COME ANY TOUGHUH.
A COP ON OUR BLOCK USED T' CHEW HIS NAILS...
THE TWO-INCH ROOFING KIND.
TOUGH. TOUGH COPS.
HAVE A SEAT.
THANKS
SO WHAT BRINGS YOU UP HERE?
WELL, Y'KNOW THE ELECTION IS...
ELECTIONS.
AHH--I DON'T KNOW
ELECTIONS.
EVERY FOUR YEARS Y'GET T'MAKE YOUR LAST MISTAKE WORSE, Y'KNOW WHAT I MEAN?
I GOT A COUSIN WHOSE A REPRESENTATIVE F'GARRISON ...
SAYS HE WANTS T'BE A BACK-BENCHUH...
SO HE CAN LOOK DOWN ASTORIA'S DRESS.
AHH. BUT IT'S ROUGH, Y'KNOW?
ROUGH.
ROUGH. A'YOU KIDDIN'?

I SENT A REQUEST IN FOR AN OFFENSIVE MILITARY WEAPON TO PROTECT NEWCASTLE.
THEY SENT ME AN ARMY COOK WIT' TYPHOID...
I NOW. I NOW. WAL...
AND Y'CAN'T GET GOOD HELP NOWADAYS, Y'KNOW?
I GOT AN ASSISTANT THINKS Y'STOP INFLATION BY SHOOTING POOR PEOPLE.
I REMEMBER WHEN BEING POOR WAS A VERY SPECIALIZED TRADE. NOW EVERYONE'S GETTING INTO IT...
WHAT I'M HERE TO...
AN' KIDS T'DAY! LISTEN. DON'T GET ME STAHTED ON THAT.
MY YOUNGEST BOY-- I ASK HIM WHAT HE WANTS F'R 'IS BIRTHDAY.
HE SAYS "UNSHIB"
CARABUS WANTS T'NOW IF YOUAH GOING T'BE ON BOARD WITH US FOR DE ELECSHUN.

ON BOARD?
THE LAST TIME SOMEONE FRUM GREATUH IEST ASKED ME T'GET ON BOARD, THEY WAS HOLDIN' A PAIR OF OARS AN' A WHIP
GUARANTEE US AWL TEN REPRESENATIVES AN' CARABUS'LL GIVE YUH A CABINET POST.
A CABINET POST?
YAH.
Y'MEAN A CHEST O' DRAWERS WIT' A LOG INSIDE ...
NAH. NAH. A POATFOWLIO ...
F'REAL. A CABINET POST.
CHEE. DAT WOULD BE GRATE.
WHICH ONE?
WHICHEVUH ONE YUH WANT...
I DUNNO. SOMETHIN' UPBEAT Y'KNOW?
I'M AN UPBEAT COINA GUY.
I NOTICED DAT.
HOW ABOUT MINISTUH OF OPTIMISM.
SHUAH!
SOUNDS GRATE.

SAY! THIS WAS SWELLA YOU...
WAL... Y'FRUM D'OLD NEIGHBUHOOD Y'KNOW?
I KNOW WATCHA MEAN. IT'S LOYALTY, Y'KNOW?
NOBODY'S LOYAL ANYMORE.
FRIENDA MINE HADDA BASSET HOUND THAT FINGERED HIM F'TWO FRENCH POODLES AN' A CHEWY-BONE.
THING LIKE THAT'LL REALLY HURT A GUY, Y'KNOW?
SWELL. IF YOU'LL JUST SIGN THIS PIECE O' PAPUH...
SIGN. YAH. WHY NOT?
WHATSA MATTUH?
LAST TIME I DIDN'T READ THE FINE PRINT ...
AND I ENDED UP ORDERING A QUARTER-TON O' GOAT CHOW.

Fort Palin
Fort Cleese
1
Fort Dead Parrot
Fort Trof
Fort Frot
Fort Torte
Fort Tory
3
Fort Grit
PARMOOR
4
OH, FINE! SO I'M SUPPOSED TO MAINTAIN THE WORLD'S MOST SOPHISTICATED DEFENSE SYSTEM AGAINST INVADIN' BARBARIAN 'ORDES FOR THE THREE MEASLY MILLION CROWNS Y'SEND UP 'ERE ON A BLEEDIN' TURTLE WITH GOUT AFTER EVERY DAM BLEEDIN' BUDGET IS PASSED BY THAT QUIBBLIN' QUORUM OF HALF-FORMED INTELLIGENCES YOU CALL A LEGISLATURE; NOT TO MENTION THE FACT THAT THE BUNDLE ENDS UP BEING AT LEAST FORTY THOUSAND CROWNS SHY OF A LOAD EVERY BLEEDIN' TIME IT GETS 'ERE.
AN' NOW 'ERE YOU ARE, REGULAR AS FLAMIN' CLOCKWORK, SNIFFIN' AROUND PARMOOR'S ELECTORAL CROTCH FOR TARIM-ONLY-KNOWS WHAT KIND OF A CONTRA-MORAL SELLOUT OF WOT Y'SNIGGERINGLY REFER TO AS THE COMMON PEOPLE, WITHOUT SO MUCH AS AN 'ALF-CROWN'S NOTICE OF THE GREAT FESTERIN' PIMPLE OF RESENTMENT THAT 'AS BEEN GROWIN' FOR DECADES TOWARDS A PUSTULOID EXPLOSION OF SUCH OMINOUS PROPORTIONS, THAT IT IS ONCE MORE LEFT T'YOUR OBEDIENT SERVANT ALONE...
TO ATTEMPT TO ALERT THE SELF-DELUDIN', BOTTOM-WIPIN' TOADIES OF THE REAL POWER-BROKERS TO THE IMMINENT COLLAPSE OF THE FRONTIERS OF THIS RIDICULOUS EXCUSE FOR A CITY-STATE DESPITE THE BEST EFFORTS OF THE LAST OF THE TRULY PATRIOTIC AND INCORRUPTIBLE ELEMENTS IN THIS ULCEROUS SORE OF AN 'ODGE-PODGE REPUBLICAN DOG'S BREAKFAST IN THE 'OPES THAT BY SOME MANNER OF COW-TOWIN' OSMOSIS
THE MESSAGE OF SAID IMMINENT COLLAPSE MIGHT, THROUGH SOME 'ITHERTO UNEXPLORED AUDITORY AVENUE, REACH THE LAVENDAR-SCENTED EAR OF SOME UNSEEN, ILL-EQUIPPED AND SELF-APPOINTED PULLER OF STRINGS, WHO MIGHT, 'OWEVER IMPROBABLE IT MIGHT SEEM, TAKE 'IS THUMB OUT OF 'IS BLEEDIN' GOB, LONG ENOUGH T'TAKE SOME NOTICE AND TAKE THE FIRST BLEEDIN' STEP TOWARDS ANYTHIN' FAINTLY RESEMBLIN' POSITIVE BLEEDIN' ACTION.
THUNK!

FURTHERMORE, IF THERE IS NO MOVEMENT TOWARD SUBSTANTIALLY INCREASIN' THE SAID NIGGARDLY SUM OF THREE MILLION CROWNS, I CAN QUI'E ASSURE THE CANDIDATE THAT WITHIN A FORTNIGHT, WE SHALL BE UP TO OUR COD-PIECES IN FOUL-SMELLIN', GIBBERISH-SPOUTIN', VIRGIN-RAPIN', SHORT, YELLOW, SLANTY-EYED HSIFFIES, TO WHOM, HAVIN' DONE MY BEST FOR TARIM AND COUNTRY, I'LL BE PLEASED TO GIVE DETAILED AND COMPLETE INSTRUCTIONS ON ALL ROADS LEADIN' TO THE REGENCY 'OTEL WITH A DETAILED FLOOR PLAN OF THE FIFTH LEVEL AND A BRIGHT RED "X" INDICATING THE PRECISE LOCATION OF THE AMBASSADOR SUITE.
THUNK!
HOW ABOUT WE STICK WITH THE THREE MILLION, BUT CEREBUS WILL AGREE TO DEPOSIT FIFTEEN THOUSAND CROWNS IN YOUR LEGENDARY UNNUMBERED T'CAPMIN BANK ACCOUNT
THIRTY.
TWENTY.
TWENTY FIVE.
SOLD.

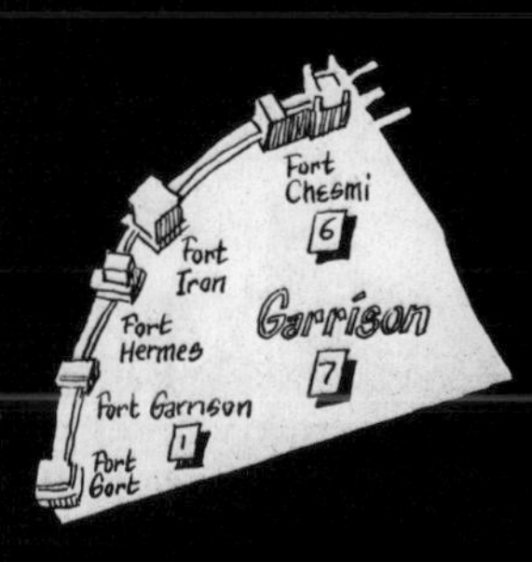

I FEEL COMPELLED TO REITERATE THAT THE ELECTION OF 1413 WAS A GIANT STEP FORWARD FOR ESTARCION DESPITE THE BEST EFFORTS OF THE RULING CLASSES TO DOWNPLAY ITS SIGNIFICANCE. FOR THE FIRST TIME AN ELECTION INCLUDED ALL ELEMENTS OF A SOCIETY-- SOLDIERS, MERCHANTS, LABOURERS, FARMERS. THERE WAS DOUBLE-VOTING, SPOILED BALLOTS, CORRUPTION OF ALL KINDS -- BUT THE PROCESS ITSELF MUST BE VIEWED AS FAR PURER THAN THE OLIGARCHY, THE THEOCRATIC APPOINTMENT, THE MILITARY DICTATORSHIP. WHETHER SUCH A CHANCE JUXTAPOSITION OF ELEMENTS WILL EVER OCCUR AGAIN IS DOUBTFUL. I CAN'T HELP BUT FEEL THAT OUR SOCIETY IS THE POORER FOR IT. (EDITOR'S NOTE - THE READER SHOULD BEAR IN MIND THAT SUENTEUS PO IS AN ANARCHIST. CONSEQUENTLY, WHERE HE ATTEMPTS TO INTERPRET, RATHER THAN *DOCUMENT* EVENTS, HIS VIEWS SHOULD BE DISCOUNTED UTTERLY).

YOU WERE SAYING... AH! THE PRIME MINISTER! GOOD MAN THAT GATSON
DAMN GOOD MAN.
GATSON RESIGNED IN DISGRACE... I'M CEREBUS ...I'M CAMPAIGNING FOR PRIME MINISTER
AH! CAMPAIGNING! YES...
BEEN FOUR YEARS ALREADY HAS IT?
REMARKABLE.
SINCE ALL THE SOLDIERS HERE ARE UNDER YOUR DIRECT COMMAND... CEREBUS WANTS TO KNOW IF THERE'S ANYTHING YOU...
...NEED.
NEED?
WELL, I COULD USE SOME MORE CROSSBOWMEN-- I CAN TELL YOU THAT MUCH...
THEN YOU'D BE WILLING TO SIGN THIS PAPER?
PAPER?
GUARANTEEING CEREBUS ALL SEVEN OF THIS PROVINCES REPRESENTATIVES
YOU CAN JUST WRITE "TWO HUNDRED CROSSBOWMEN" IN THE BLANK SPACE
THIS SEEMS TO BE IN ORDER. YES.
THIS WILL BE JUST FINE.
PLEASURE DOING BUSINESS WITH YOU.
LIKEWISE, I'M SURE
OO WAS THAT COMMANDER?
MM?
OH, THAT WAS THE GOAT THEY SAY IS RUNNING FOR PRIME MINISTER

THE REGENCY
TWO WEEKS LATER
ALL RIGHT. CEREBUS WILL EXPLAIN IT ONCE MORE
THE FIRST THIRTY-EIGHT SEATS IN GREATER IEST, BLAKELY AND HARBOURSIDE, ASTORIA KNEW ABOUT. THEN CEREBUS GOT FIFTEEN REPRESENTATIVES FROM GRACE DISTRICT THAT ASTORIA DIDN'T KNOW ABOUT
THEN WE SIGNED A DEAL WITH OLDHAM SHE DID KNOW ABOUT FOR SIX MORE SEATS
THEN WE SIGNED A DEAL WITH OLDCASTLE, SHE KNEW ABOUT, FOR ANOTHER TEN AFTER THE TWENTY IN GREATER IEST WERE REDUCED TO EIGHT...
MEANING WE LOST TWELVE BUT GAINED TEN, AFTER WHICH, CEREBUS PICKED UP FOURTEEN MORE FROM T'ANA, FORT TORY AND GARRISON THAT ASTORIA DIDN'T KNOW ABOUT

SO CEREBUS ENDED UP WITH FIFTY-NINE GUARANTEED SEATS IN THE LEGISLATURE, HAVING NEEDED ONLY FIFTY-ONE SEATS FOR A MAJORITY GOVERNMENT.
WHILE ASTORIA ...
GLP
GLP
GLP
WHILE ASTORIA ONLY KNOWS OF FORTY-FOUR SEATS GUARANTEED FOR CEREBUS, SEVEN SEATS SHY OF A MAJORITY GOVERNMENT
SO THAT'S WHERE SHE IS NOW...
OUT THERE.
SOMEWHERE.
WADING THROUGH HIP...DEEP...SNOW.
HER AND THAT SIX FOOT BUG OF HERS
LOOKING FOR SEVEN MORE REPRESENTATIVES
WHY DID YOU SMILE WHEN YOU SAID THAT?
DID CEREBUS SMILE WHEN HE SAID THAT?
YES, YOU DEFINITELY SMILED WHEN YOU SAID THAT...

F-FROSTONITE
EV-EVERYWHERE
G-GETTING
W-WEAK
FROSTONITE: FRAGMENTS OF INTENSE COLD FORMED WHEN THE MOON ROACH'S NATIVE PLANET FROSTON EXPLODED.
TH-TH-ANK Y-Y-YOU K-KEVITCH
D-D-DADDY?
M-M-MARLON?
S-SOMEBODY?
G-G-GREAT FROSTON! -- A-A-ASTORIA C-C-COMING TH-THIS WAY! IF SH-SH-SHE SEES ME SH-SH-SHIVERING LIKE TH-THIS
SH-SHE'LL KNOW I'M TH-THE MOON R-R-ROACH...

HERE!
I MANAGED TO FIND A SHOPKEEPER WHO HAD ONE FOR SALE
THE NEXT TIME I TELL YOU IT'S TOO COLD TO GO OUT IN JUST A BODY-STOCKING
YOU DAMN WELL BETTER LISTEN!
FORTUNATELY, ASTORIA IS DISTRACTED AND FAILS TO NOTICE HOW HIS BODY IS SHAKING...
YOU'RE LIKE A THREE-YEAR-OLD --EXCEPT YOU HAVEN'T GOT HALF THE COMMON SENSE OF ONE...
HIS SECRET IS SAFE --BUT FOR HOW LONG?!
HOW LONG?

AS FOR THE SO-CALLED "ONE-SHEETS," ONE WOULD BE HARD-PRESSED TO FIND A LESS SUITABLE APPENDAGE TO THE BODY POLITIC. IF, AS WAS DEVOUTLY WISHED IN THE PREVIOUS CHAPTER, WE ARE SOME DAY TO WITNESS FULL-BLOWN REPUBLICANISM IN IEST, SURELY THE FIRST CASUALTY OF THE PEOPLE'S WILL WOULD BE THESE BRAZEN TESTIMONIALS TO THE COLOSSAL VANITY OF THE RULING CLASSES! SHAMELESSLY SLANTED, IMPERVIOUS TO TRUTH AND CATERING ONLY TO THOSE ASPECTS OF HUMAN NATURE WHICH MIGHT BEST BE DESCRIBED AS "BASE..."

THE SUN
AARDVARK CLAIMS VICTORY
"NO COMMENT," SAYS GOAT

The Times

"AARDVARK CHEATING"

GOAT BREAKS SILENCE ON CONTROVERSY

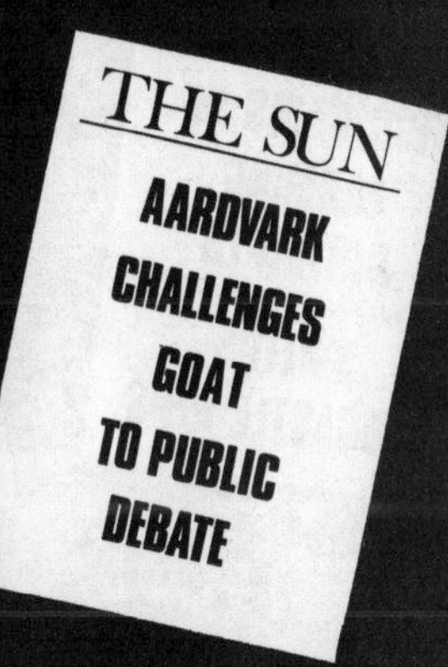

THE SUN
AARDVARK CHALLENGES GOAT TO PUBLIC DEBATE

...DEVOID OF EVEN ELEMENTARY GRAMMAR AND SYNTAX, RELIANT ON THE PRESENT PERFECT TENSE (EVIDENTLY TO CREATE SOME SHODDY ILLUSION OF IMMEDIACY) THE "ONE-SHEETS" GAINED SOME SMALL ADMIRATION FOR PROVIDING THE MASSES WITH THEIR OWN LITERATURE (THOUGH ONE HESITATES TO DIGNIFY IT WITH SUCH A LABEL).

The Times

GOAT LOSES VOICE IN FREAK ACCIDENT

"..." SAYS GOAT!

THE SUN

"MUTE GOAT UNSUITED TO BE P.M." SAYS AARDVARK

The Times

GOAT ACCUSES AARDVARK OF PREJUDICE AGAINST HANDICAPPED

"..." SAYS GOAT

THE SUN

"FARM ANIMALS UNSUITED FOR POLITICS" SAYS AARDVARK

The Times

CHICKENS, COWS, HORSES PLAN PROTEST RALLY TO SUPPORT GOAT

ONE CAN, AT LEAST, FEEL CERTAIN THAT THESE MELODRAMATIC PAPERS WOULD NOT LAST LONG IN A FREELY-GOVERNED, FREELY-ELECTED SOCIETY! SURELY THE REPRESENTATIVES OF THE PEOPLE'S WILL WOULD TEAR AWAY THE MASKS CONCEALING THE PRODUCERS OF SUCH ILL-MINDED, SELF-SERVING CLAPTRAP...

THE SUN
AARDVARK MAKES BIG GAINS IN FARMING DISTRICTS
SWEEPS OLDCASTLE REPS

The Times
"BAAAH" SAYS GOAT. "AARDVARK COUNTING VOTES BEFORE ELECTION DAY"

THE SUN
AARDVARK URGES PUBLIC DEBATE AS GOAT RECOVERS VOICE

...AND THAT THE PEOPLE, WHEN THEY REALIZED THE SPECIAL INTERESTS OF THE PRODUCERS, WOULD DEMAND INSTEAD PUBLICATION OF "TRUTH" AS DETERMINED BY A MAJORITY OF THEIR OWN FREELY-ELECTED REPRESENTATIVES...

The Times
"..." SAYS GOAT AS RELAPSE CLAIMS VOICE

THE SUN
ASTORIA OFFERS TO DEBATE LORD JULIUS AFTER RELAPSE

The Times
"..." SAYS LORD JULIUS AS "MUTE PLAGUE" SPREADS

THE SUN
AARDVARK LEADS IN ALL DISTRICTS
VICTORY ASSURED

The Times
ELECTION TOMORROW
VOTE GOAT!

THE SUN
AARDVARK PREPARES MASSIVE VICTORY CELEBRATION
ELECTION TOMORROW

...ONLY THEN WOULD REPUBLICANISM REACH ITS ULTIMATE GOAL OF GOVERNMENT FOR THE MASSES, BY THE MASSES, AND OF THE MASSES.

Election Night

YOU'RE BEING RIDICULOUS.

THAT'S YOUR OPINION.

IT'S THE TRUTH!
MOST OF THOSE PEOPLE OUT THERE ARE MEMBERS OF YOUR OWN PARTY!

THEY'RE THE ONES WHO HANG AROUND THE SALONS, SIPPING WINE WITH THEIR PINKIES OUT AND USING BIG WORDS!!

WHUT'S TH' MATTER?

HE REFUSES TO GO OUT! HE SAYS THEY'RE GOING TO LAUGH AT HIM.

HEHHEHHEH! WHY THET'S TH' STOOPIDEST THANG AH EVER...

WHUT AH MEANT TUH SAY, YER MERCIFULNESS ...

ALL THE GREAT POPULISTS AND REPUBLICANS OF THE AGE WERE GATHERED THAT EVENING--HAD STREAMED INTO THE HALL SINCE BEFORE DAWN.

AT LAST, THE PARTY SPEAKER WAS HANDED A SLIP OF PAPER

GREATER IEST VOTES ALL EIGHT REPRESENTATIVES TO CEREBUS THE AARDVARK ...

THE TENSION WAS BROKEN BY THUNDEROUS APPLAUSE. THOUGH THE AMBASSADOR BALCONY REMAINED EMPTY, OUR FERVOR WAS UNDIMMED.

WE LAUGHED, SHOUTED, SHOOK EACH OTHER. IT SUDDENLY SEEMED POSSIBLE; SO INSANELY WITHIN REACH!
LISTEN TO THAT!
HOW CAN YOU SAY THEY'LL LAUGH AT YOU?
WHAT IF CEREBUS DOESN'T WIN THE NEXT DISTRICT?! ...
THEY ADORE YOU!
LET THEM, DAMMIT!
CEREBUS WOULD PREFER THAT THEY ADORE HIM THROUGH THE CURTAIN! THANKS!
SPONTANEOUSLY, WE BEGAN A RHYTHMIC CLAPPING AND A CHANT OF "AARDVARK AARDVARK"
WE FAIRLY GLOWED WITH OPTIMISM.
YOU SEE? YOU SEE?
NOW THEY'RE MAKING FUN OF CEREBUS' SPECIES
WHAT'S WRONG?
HE'S BEING A PERFECT ASS-- THAT'S WHAT'S WRONG!
HE THINKS THEY'RE GOING TO LAUGH AT HIM
I'VE TOLD HIM AND I'VE TOLD HIM...
YES.
I'M SURE YOU HAVE.
EXCUSE US FOR A FEW MINUTES.

CEREBUS JUST DOESN'T WANT TO GO OUT THERE!...
I QUITE UNDERSTAND.
IT DOESN'T MATTER WHAT
YOU DO?
OF COURSE ...
YOU ARE THE EARTH-PIG BORN...

AS LESSER BEINGS...
WE SHOULD BE GRATEFUL THAT YOU DEIGN TO CONSORT WITH US...
LEST WE DRIVE YOU FROM OUR MIDST...
YEAH.
DAMN RIGHT.

...I BELIEVE, GREAT CEREBUS, THAT THE CITIZENRY WISHES ONLY TO PROVE ITS GRATITUDE BEFORE YOUR MAGNIFICENT PERSON.
YEAH?
WELL, MAYBE JUST A FEW SECONDS, THEN.

BOROUGH OF T'AGATH, BOROUGH OF HARNE, BOROUGH OF MANN, BOROUGH OF KIEL, AND BOROUGH OF MERCER VOTE ONE REPRESENTATIVE EACH TO THE NEXT PRIME MINISTER OF THE CITY-STATE OF IEST ...
...JULIUS GOAT.

FORGET IT! CEREBUS IS NOT GOING OUT THERE!
BUT SURELY
LISTEN, MAC MUFIN, CEREBUS DOES NOT INTEND TO MAKE A FOOL
OF
HIM
DID YOU SEND OUT FOR AN ALBINO?
THOSE PEOPLE ARE WAITING TO SEE SOMEONE IMPORTANT. IF A THEOCRAT WON'T GO OUT THERE
THEN MAYBE I NEED A DEVOTIONALIST.
IT'S LIKE MAH DADDY USED TUH SAY, SON "Y'CAINT HAVE TH' BUTTERFLIES IF Y'AINT GOT THE STOMACH"
GUTS, THAT IS!
Y'ALL JUST PUT Y'THUMB IN Y'MOUTH AN' WHEN AHM ELECTED, AH'LL TRY AN' FIND Y'A JOB AS ONE O'MAH VALETS!
BUT F'R NOW ...
...CUE...
..AH SAY--CUE TH' FANFARE!

WHOA!
WHOOOOOOOAA
SON! WHOA, SON! WHAT-- I SAY-- WHAT ARE Y'DOING?
VIOLENCE-- I SAY-- VIOLENCE NEVUH SOLVED ANYTHING, SON!
BUT EVEN AS WE DISCUSSED THE RETURNS FROM LOWER IEST, A TUMBLER WEARING THE CEREMONIAL COSTUME OF THE PALNAN ARISTOCRACY WAS "HURLED" FROM THE BALCONY...
IT WAS A MAGNIFICENT ALLEGORY, OBVIOUSLY DESIGNED TO BUOY OUR SAGGING SPIRITS.
JOYFULLY, WE PASSED THE LIMP FORM OF THE TUMBLER OVER OUR HEADS LIKE PRIMEVAL HUNTERS WHO HAD, AT LAST, CAPTURED A PARTICULARLY WORRISOME BEAST OF PREY.
Y'ALL WOULDN'T HAPPEN T'KNOW WHAR AH COULD FIND TWENTY POUNDS OF PLASTER O'PARIS IN THE SHAPE OF A LEG, WOULD Y'BOY?

SH, IT'S ANOTHER RETURN ...
THE CITY-STATE OF IEST'S MUNICIPALITY OF HARBOURSIDE...
HARBOURSIDE THAT'S ONE OF OURS
GET READY.
YOU'RE SURE?
VOTES ALL SIX REPRESENTATIVES ...
REMEMBER TO WAVE...
NOT NOW-- WHEN WE'RE ON THE BALCONY
TO THE PALNAN GOAT...
THERE WAS AN UN-SPOKEN AGREEMENT AFTER THE HARBOURSIDE RESULTS. A SIMULTANEOUS DREAD...
THAT SOMEHOW LORD JULIUS HAD MANAGED TO "FIX" THE ELECTION.
AS WE STARED UP AT THE FIFTH FLOOR WE COULD ONLY PRAY THAT OUR LEADERS WERE FINDING A WAY TO ENSURE THAT VICTORY WAS NOT SNATCHED FROM OUR GRASP...
IT'S ALL YOUR FAULT
MY FAULT?
WELL, IT'S CERTAINLY NOT MY FAULT.

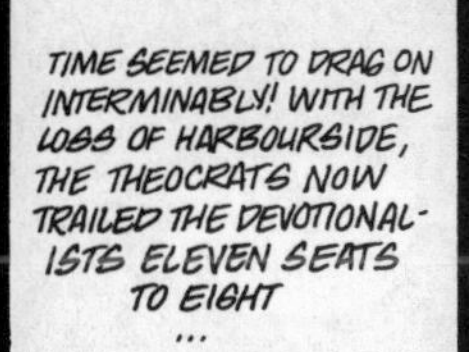
TIME SEEMED TO DRAG ON INTERMINABLY! WITH THE LOSS OF HARBOURSIDE, THE THEOCRATS NOW TRAILED THE DEVOTIONAL-ISTS ELEVEN SEATS TO EIGHT
...

I SHOULD NEVER HAVE TRUSTED ADDISON WHEN HE SAID HE COULD KEEP THE GUILD EXECUTIVE ON BOARD...

IS IT ADDISON'S FAULT? OR DID LORD JULIUS RIG THE RESULTS?

IT'S MY FAULT-- I SHOULD HAVE APPOINTED SOMEONE I COULD TRUST...

CEREBUS HAS ALWAYS SAID THAT YOU'RE ONLY AS GOOD AS THE PEOPLE CARRYING OUT YOUR ORDERS
...

I THOUGHT THAT I COULD...
SHH.
THE CITY-STATE OF IEST'S GARDEN MUNICIPALITY OF OLDHAM...

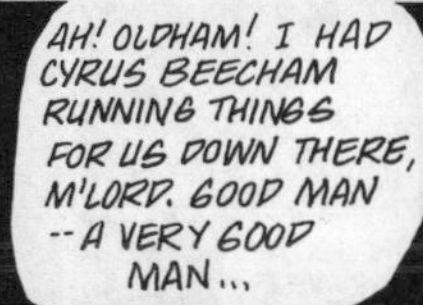
AH! OLDHAM! I HAD CYRUS BEECHAM RUNNING THINGS FOR US DOWN THERE, M'LORD. GOOD MAN --A VERY GOOD MAN...

AYE?

BIRTHPLACE OF WILLIAM LYON -- INVENTOR OF THE CONTINUOUS ACTION LOOM...

MMM. A REAL MOVER. A TAKE-CHARGE TYPE. LOVES A GOOD CHALLENGE
...

VOTES ALL SIX REPRESENTATIVES
...
...TO THE NEXT PRIME MINISTER OF IEST.

I WAS THINKING OF BRINGING HIM BY FOR A CHAT WHEN WE'RE LOOKING FOR SOMEONE TO HEAD UP EXTERNAL AFFAIRS.

JULIUS GOAT.

BUT THEN I DECIDED TO FIRE THE INCOMPETENT LITTLE TWIT, INSTEAD.
I SHOULDN'T WORRY ABOUT IT TOO MUCH IF I WERE YOU, M'LORD.
I THINK I CAN SAFELY SAY, WITHOUT FEAR OF CONTRADICTION, THAT NELSON WILL GO FOR THE NEW REPUBLICANISM IN A BIG WAY...
WHO'A' YOU KIDDIN'?
NELSON IS A HULLY-OWNED SUBSIDEE-AIRY OF DA PALNOO OVUHLAND TRADIN' COMP'NY.

THE SUBURBAN RIDINGS HAVE ALWAYS BEEN UNPREDICTABLE.
EXCEPT NELSON, OF COURSE ...
THAT, SIR, IS A SCANDALOUS SPECULATION ON YOUR PART!! ...
DAT AIN'T NO SCANDALOUS SPECULATION, MOY FRIEN'-- DAT IS A WELL-KNOWN SECRET ...

A WELL-KNOWN SECRET? OR A WELL-USED BIT OF GOSSIP?

I GOT FIFTY CROWNS SEZ IT'S A WELL-KNOWN SECRET ...

I HAVE ONE HUNDRED CROWNS WHICH SAYS THAT IT IS AN UN-SUBSTANTIATED RUMOUR!!
BANK of IEST

THE CITY-STATE OF IEST'S TOWNSHIP OF NELSON...

A HUNNERD 'N' FIFTY...
VOTES ALL SIX OF ITS REPRESENTATIVES TO THE PEOPLE'S CHOICE FOR PRIME MINISTER ...
TWO HUNDRED
Y'R ON!
JULIUS THE GOAT...
NOW EAST CHAPEL --DERE IS A TOWN DAT IS READY F'YUH NOO RUHPUBLIC'NIZM...
COME, NOW. EAST CHAPEL WOULD NEVER VOTE FOR A REPUBLICAN PARTY... THEY'RE STILL LOYAL TO HIS HOLINESS...
"WHEN DA CAT'S AWAY..."
RIDICULOUS NAIVE AND...
FIFTY?
A HUNNERD
YOU ARE ON...
HIS HOLINESS' LOYAL HOLY VILLAGE OF EAST CHAPEL, HOME OF HIS HOLINESS...
WITH FAINT INTEREST AND NO LITTLE DISTASTE, VOTES ITS SINGLE REPRESENTATIVE TO THE LESSER OF TWO EVILS...
JULIUS LORD GOAT...

YOU SEE? YOU SEE?
LET THAT BE A LESSON TO YOU ABOUT POLITICAL INSTINCTS, YOU ILLITERATE BUFFOON!
EAST CHAPEL WOULD RATHER HAVE VOTED FOR A DEAD MOLLUSK FOR PRIME MINISTER THAN VOTE FOR C...
...OMEONE ELSE.
BUT...
UH...
BUT THE REAL VILLAIN IS HIM!
HMPH-- IS HE! PRETENDING TO BE A REPUBLICAN, WHEN HE IS NOTHING MORE THAN A BLATANT OPPORTUNIST!
A MONEY-GRUBBING LEECH!
NOW WAIT A MINNIT!
"WAIT A MINUTE" HE SAYS; AS IF A MERE MINUTE WOULD SUFFICE TO STAVE OFF THE CRITICISM HE SO RICHLY DESERVES...
IF HE WOULD DEFEND HIM-SELF, THEN LET HIM ANSWER THIS...
WHAT HAS HE EVER DONE TO ADVANCE THE CAUSE OF REPUB-LICANISM?!
THE CITY-STATE OF IEST'S MUNICIPALITIES OF B'ORN, GRACE, DUNHAM AND THE DOCKS, IN ACCORDANCE WITH THE WISHES OF REPRESENTATIVE FILGATE WHOM THEY REVERE MORE THAN LIFE ITSELF, UNANIMOUSLY VOTE ALL TEN REPRESENT-ATIVES TO THEIR NEXT PRIME MINISTER, CEREBUS THE AARDVARK...

WE WERE NOW TRAILING TWENTY-FOUR SEATS TO EIGHTEEN...
WITH HALF THE RETURNS IN...

I THINK WE HAD BETTER ASSUME WE ARE GOING TO BE THE OPPOSITION PARTY...
IN CASE LORD JULIUS DECIDES TO ARREST HIS OPPONENTS PERHAPS WE SHOULD LEAVE NOW...
YES! YES! RIGHT NOW! I'VE GOT SOME LADS WE CAN SEND IN TO STIR THINGS UP IF HE TRIES TO CONVENE THE LEGISLATURE.
BUT FOR THE MOMENT, WE CAN'T LET HIM ROLL OVER US IN THE HEAT OF VICTORY!
I GOT ENOUGH TROOPS TUH HOLD D'UPPAH CITY IF WE C'N GET D'PEOPLE BEHIND US...
BUT RIGHT NOW, WE BETTUH START PACKIN'...

YOU CAN ALL LEAVE IF YOU WANT TO BUT CEREBUS IS STAYING RIGHT HERE!
WE ALL FELT BITTERLY DISAPPOINTED. NOT A SINGLE SEAT IN ANY PROVINCE... EXCEPT THE DOCKS.
THE DOCKS.
THE QUIET INTELLECTUAL REVOLUTION WE HAD DREAMED OF, WAS NOW A BAD JOKE...

EVERY TIME HIS MUSTACHE TWITCHES YOU ALL RUN FOR THE HILLS!
WELL, NOT CEREBUS THE AARDVARK

IF CEREBUS DOESN'T BEAT HIM IN THE ELECTION
CEREBUS WILL BEAT HIM IN A WAR!!

I SHALL NEVER FORGET THAT MOMENT OF EXULTATION, AS WE CHEERED AND APPLAUDED! A WAR! A WAR! TO THINK THAT WE MIGHT BE HACKED TO PIECES BY LORD JULIUS' TROOPS IN THE NAME OF OUR GRAND REPUBLICAN CAUSE...
WHO COULD ASK FOR A NOBLER DEATH?

DID YOU HEAR WHAT HE JUST SAID, BASKIN?
YES, LORD JULIUS-- I BELIEVE EVERYONE IN THE HOTEL DID.
A FINE THING. AFTER ALL I'VE DONE FOR HIM! I GAVE HIM A JOB...
PUT A ROOF OVER HIS HEAD
THAT'S RIGHT! I INVITED HIM TO ALL MY BEST PARTIES
YOU GAVE HIM A WIFE YOU'D HARDLY USED YET
THAT'S RIGHT.
I GAVE HIM A...
YOU WOULDN'T SAY THAT IF YOU WEREN'T GUARANTEED TWENTY-SIX WEEKS OF SEVERANCE PAY...
NYAH! NYAH!

FLEAGLE-- GET SOME THUGS FROM THE TAVERN EIGHT BLOCKS DOWN, TWENTY OR SO. GIVE THEM A HALF-CROWN EACH AND TELL THEM TO HOLD THIS SUITE OF ROOMS AT ALL COSTS...
YES, YER ASSERTIVENESS.
BRAN --TAKE A CARRIAGE AND FIND ME TWO DIVISIONS OF HEAVY PIKE ON THE BLACK MARKET
SPLIT THEM AND STATION THEM AT EACH ENTRY POINT TO THE REGENCY GROUNDS
YES, GREAT CEREBUS...
TELL THEM THEY'LL BE FACING PALNAN CROSSBOWMEN AND SKIRMISH TROOPS ...
NORTHBELL, THE BREADBASKET OF THE CITY-STATE OF IEST...
VOTES TWO REPRESENTATIVES TO LORD JULIUS GOAT AND TWO REPRESENTATIVES TO CEREBUS
WHAT DOES THAT GIVE US?
WE HAVE TWENTY SEATS. THEY HAVE TWENTY-SIX... THEY'RE PAST THE HALFWAY POINT FOR A MAJORITY
NINE RIDINGS STILL TO BE HEARD FROM.

HA
HA
HA
HA
HA
HA
HA
INTEREST
RATES

HER REVERENCE, THE ABBESS OF ALL GRACE PROVINCE EXTENDS GREETINGS TO ALL FREE PEOPLE ...
QUIT SHOVING!
CEREBUS WAS HERE FIRST!
...AND APPOINTS FIVE REPRESENTATIVES TO CEREBUS AND TEN TO LORD JULIUS' GOAT...
WHAT DOES THAT GIVE US?
THIRTY-SIX SEATS, LORD JULIUS.
THIRTY-SIX TO TWENTY-FIVE...
THEY'RE PAST THE TWO-THIRDS MARK.
MARK MY WORDS, BASKIN MY BOY -- THE WAY TO AN ABBESS' HEART IS THROUGH HER WARTS...
THE RIVERSIDE PROVINCE OF RIVERSHIRE ...
VOTES BOTH REPRESENTATIVES TO JULIUS, LORD OF GOATS...
DID YOU BRING THE CONFETTI?
YES, LORD JULIUS.
AND THE NOISE-MAKERS?
YES, LORD JULIUS.
WE MAY HAVE TO CONSIDER ARMED REBELLION.
CEREBUS THOUGHT OF THAT...
NO DANCING GIRLS? WHAT IS THIS? SOME KIND OF JOKE?
THEY GOT SNOWED IN IN THE LOWER CITY, LORD JULIUS.
THE TWO DIVISIONS OF PIKE ARE IN PLACE AS YOU ORDERED, GREAT CEREBUS.
SEVEN RIDINGS STILL TO REPORT ...

GOPHER FLEAGLE REPORTING IN...
YER THUGS'RE IN PLACE AT ALL THREE DOORS, YER POWER-FULNESS ...

NO ONE GETS IN UNLESS CEREBUS, ASTORIA OR BRAN MAK MUFIN CLEARS THEM.
YESSIR!

AS THE DESK CLERK, I MUST PROTEST THE UNCALLED-FOR INFLUX OF RIFF-RAFF... FURTHERMORE...
SOMEBODY DITCH THE WIND-BAG!

SORRY, YER OBNOXIOUSNESS, BUT ORDERS IS ORDERS...
WHAT ARE YOU DOING!
SEE HERE!

IT WAS A TUMBLER DRESSED AS THE REGENCY DESK CLERK... ONCE MORE WE ROARED OUR APPROVAL--NO ONE WAS GOING TO INTIMIDATE THE THEOCRATS...

LORD JULIUS! LORD JULIUS!
THE THEOCRATS HAVE THE GROUNDS SURROUNDED BY HEAVY PIKE!

WE'LL HAVE TO SEND IN OUR HEAVY PIKE, THEN...
WE CAN'T LORD JULIUS
AND WHY NOT?

YOU TOLD ME TO SELL THEM ON THE BLACK MARKET TO FINANCE YOUR CAMPAIGN.

OH! SO NOW IT'S MY FAULT, IS IT?

T'ANA AND DISTRICT, IEST'S GOLDEN PROVINCE OF THE NORTH...

VOTES TWO REPRESENTATIVES TO CEREBUS AND TWO REPRESENTATIVES TO LORD GOAT OF PALNU.

FORTY TO TWENTY-SEVEN...
SIX RIDINGS LEFT...

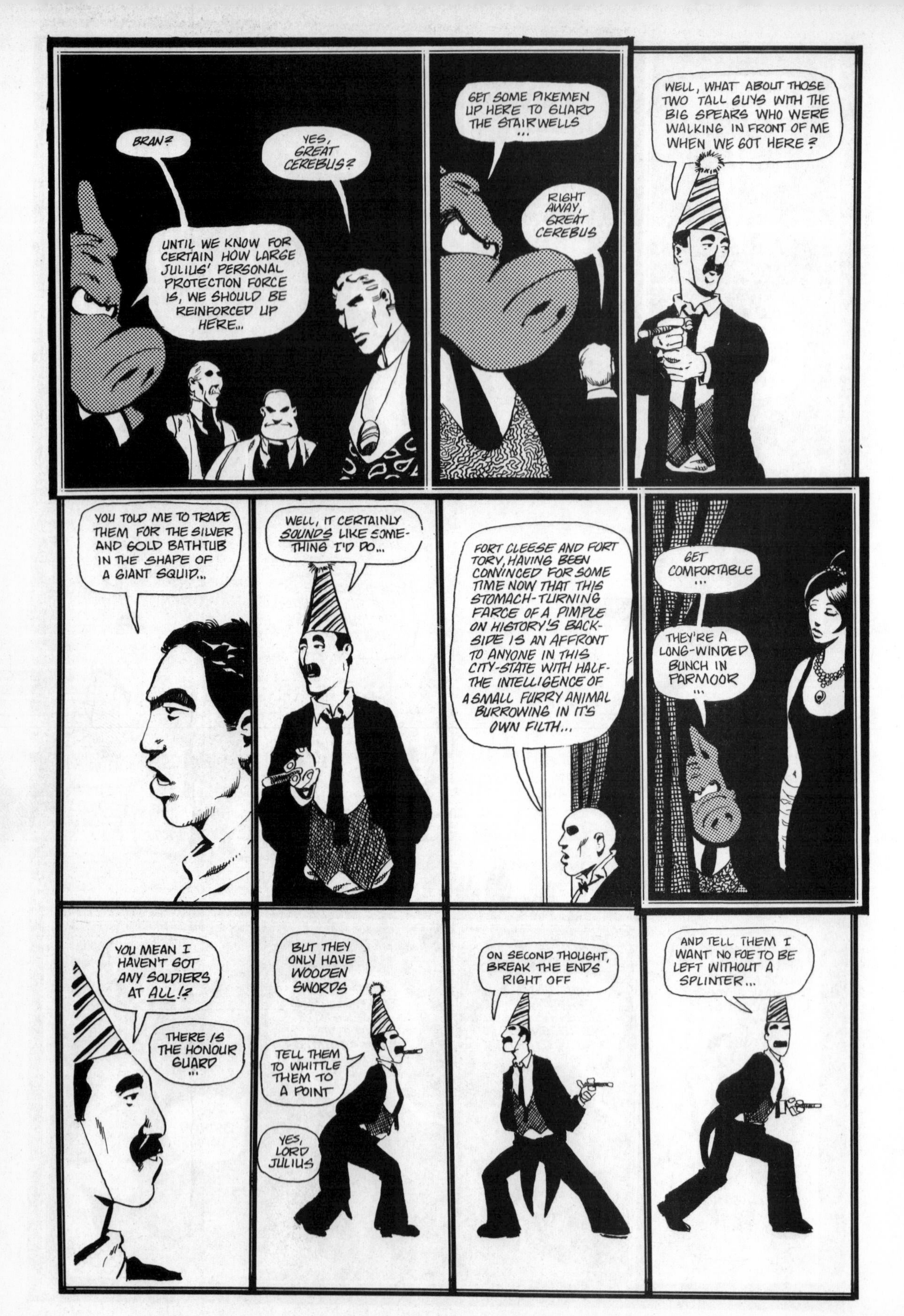
BRAN?
YES, GREAT CEREBUS?
UNTIL WE KNOW FOR CERTAIN HOW LARGE JULIUS' PERSONAL PROTECTION FORCE IS, WE SHOULD BE REINFORCED UP HERE...
GET SOME PIKEMEN UP HERE TO GUARD THE STAIRWELLS ...
RIGHT AWAY, GREAT CEREBUS
WELL, WHAT ABOUT THOSE TWO TALL GUYS WITH THE BIG SPEARS WHO WERE WALKING IN FRONT OF ME WHEN WE GOT HERE?
YOU TOLD ME TO TRADE THEM FOR THE SILVER AND GOLD BATHTUB IN THE SHAPE OF A GIANT SQUID...
WELL, IT CERTAINLY SOUNDS LIKE SOMETHING I'D DO...
FORT CLEESE AND FORT TORY, HAVING BEEN CONVINCED FOR SOME TIME NOW THAT THIS STOMACH-TURNING FARCE OF A PIMPLE ON HISTORY'S BACKSIDE IS AN AFFRONT TO ANYONE IN THIS CITY-STATE WITH HALF THE INTELLIGENCE OF A SMALL FURRY ANIMAL BURROWING IN IT'S OWN FILTH...
GET COMFORTABLE ...
THEY'RE A LONG-WINDED BUNCH IN PARMOOR ...
YOU MEAN I HAVEN'T GOT ANY SOLDIERS AT ALL!?
THERE IS THE HONOUR GUARD ...
BUT THEY ONLY HAVE WOODEN SWORDS
TELL THEM TO WHITTLE THEM TO A POINT
YES, LORD JULIUS
ON SECOND THOUGHT, BREAK THE ENDS RIGHT OFF
AND TELL THEM I WANT NO FOE TO BE LEFT WITHOUT A SPLINTER...

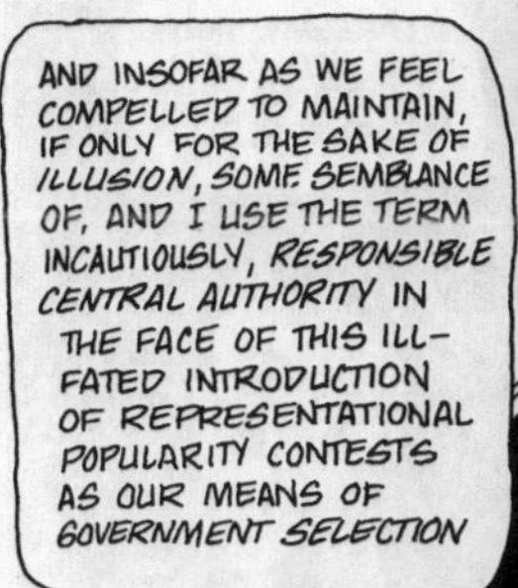

AND INSOFAR AS WE FEEL COMPELLED TO MAINTAIN, IF ONLY FOR THE SAKE OF ILLUSION, SOME SEMBLANCE OF, AND I USE THE TERM INCAUTIOUSLY, RESPONSIBLE CENTRAL AUTHORITY IN THE FACE OF THIS ILL-FATED INTRODUCTION OF REPRESENTATIONAL POPULARITY CONTESTS AS OUR MEANS OF GOVERNMENT SELECTION

IT'S ALL ONE SENTENCE...
CEREBUS USUALLY PASSES THE TIME COUNTING ADVERBS ...

TRIFLE WITH ME, WILL HE?

BUT THEY HAVE MANAGED TO ROUND UP A FEW BUTTER KNIVES...

THEREFORE, FORT CLEESE AND FORT TORY HAVE NO RECOURSE BUT TO LOWER THEMSELVES TO THE SAME DISGUSTING DEPTHS OF DEPRAVITY AS EVERYONE ELSE IN THIS SNIVELLING AND DEMENTED HALF-WIT OF A THEOCRACY, AND SO ANNOUNCE BEFORE THIS DEPRAVED COMPANY OF VILE REPUBLICANISM THEIR INTENTION TO VOTE ALL FOUR REPRESENTATIVES TO THE STUPID BLEEDING GOAT ...

A GREAT VICTORY! THE TIDE IS TURNING! TO ARMS! TO ARMS!

I'M VERY SORRY, LORD JULIUS, BUT THIS IS ALL THE BOILING OIL THE KITCHEN COULD SPARE ...

...THEY'RE DEEP-FRYING CHICKEN BREASTS THIS EVENING.
REMEMBER MEN!...

...DON'T CHARGE 'TIL YOU SEE THE "MADE IN PALNU" STAMP ON THEIR TUNICS...

FORTY-FOUR SEATS TO TWENTY-SEVEN NOW.
THEY ONLY NEED SEVEN MORE FOR A MAJORITY ...
FOUR RIDINGS LEFT...

ACCORDING TO OUR BEST INFORMATION, LORD JULIUS HAS AN ELITE HONOUR GUARD, A NEW DEVICE THAT SHOOTS STREAMS OF BOILING OIL AND SOME KIND OF A SECRET WEAPON ...
HE CALLS IT "THE HUMAN TORCH".

NO! DADDY! PLEASE!
AND HE THROWS FIREBALLS WITH EITHER HAND!!
KEROSENE

THE PROVINCE OF BLAKELY, BIRTHPLACE AND NAMESAKE OF THE FIRST PRIME MINISTER OF IEST, WITH UTMOST GRATITUDE TO THE FIRST BLAKELY'S DESCENDANT, CYRUS N. BLAKELY, VOTES ALL TWELVE REPRESENTATIVES TO CEREBUS ...
OUR CLAPPING AND STAMPING GAINED NEW LIFE AND ENERGY...
HUNH! I WOULD RADDUH BE RE-VERED MORE DAN LIFE ITSELF DAN HAVE A BUNCHA UTMOST GRATUHTOOD...
OF COURSE YOU WOULD...
I DARESAY THAT'S WHY YOU KEEP GETTING RE-ELECTED.
IF I LIVED IN THE DOCKS I WOULD PROBABLY REVERE ANYTHING MORE THAN LIFE ITSELF...
FORTY-FOUR SEATS TO THIRTY-NINE ...
THREE RIDINGS LEFT
IF WE MANAGE TO GET OUT OF THIS ALIVE REMIND ME TO TAKE BLAKELY'S NAME OFF OF THE INVITATION LIST FOR THE FESTIVAL OF PETUNIAS...
YES, LORD JULIUS.
WHICH THREE?
CHESMI, GARRISON AND...
AARD-VARK! AARD-VARK!
AND...
THAT'S ODD...
CHESMI, GARRISON AND...
AND...
AND WHAT?!
AND...
CHEE. DIS IS EXCOITING.

THE ANCIENT NORTHERN PROVINCE OF OLDCASTLE, IN THIS ELECTION OF FOURTEEN-THIRTEEN ...
OH. RIGHT! OLDCASTLE ...
WITH LORD WHAT'S-HIS-NAME ...
LOAHD RODNEY.
VOTES ALL TEN OF ITS ABLE REPRESENTATIVES ...
TO THE NEXT PRIME MINISTER OF IEST...
CEREBUS THE
NONE OF US HEARD THE END OF THE SPEECH...
REMIND ME TO OFFER LORD WHAT'S-HIS-NAME A JOB.
YOU ALREADY DID--HE'S GOING TO BE IN YOUR CABINET ...
OR CEREBUS' SHADOW CABINET ...
LORD JULIUS! YOU CAN'T GIVE UP NOW!
I'M NOT GIVING UP, I'M JUST GOING TO JUMP OUT THIS WINDOW FOR A MINUTE....
THEY STILL NEED TWO REPRESENTATIVES ...
WE ONLY NEED TWO OF THE REMAINING SEVEN SEATS
TWO SEATS.
THE PROVINCE OF GARRISON...
THIS IS IT...
SITE OF THE BATTLE OF IEST AND THE CHESMI RIVER REBELLION...
C'MON! SKIP THE HISTORY LESSON ...
VOTES ITS SEVEN REPRESENTATIVES AS FOLLOWS...

ONE REPRESENTATIVE FOR CEREBUS THE AARDVARK
NO

NO! IT CAN'T BE

...AND THE OTHER SIX REPRESENTATIVES TO LORD JULIUS GOAT

IT'S OVER.

FORTY NINE PLUS ONE...

CEREBUS LOST.

FORTY-FOUR PLUS ...

AGAIN.

SOMETHING IS WRONG HERE...
MM?

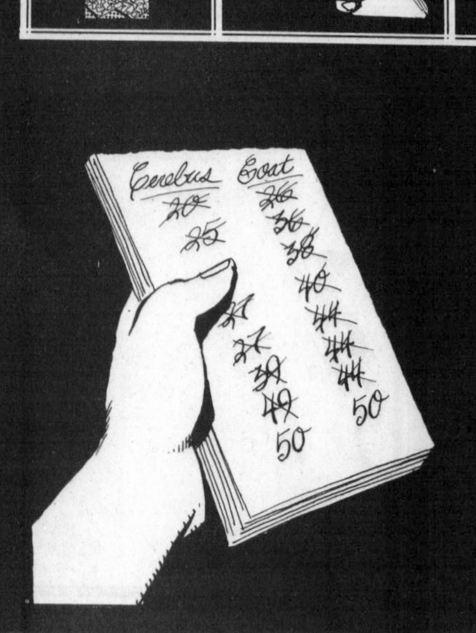
Cerebus Goat
50
50
IT'S A TIE!

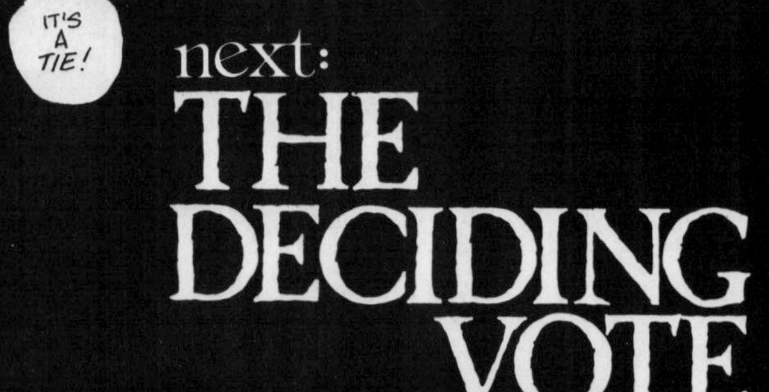
next:
THE DECIDING VOTE

the deciding vote

THE SPECIAL "WARMTHO" SHIELDING IN HIS NEW FUR COSTUME SCREENS OUT THE POISONOUS FROSTONITE RAYS... AND SO, IN HIS GUISE AS MILD-MANNERED SERGEANT PRESTON OF THE NORTHERN IESTAN MOUNTED POLICE HE IS NOW ABLE TO DO HIS DUTY

...TO INSURE THAT NO HARM BEFALLS THE NEXT PRIME MINISTER AND HIS BEAUTIFUL YOUNG MISTRESS...

"ON, HUSKIES" HE CRIES, THIS STALWART AND PURE DEFENDER OF THE TRUE NORTH, STRONG AND FREE!

THE WILDS OF NORTH-BELL FLASH BY HIM AS HE HASTENS TOWARD STORM'S END MANOR AND THE IMPORTANT MEETING THERE TO TRANS-PIRE...

"SO LONG AS I LIVE," HE SWEARS TO THE SNOW-SHROUDED MOUNTAINS, "FREEDOM SHALL BE SAFE FROM DEMOCRACY"
"AND THE PRIME MINISTER, AS WELL..."

I THINK HE'S COMPLETELY LOST HIS MIND...
IT'S OKAY -- YOU DON'T MISS WHAT YOU NEVER HAD IN THE FIRST PLACE ...

THE PRIME MINISTER'S HOT-BLOODED AND WELL-KNOWN MISTRESS STEPS GINGERLY FROM THE OFFICIAL SLED, BRUSHING SERGEANT PRESTON'S ARM AS SHE DOES SO...
SERGEANT PRESTON KNOWS ONLY TOO WELL THE SEETHING PASSION THAT THE PRIME MINISTER'S MISTRESS FEELS FOR HIM...
POOR OBSESSED CHICK.
I WUZ WONDRIN' WHEN YOU FOLKS'D GET HERE ...
WE HAVE A GREAT DEAL TO DISCUSS.
DON'T WE THOUGH?
PLEASE. STEP INTA MAH OFFICE...
IT'S...
IT'S AWFULLY DARK IN HERE.
LORD STORM'SEND?
SLAM
KLICK
BANG! BANG!
LORD STORM'SEND
ARTEMIS! KEEP YOUR HANDS TO YOURSELF!
WAP
THOUGH INTELLIGENT, THE PRIME MINISTER'S MISTRESS HAS TROUBLE EXPRESSING HER TRUE FEELINGS.
PUT THEM SNOWSHOES ON AND FOLLA ME. I GOT FENCES T'MEND
IF I'M GOING TO TALK TO A POLY-TICIAN I WANT TO MAKE SURE I DO SOME-THIN' USEFUL AT THE SAME TIME...
CEREBUS?
CEREBUS!?
DON'T YOU DARE SIGN ANY AGREE-MENT WITHOUT CONSULTING ME!

ARE YOU SURE THEY'LL BE...
UMPH!
...OKAY?
WUFFA-WUFFA-WUFFA- WUFFA
WHUF
OKAY?
THEY'LL BE MORE THAN OKAY.
WHUF WHUF WHUF
THAT'S THE SHED WHERE I KEEP M' WHITE LIGHTNIN'.
THE MOON ROACH GROPES BENEATH HIS ROACH CAPE FOR THE SECRET COMPARTMENT WITH THE SECRET ROACH MATCHES ...
GET-YOUR-MITTEN-OUT OF THERE THIS INSTANT !!
WAP !
WRONG SECRET COMPARTMENT ...
SHUT UP, KEVITCH...
FSSSS!
OOOOOOOOOOOHH!
WHUFFA-WHUFFA- WHUFFA
WHUF!
WHUF WUF WUF
I'LL BET THEY GET THROUGH HALF A MASON JAR EACH B'FORE THEY COMMENCE T'PASSIN' OUT

BRINGING ALL SEVEN OF HIS ROACH SENSES TO BEAR ON IT, SERGEANT PRESTON BEGINS HIS EXAMINATION OF WHAT HE SUSPECTS IS AN ILLICIT SUBSTANCE, WUBBA WUBBA TINGLE TINGLE TINGLE
IT SORT OF SMELLS LIKE HONEY.
SO NOW THAT THE ELECTION HAS ENDED IN A TIE, YOU'RE BACK UP HERE AGAIN, LOOKING FER A FAVOUR--A HANDOUT!
LOOK...
"GRAMPAW"
CEREBUS JUST WANTS TO KNOW WHO GETS THE FIFTH REPRESENTATIVE... YOU CAN ACT IT OUT IF THAT'S ANY EASIER FOR YOU.
IT DOESN'T REALLY TASTE LIKE ANYTHING.
LOOK, "SONNY" YOU REMIND ME OF A MULE I ONCE OWNED. JEST LIKE YOU, SHE WAS ALWAYS MAKIN' NOISE AN' SHE NEVER LISTENED TO A WORD I SAID
I FINALLY HAD HER DESTROYED AND SHE COULD SNOWSHOE A DAMN SIGHT BETTER'N YOU CAN...
I HOPE I MAKE MYSELF CLEAR...
WHERE ARE WE?
IS IT SAFE?
ON THE FLOOR...
AS LONG AS WE DON'T MOVE...
NOOO PROBLEM.

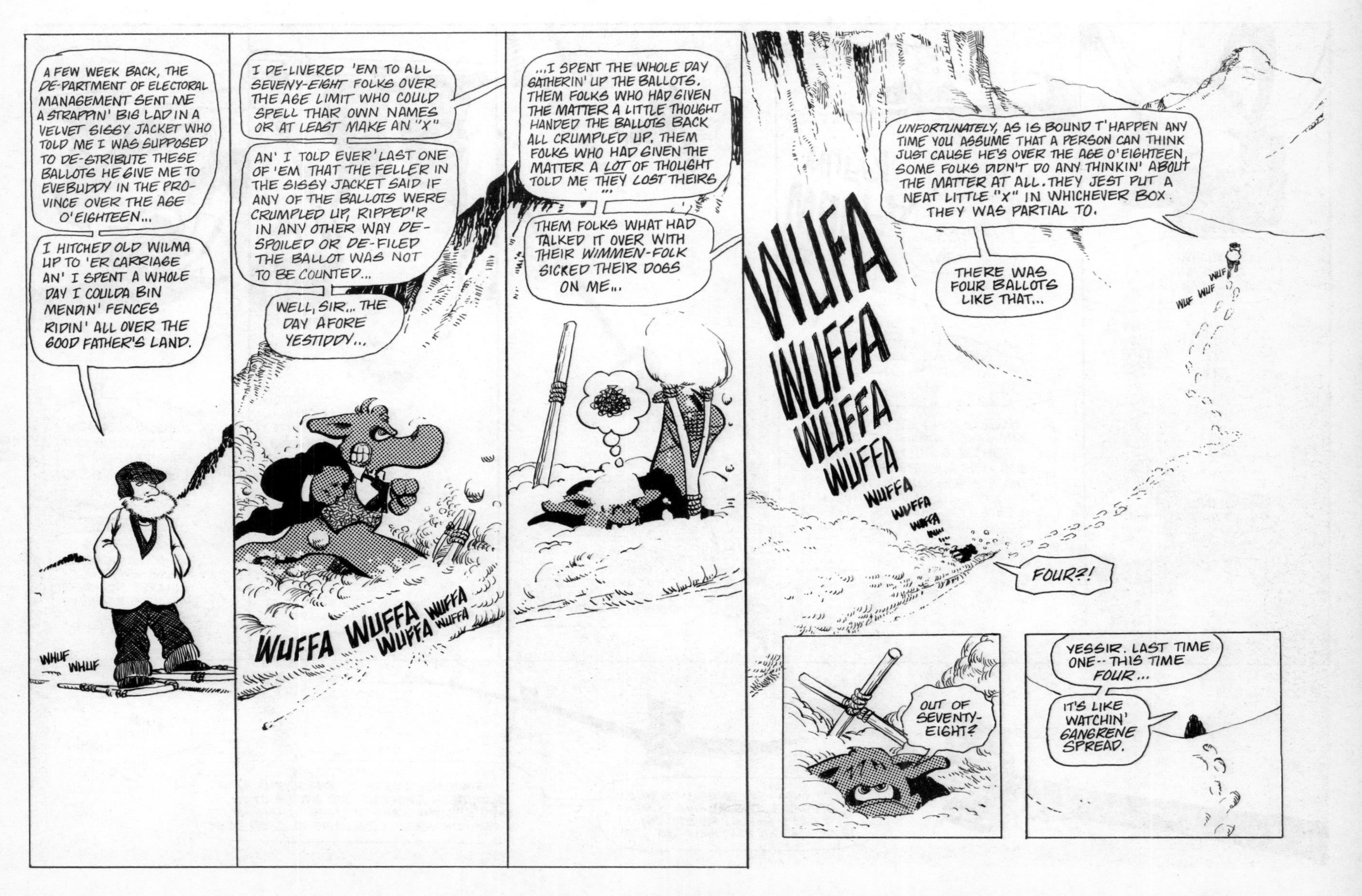

A FEW WEEK BACK, THE DE-PARTMENT OF ELECTORAL MANAGEMENT SENT ME A STRAPPIN' BIG LAD IN A VELVET SISSY JACKET WHO TOLD ME I WAS SUPPOSED TO DE-STRIBUTE THESE BALLOTS HE GIVE ME TO EVEBUDDY IN THE PRO-VINCE OVER THE AGE O'EIGHTEEN...
I HITCHED OLD WILMA UP TO 'ER CARRIAGE AN' I SPENT A WHOLE DAY I COULDA BIN MENDIN' FENCES RIDIN' ALL OVER THE GOOD FATHER'S LAND.
WHUF WHUF
I DE-LIVERED 'EM TO ALL SEVENY-EIGHT FOLKS OVER THE AGE LIMIT WHO COULD SPELL THAR OWN NAMES OR AT LEAST MAKE AN "X"
AN' I TOLD EVER' LAST ONE OF 'EM THAT THE FELLER IN THE SISSY JACKET SAID IF ANY OF THE BALLOTS WERE CRUMPLED UP, RIPPED'R IN ANY OTHER WAY DE-SPOILED OR DE-FILED THE BALLOT WAS NOT TO BE COUNTED...
WELL, SIR... THE DAY AFORE YESTIDDY...
WUFFA WUFFA WUFFA WUFFA WUFFA
...I SPENT THE WHOLE DAY GATHERIN' UP THE BALLOTS. THEM FOLKS WHO HAD GIVEN THE MATTER A LITTLE THOUGHT HANDED THE BALLOTS BACK ALL CRUMPLED UP. THEM FOLKS WHO HAD GIVEN THE MATTER A LOT OF THOUGHT TOLD ME THEY LOST THEIRS ...
THEM FOLKS WHAT HAD TALKED IT OVER WITH THEIR WIMMEN-FOLK SICKED THEIR DOGS ON ME...
WUFA WUFFA WUFFA WUFFA WUFFA WUFFA WUFFA
UNFORTUNATELY, AS IS BOUND T'HAPPEN ANY TIME YOU ASSUME THAT A PERSON CAN THINK JUST CAUSE HE'S OVER THE AGE O'EIGHTEEN, SOME FOLKS DIDN'T DO ANY THINKIN' ABOUT THE MATTER AT ALL. THEY JEST PUT A NEAT LITTLE "X" IN WHICHEVER BOX THEY WAS PARTIAL TO.
THERE WAS FOUR BALLOTS LIKE THAT...
WHUF WHUF WHUF
FOUR?!
OUT OF SEVENTY-EIGHT?
YESSIR. LAST TIME ONE-- THIS TIME FOUR...
IT'S LIKE WATCHIN' GANGRENE SPREAD.

WUFFA WUFFA
WUFFA WUFFA
WUF WUF WUF
AH DE-CIDED TO SEND TWO REPRESENTATIVES TO YOU AN' TWO TO THE GOAT, SINCE THAT'S THE WAY THE BALLOTS COME OUT, AND HOPE NOBUDDY'D NOTICE THERE WAS A REPRESENTATIVE MISSING...
WELL, SIR, WHEN LORD JULIUS SHOWED UP AND TOLD ME IT WAS A TIE, I KNEW IT WAS THE GOOD FATHER'S NATURAL JUSTICE AT WORK...
... PAYING ME BACK FER AIDING AN' ABETTING POLYTICIANS IN THE COMMISSION OF AN ELECTION...
NOW I GOTTA DE-CIDE WHICH ONE O' YOU TWO BOZOS GETS THE WHOLE BLAMED CITY-STATE ON A SILVER PLATTER ...
WHAT ≡PUFF≡ DID YOU SAY ≡PANT≡ TO LORD JULIUS?
I ASKED HIM IF'N HE HAD THE ALBATROSS, AND HE SAID "NO." I EXPECT YOU AIN'T GOT IT NEITHER...
CEREBUS ≡PANT≡ ALMOST ≡PUFF≡ HAD IT.
IF'N Y'MEAN TH' RANSOM THE McGREW BROTHERS PICKED UP FOR YOU -- THAT ONE WAS A FAKE...
WHUF WHUF WHUF
WHUFA WHUFA WHUFA
THE KEVILLISTS SENT THAT ONE HOPIN' YOU'D THINK IT WAS THE REAL ONE AND TIP YOUR HAND EARLY. TWENNY PEOPLE DIED AFORE SUMBUDDY HAD THE SENSE TO CHIP OFF THE ENAMEL T'FIND OUT IT WAS ONLY LEAD UNNERNEATH.
WHAT ≡PUFF≡ IS THE ≡PANT≡ ALBATROSS FOR? ...
WUFFA WUFFA WUFFA
Y'MEAN YOU DON'T KNOW?!
≡PUFF≡ NO.
WHY THE HECK DO YOU WANNA BE PRIME MINISTER, THEN?
FOR ≡PUFF≡ THE MONEY.
YOU TRYIN' T'BE REFRESHIN' OR SOMETHING?

WOOOO...
IT'S A GOOD THING THAT STUFF DOESN'T LAST VERY LONG... I WAS...
MY ARM!
LOOK AT MY ARM!!
IT'S STRETCHING!! IT'S STRETCHING!!
MY OTHER ARM...
IT'S COVERED IN ORANGE ROCKS!!
WHAT TH'...?
I'M...
I'M CHANGING
GETTING TALL!
RIP.
RIP.
RIP.
STRONG!
GREEN!
ROACH-HULK KILL!
THWIPP THWIPP
YOUR FACE IS COVERED WITH WEB-FLUID...
AAAARGHH!
HEE HEE

THEN THERE'S BRAN MAK ≥PANT≤ MUFIN ... ASTORIA ≥PUFF≤ MADE HIM CEREBUS' ≥GASP≤ PERSONAL ADVISOR ≥PANT≤
WUF! WUF!
WHY?
≥PUFF≤ BECAUSE HE WAS ≥PANT≤ THE ONE WHO ≥PUFF≤ SAID CEREBUS ≥GASP≤ SHOULD BE PRIME ≥PUFF≤ MINISTER...
≥PUFF≤ CEREBUS ≥PANT≤ KEPT THE ≥PANT≤ McBREWS ≥PUFF≤ SO THEY COULDN'T ≥PANT≤ TELL ANY ≥PUFF≤ BODY ABOUT CEREBUS ≥PANT≤ KIDNAPPING ≥PUFF≤ HIMSELF...
WUF
BLAKELY ≥PUFF≤ AND ≥GASP≤ FILGATE ≥PANT≤ BECAUSE ≥PUFF≤ THEY ≥PANT≤ COULD ≥WHEEZE≤ GUARANTEE ≥PUFF≤ REPRE≥GASP≤ SENTATIVES
IS THERE ENYBUDDY ELSE?
≥PANT≤ THERESA ≥PUFF≤ A ≥GASP≤ STORIA'S ≥PANT≤ A ≥GASP≤ SSISTANT AND ≥GASP≤ THE ≥PANT≤ MOON ≥GASP≤ ROACH ≥PANT≤ HE'S ≥PANT≤ HE'S ≥GASP≤ HE'S ≥GASP≤
WUF WUF WUF
... THE FELLER WHO LOOKS LIKE A SIX-FOOT BLEACHED BUMBLEBEE ...
≥YES≤
≥GASP≤
≥PANT≤
GOT A MATCH?
HERE ≥GASP≤ ≥PANT≤ ≥PUFF≤ ≥GASP≤
FWOOOOSHH!

BRINGING THE FULL FORCE OF HIS LATENT PSIONIC ROACH POWERS TO BEAR, PSI-ROACH BATTERS MERCILESSLY AT HER DEFENCES
HMMLRACKLE ZAKKTTT
SHE DEFLECTS HIS PSI-BLASTS WITH RIDICULOUS EASE
HUMMZ!!
HE INCREASES THE INTENSITY TO PSIONIC FORCE LEVEL FIVE OVER NINE-R SQUARED TO THE FIFTH POWER...
HZZRAKKT ZWAMZWAM
CLOSER CLOSER CLOSER ...
SO CLOSE SHE CAN SMELL HIS BREATH -- SMELL HIS ARM-PITS -- IT IS THEN THAT SHE REALIZES WHY HE HAS NEVER HAD A GIRL-FRIEND
HE FEELS HIS PSIONIC MASCU-SHIELDS CRUMBLING
STRUGGLES... TO... MAINTAIN... THEM...
THIS... IS... RIDICULOUS! THERE'S ONLY ONE WAY... TO ...PROVE... WHO... IS... STRONGER
YOU'RE RIGHT.

Y'SEE THET FELLER SITTIN' UP ON HIS HORSE? THE ONE OVER YONDER ON THE NEXT RIDGE? WITH THE HAT LIKE MINE?
≥GASP≤ UH-HUH.
WELL, SIR--THET'S M'COUSIN ELMO...
BY LIGHTIN' THET TORCH, I JUST GIVE ELMO A SIGNAL...
A SIGNAL AS T'WHO I'VE CHOSE T'BE THE NEXT PRIME MINISTER...
WUF WUF WUF WUF WUF WUF WUF WUF
AN' RIGHT NOW, ELMO IS HEADED FER THE REGENCY HOTEL T'ANNOUNCE THET TH' CHOICE HAS BEEN MADE AND WHO THE LUCKY GOAT.... OR AARDVARK ... BE!
WHO ≥GASP≤ ≥PANT≤
WHO ≥GASP≤ IS... IT?
WUF WUF WUF
SEEIN' AS HOW YOU POLYTICIANS'RE SO PARTIAL T' SURPRISE TAXES 'N' SURPRISE ELECTIONS 'N' SURPRISE VOTES 'N' SURPRISE BILLS ...
WUF WUF WUF
OH NO.
YOU HAVE A NICE TRIP BACK, NOW... Y'HEAR?

WUFFA WUFFA WUFFA WUFFA WUFFA WUFFA WUFFA WUFFA WUFFA WUFFA WUFFA WUFFA
WUFFA WUFFA WUFFAWUFFAWU
FFAWUFFAWUFFAWUFF
THE CHOICE HAS BEEN MADE?
YUP.
COULDN'T CHANGE YOUR MIND EVEN IF YOU WANTED TO?
NOPE.
YOU'RE SURE?
YUP.
WHAM!
WUFFAWUFFAWUFFAWUFFA WUFFAWU
CEREBUS WONDERS IF THAT WAS HIS FIRST OFFICIAL ACT AS PRIME MINISTER OR AS LEADER OF THE OPPOSITION...

...SO...?
...SO...?
...READY T' GIVUP....?
...NOPE...
...ARE YOO?...
...NOPE...
MEEN EITHER ....
...READY T' THROW UP...?
...YUP. ARE YOO?...
...YUP...
...ME ALTSO...
...ONE...
...TWO...
...THREE...

WUFFA WUFFA
WUFFA WUFFA
WUFFA WUFFA WUFFA WUFFA
SMASH BASH CRASH SPLINTER SMASH
ASTORIA! COOTIE!--LET'S GO! HE'S MADE UP HIS MIND, BUT WE WON'T KNOW WHO WON UNTIL WE GET BACK TO THE...
HIC
WHOOIZZIT...?
I DUNNO, BUT I HOPE'T'S TH' JANITOR! THIS MESS IS A PLACE!!!

...UN=HIC= UNHAND ME FOR I ALONE WIELD TH' POWER =HIC= COSMIC....
UNHAND ME ALTSO...FOR I ALONE CONTROL THE =HIC= X-FACTOR
NGH!
IT'S =HIC= NO USE, 'STORIA--
..HMM...?
HE'S MADE OF GRAY FROSTONITE..TH' ONLY SUBSTNCE THAT C'N REMOVE OUR POWERS 'N' MAKE THE WORLD SPIN =HIC= IN TH' OPPOPPOSITE D'RECTION ......
GREAT =HIC= FROSTON ....
YOU WOULDN' HAPPENAHAVE A FEW YARDS'F LEAD FOIL ON YOU?......
I THINKI LEFT IT IN M'OTHER COAT.......
WITHA KRAK OF HISSWIP TH'CANDIDIDATE ISOFFAG'IN IN SERCHUV TH' ELU=HIC= TH'ELUS=HIC= TH' HARD'T'GIT PRIME MINISTERSHIP....
NEETHER SNORE NOR SLEET NOR SMELLUV PUKE SHALL STAYTHIS EEGER EARTH-PIG FROM AN ALMOS' =HIC= HONEST JOB

MUCH LATER
AN' SO HE RASES ON ON ≷HIC≶ ON INDO TH' SNIRLING SWOW GRIMN'SS'N'DENERM'N ≷HIC≶ DENERMINISHUN ETCHED ON 'IS EVERY FACE! HE PORES FORTH EV'RY OUNCE UF EGERNY 'N HIS BID T'REASH THE FELD RIV'R AND THENCE T'TH' REGETCY HO≷HIC≶ HO ≷HIC≶ HO≷HIC≶ ABASSADER SWEET......
WILLY BE THE NOO PRIMINNISER'R LIDDLE MORE TH'N'N ASTER ≷HIC≶ ASTER ≷HIC≶ FOOTNOTE IN TH' HISTORY OF PAGES..... THERES NO WAY FER'M T'KNOW AS'E URGES HIS URGES ONTO MORE URGENT URGES THEN NEVER B'FORE ≷HIC≶ ......
FAME 'R' OBLIVION? TH' TOO CHASE EASH UTHER ROUND'N'ROUND 'IS L'IL GRAY HEAD! WISH'LL IT BE?.... A LIFE-TIME OF ADU≷HIC≶ ADULA ≷HIC≶ AD ≷HIC≶ ASS-KISSING OR DERRRISIVE LAFFTER AT THIS RIDDIKILUSS ......
UMPH ....
ABRUPPLY HE REIGNS IN TH' HORSE..... HAS TH' PRESHER PROVEDOO GRATE? HAS HE GIVENUP? .....
HE REASHES OVER THE BACK UF TH'SEAT 'N' RAISES TH'MOOON ROASH'S FROST'NITE PARAL ≷HIC≶ PARALY ≷HIC≶ STIFF'NED ARM...... AN' REMOVES TH' MITT'N FRUM TH' EQWULLY STIFF'NED LEFT HAND ......
TH' WHITE MITTEN OF SURREN'ER? CAN IT BE TROO? IS THIS WHERE TH' QUEST EN'S? WITHOUT ONE ELF IN SITE? SEEZING THE MOOON ROASH'S JAW, HE TALA WALA WILLA WULLA MMF!!
MFMF? MFFMFF FMFFMM MFF?..... MFFFM! MFFMF MFFMFM MFMFF MFFMF MFFMF MFFMF MFFMF ......

MUCH, MUCH LATER
WHOOOA...
EVENING.
EVENIN'...
CEREBUS HAS BEEN TRYING TO REACH THE FELD RIVER SINCE EARLY THIS AFTERNOON...
HOW MUCH FARTHER IS IT?
WELL, SIR...
THET DEPENDS...
DEPENDS?...
DEPENDS ON WHAT...!?
DEPENDS ON WHETHER YOU KEEP GOING WEST OR WHETHER YOU DECIDE T'TURN SOUTH SOMETIME...
OH.
IF'N YOU DO DECIDE T'TURN SOUTH, IT'S ABOUT A TWO-HOUR TRIP...
THE MOON ROACH IS SUDDENLY GRATEFUL FOR THE MITTEN SHOVED IN HIS MOUTH...
UNMUFFLED GIGGLING WOULD HAVE CAUSED HIM TO BE SEVERELY BEATEN ABOUT THE HEAD AND SHOULDERS WITH GRAY FROSTONITE FISTS...

HEY!
HEY, YOU! THE BRIDGE IS OUT!
SURE IS -- I EXPECT YOU'LL BE WANTIN' A ROOM ...
NO--JUST INSTRUCTIONS ON HOW TO GET TO THE NEXT BRIDGE.
THE NEXT BRIDGE IS EIGHTEEN MILE DOWNRIVER...
THANKS.
BUT IT'S OUT, TOO
AND THE NEXT BRIDGE AFTER THAT ONE?
ANOTHER EIGHT MILE FURTHER ON.
BUT IT'S OUT TOO, RIGHT?
NO -- IT'S JEST FINE...
WONDERFUL. THANKS FOR YOUR TIME.
DOESN'T GIT USED MUCH SINCE THE AVALANCHE CLOSED TH' ROAD, THOUGH.
OKAY.
HOW DOES SOMEONE GET TO GREATER IEST?
WELL, SIR.

YOU'LL JEST HAFTA WAIT A WEEK 'TIL THE TEMPORARY BRIDGE IS BUILT.
TEMPORARY BRIDGE.
YESSIR.
ISN'T IT A LUCKY THING THIS HOTEL WAS RIGHT HERE NEXT TO THE BRIDGE,
I'D SAY SO...
A VERY LUCKY THING, INDEED.
RIGHT.
HOW MUCH FOR A ROOM ...
ACTUALLY, THAT'S ANOTHER PIECE OF LUCK...
THIS HERE WEEK IS OUR "ANNUAL BRIDGE-BUILDER SPECIAL"
ANNUAL BRIDGE BUILDER SPECIAL
ANNUAL...
BRIDGE-BUILDER SPECIAL?
YESSIR-- ROOM WITH A VIEW OF TH' BRIDGE BEIN' BUILT... FER ONE WEEK, PLUS MEALS, TOWELS 'N' LINENS CHANGED TWICE FER FIVE CROWNS EVEN, WHICH INCLUDES YER TIPS 'N' YER GRATUITIES ...
THE BRIDGE COLLAPSES FAIRLY OFTEN, DOES IT? ...
YESSIR...
AFTER JEST 'BOUT EVER' HEAVY SNOWFALL ...
EVER THOUGHT OF BUILDING A STURDIER BRIDGE? ...
CONSIDERED IT...
BUT FOLKS HEREABOUTS WERE AFRAID IT MIGHT HURT THE TOURIST TRADE...
...SIGN HERE ...

SKRTCHA SKRTCHA SKIT
FIVE CROWNS, EH?
YUP.
"CEREBUS".
ANY RELATION T'THE NEW PRIME MINISTER?
ACTUALLY, CEREBUS ...
NEW...
PRIME MINISTER?
YUP. COUSIN ELMO WAS BY EARLIER T'DAY... HE TOLD ME TH' DECISION HAS BIN MADE...
I'M... HIM!!... HE!
I MEAN... CEREBUS IS THE NEW ME!
I WAS ALWAYS ME--BUT NOW I'M THE NEW HIM!!
WELL, I'LL BE... THE NEW PRIME MINISTER STAYIN' AT MY HOTEL...
YEAH!
WOW!
YOU GOT ANY LUGGAGE, MR. PRIME MINISTER, SIR?
WHAT?
LUGGAGE?
UH-- NO!
BUT CEREBUS HAS TWO DRUNKS OUTSIDE IN HIS SLED...!

FINE. FINE. HERE'S YER ROOM KEY 'N' A BOTTLE T' HELP YOU PASS THE TIME, MR. PRIME MINISTER
ON THE HOUSE ...
ON THE HOUSE WELL, THANK YOU...
THANK YOU VERY MUCH ...
YOU JEST GO UP THOSE STAIRS T'YER ROOM 'N' RELAX...
ROOM RELAX
AN' I'LL BE BRINGING YER DRUNKS UP IN A FEW MINUTES ...
Dear Chancellor of the Exchequer:
I am enclosing my hotel's bill for eight hundred and fifty crowns for use of the Diplomatic Suite for one week by the new Prime Minister and his staff, with a supplemental laundry bill of fifty crowns and a liquor bill of

Cerebus the Aardvark
CEREBUS' SIX CRISES
crisis number one
THE BUREAUCRATIC REBELLION
THE RANKING DIPLOMATIC REPRESENTATIVE OF ESHNOSOPUR REQUESTS AN AUDIENCE WITH THE RIGHT HONOURABLE PRIME MINISTER OF IEST...
PLEASE ACCEPT THE PRIME MINISTER'S REGRETS, BUT HE IS NOT RECEIVING VISITORS AT THIS TIME...
The Times
GOAT GOES INTO HIDING AS AARDVARK TAKES OATH OF OFFICE
PURGE FEARED
THE EXECUTIVE VICE PRESIDENT AND PRESIDENT OF THE MERCHANTS' GUILD DESIRE A BRIEF MEETING AT THE PRIME MINISTER'S CONVENIENCE ...
THE MINISTRY OF TRADE IS IN GOVERNMENT HOUSE DOWN THE STREET. SOMEONE WILL SPEAK TO YOU THERE ...
I REPRESENT MR. R.H. DIPP OF HADDEN, HADDEN AND DIPP...
PLEASE TELL MR. DIPP WE CAN'T IMAGINE WHAT HAS HAPPENED TO THE RECEIPT FOR HIS VERY GENEROUS CAMPAIGN CONTRIBUTION-- BUT WE WILL CERTAINLY SEND IT OVER AS SOON AS SOMEONE FINDS IT...
OY! MISSY! AM I UNDER ARREST? YOU CAN'T PIN THAT BREAK-IN ON ME. I DIDN'T EVEN KNOW THE ...
AH. MR. "BALDY" PATE I BELIEVE...
THE PRIME MINISTER ASKED ME TO HAVE YOU WAIT... HE'S IN A MEETING RIGHT NOW...
THE SUN
CEREBUS SWORN IN AS PRIME MINISTER

THE SUN P.M. DISBANDS LEGIS-LATURE HUNDREDS OF HSIFFY SPIES ARRESTED
The Times "DON'T SAY WE DIDN'T WARN YOU" GOAT ORGANIZES RESISTANCE MOVEMENT
THE SUN P.M. ANNOUNCES NEW AMNESTY PROGRAM TURN IN ALL TRAITORS OR BE EXECUTED YOURSELF
The Times LORD JULIUS FLEES CITY GOAT ARRESTED ON MORALS CHARGE
AND IN LIGHT OF THE IESTAN GUILD OF GOVERNMENT EMPLOYEES HAVING ELECTED ME AS SPOKESMAN FOR THEM, I WISH TO PROTEST IN THE STRONGEST POSSIBLE TERMS, THE COMPLETE AND UTTER PERVERSION OF ALL ACCEPTABLE STANDARDS OF GOOD GOVERNMENT AND DUE PROCESS OF LAW, MR. PRIME MINISTER, AND TO URGENTLY REQUEST THAT YOU TAKE IMMEDIATE AND DECISIVE STEPS TO RESTORE SUCH STANDARDS...
PLEASE GIVE THE PRIME MINISTER YOUR HAND ...
MY... HAND?
THE PRIME MINISTER WISHES TO DEMON-STRATE HOW HE FEELS WE CAN ALL WORK TOGETHER TO RESTORE OUR CONFIDENCE AND BRING ABOUT A NEW AGE OF PROSPERITY...
OH.
PICTURE YOUR THUMB AS ME...
YOUR PRIME MINISTER...
YOUR FINGERS AS THE VAST BUREAUCRACY OF THIS GREAT CITY-STATE...

WHEN THE PRIME MINISTER --YOUR THUMB-- IS UNITED WITH THE BUREAUCRACY -- YOUR FINGERS--GREAT WORKS CAN BE ACCOMPLISHED. THE LIFTING OF SPIRITS THE GRASPING OF IDEAS
WE HOLD THE FUTURE BETWEEN US...
IF, HOWEVER, THE PRIME MINISTER AND HIS BUREAUCRACY ARE NOT UNITED...
LIKE...
GAHH
SO!
WE HAVE WHAT?
DISUNITY
WHAT ELSE?
DISHARMONY
WHAT ELSE?
AGONY
WHAT ELSE?
OUCH!
WHAT ELSE?
BAD!
NO GOOD!
ANARCHY!
REVOLUTION!
COMPLETE BREAKDOWN OF MORALITY!
SO WHAT SHOULD YOUR FINGERS DO?
SWEAR COMPLETE AND EVER-LASTING LOYALTY TO MY THUMB!

IF ANY MEMBER OF YOUR STAFF HAS TROUBLE UNDERSTANDING HOW IMPORTANT COOPERATION IS, FEEL FREE TO BORROW MY LITTLE DEMONSTRATION...
YES, MR. PRIME MINISTER...
AND IF YOU HAVE TROUBLE REMEMBERING HOW IT GOES, I HAVE ANOTHER ONE WHERE THE PRIME MINISTER AND THE ARMY ARE A PAIR OF PLIERS AND YOUR BIG TOE IS THE BUREAUCRACY
YES, MR. PRIME MINISTER
NEXT?
CEREBUS, OLD MATE!
HOW LONG HAS IT BEEN? LAST TIME I SAW YOU WAS...
OOOMPH!
YOU'RE SUPPOSED TO BOW, BALDY
"OLD MATE"
S ≥COUGH≤ SORRY
SORRY, MR. PRIME MINISTER, SIR!
SO-SORRY, MR PRIME MINISTER SIR
MUCH BETTER...
NOW!
HOW MUCH DO YOU SUPPOSE WE COULD'VE GOT FOR THE INAUGURATION JEWELS IN THE OLD DAYS?
COR! A HUNNERD THOUSAN' EASY!

MR. PRIME MINISTER, SIR...
SO, THE PRIME MINISTER WOULD NOT BE AMISS IN EXPECTING TO REALIZE --SAY-- A QUARTER OF A MILLION PALNAN CROWNS...
...OR THE CORRESPONDING VALUE IN --SAY-- T'CAPMIN CROSSBOWMEN?
I THINK I COULD MANAGE THAT...
MR. PRIME MINISTER SIR...
EXCELLENT. NATURALLY YOU WILL BE PERMITTED TO KEEP ANY EXCESS PROFIT... JUST HAVE THE CROSSBOWMEN SENT TO OUR BORDER OUTPOSTS ON THE OESIS RIVER...
OH.
I ALMOST FORGOT.
I'LL BE REPORTING THE JEWELS STOLEN IN ORDER TO COLLECT THE INSURANCE, SO YOU ONLY HAVE UNTIL SUNDOWN TO GET THEM OUTSIDE OF IEST'S JURISDICTION.
IF YOU'RE CAUGHT I WILL BE UNABLE TO KEEP YOU FROM BEING EXECUTED...
WOT?!
BUT...
BUT...
SLAM!!
THE SUN
INAUGURATION JEWELS STOLEN
DEVOTIONALISTS SUSPECTED
The Times
SUDDEN WEALTH FOR THEOCRATS
INAUGURATION JEWELS SUSPECTED

WHAT I MEAN TO SAY, MR. PRIME MINISTER IS THAT THE IDEALS OF THE NEW REPUBLICANISM SEEM SOMEHOW.... AT ODDS WITH THE SWEEPING...
...REFORMS...
OF THE LAST FEW DAYS.
OUR SUPPORTERS CHOSE YOU AS AN ALTERNATIVE TO LORD JULIUS -- A CARETAKER TO KEEP OUR GREAT CITY-STATE INTACT AND TO AVOID ANY DRASTIC MID-COURSE CORRECTIONS IN WHAT HAS BEEN IEST'S UNBLEMISHED RECORD OF CO-OPERATION WITH IT'S NEIGHBOUR STATES
DEATH TO THE ENEMIES OF THE LIVING TARIM!
DEATH
THE WATERS OF THE FELD, THE OESIS AND THE CHESMI WILL RUN RED WITH THE BLOOD OF THE UN-BELIEVERS!!
MIGHTY WILL HIS GREAT WRATH BE-- ALL WILL DIE IN THE UNCLEAN LANDS
YES!
WE SHALL BE HIS INSTRUMENT
WE SHALL LAY WASTE TO THE FOUL BEINGS WHO MOCK HIS NAME
DECAPITATE!
IMPALE!!
EVISCERATE!!!
THIS IS OUR MISSION!
THESE ARE OUR IDEALS!!
BLAKELY, I DON'T BELIEVE YOU'VE MET MY NEW MINISTER FOR EXTERNAL AFFAIRS.
CHARMED I'M SURE

YOU HAVE THE BANK DRAUGHT FOR THREE QUARTERS OF A MILLION PALNAN CROWNS PAYABLE TO THE PRIME MINISTER'S OFFICE?
OF COURSE. AND NOW, WITHIN A MERE FORTNIGHT WE WILL BE EVEN CLOSER NEIGHBOURS THAN EVER BEFORE, YES? HA-HA...
HAVE THE T'CAPMINS SETTLED ON A PRICE?
THREE HUNDRED THOUSAND FOR THE CAVALRY... THREE HUNDRED THOUSAND FOR THE PIKE...
A HUNDRED THOUSAND FOR FOOD, SUPPLIES ... THEY'RE READY TO MOVE AS SOON AS THE CHEQUE CLEARS ...
FINE.
HERE. TELL THEM TO KEEP THE CHANGE...
THE SUN
PAPAL FARM LANDS SOLD TO LOWER FELDA
"BALANCED BUDGET NOW WITHIN REACH" SAYS P.M.
The Times
FELDANS TO CROSS THE OESIS!
DON'T LOOK AT US -- YOU ELECTED HIM!
A BALANCED BUDGET! IN THIS DAY AND AGE! WELL, HE CAN HAVE HIS BALANCED BUDGET FOR A FEW WEEKS
THEN WE WILL BE ACROSS THE RIVER...
AND HIS BUDGET ...
WILL BE THE VERY LEAST OF HIS WORRIES ...

BUT, MR. PRIME MINISTER, SURELY YOU CAN SEE...
SEE? ALL I SEE IS A HANDFUL OF TROUBLE-MAKERS BREAKING A FEW WINDOWS AND CHANTING SOME IDIOT SLOGANS...
ALL I SEE IS MY DOMESTIC AFFAIRS ADVISOR LETTING THEM CONVINCE HIM THAT CEREBUS HAS LOST TOUCH WITH THE COMMON PEOPLE ...
TWO THOUSAND BUR-EAUCRATS IS HARDLY A MERE HANDFUL.
CEREBUS IS ALWAYS IN TOUCH WITH THE COMMON PEOPLE
ASK ANYONE --THIS JOKER FOR INSTANCE. HEY! HEY YOU! YEAH, YOU! ...
MR. PRIME MINISTER?
FORGET FOR ONE MINUTE THAT I AM CEREBUS YOUR BELOVED...
AHEM BELOVED PRIME MINISTER. SPEAKING AS AN AVERAGE CITIZEN...
...WOULD YOU SAY THAT CEREBUS HAS LOST TOUCH WITH THE COMMON PEOPLE?
I REALLY COULDN'T SAY, MR. PRIME MINISTER...
NO?!
AND WHY NOT?!
BECAUSE I'M NOT AN AVERAGE CITIZEN. I'M THE MINISTER OF ROADS AND WATERWAYS...
IF CEREBUS EVER CATCHES YOU IMPERSONATING AN AVERAGE CITIZEN AGAIN...
CEREBUS WILL HAVE YOU EXECUTED-- UNDERSTAND!?
Y-YES, MR. PRIME MINISTER...

THE SUN
P.M. GOES TO REGENCY TO MEET WITH INNER CIRCLE ON CIVIL UNREST
The Times
INNER CIRCLE?!?
YOUR GUESS IS AS GOOD AS OURS
THE MAGIC CRYSTAL REVEALS MUCH! GREAT UNCERTAINTY! GREAT UNREST! YOU DEFY TRADITION AT YOUR OWN PERIL! DISCORDIA MAY PROVE YOUR MASTER AND NOT YOUR SLAVE! OMMM.
FOR THIS CEREBUS IS GIVING YOU FREE ROOM AND BOARD?
LOOK. WHY DON'T YOU JUST TELL THE BUREAUCRACY THAT YOU'RE SELLING THE PAPAL FARM LANDS TO GET ENOUGH MONEY TO INVADE LOWER FELDA?
BECAUSE THEN THE SURPRISE INVASION WON'T BE A SURPRISE...
WHY DON'T YOU TELL THEM, BUT ALSO TELL THEM IT'S A SECRET AND THEY CAN'T TELL ANYBODY FROM LOWER FELDA
I GUESS THAT WOULDN'T WORK SO GOOD, WOULD IT?
"ABIDING FAITH IN THE PRINCIPLES OF THE NEW REPUBLICANISM"
IF HE'D JUST ADMIT THAT HE WANTS A SHARE OF CEREBUS' PROFIT, INSTEAD OF HIDING BEHIND HIS DAMN SLOGANS...
THE GREEDY SON OF A...

SON OF A WHAT?
PROFIT!
PROPHET?
EXACTLY!-THEY WANT TO SHARE IN THE PROFITS ..THAT'S ALL THEY'RE ANGRY ABOUT, BUT THEY WON'T ADMIT IT...
SO?
SO CEREBUS WILL SHARE THE PROFITS WITH THEM...
BUT YOU SPENT ALL THE PROFITS ON MERCENARIES...
YES! BUT! THOSE MERCENARIES ARE NOW PREPARING TO TAKE OVER LOWER FELDA!
CEREBUS CAN PAY THE BUREAUCRACY OUT OF THE MONEY HE MAKES BY PLUNDERING BEDUIN!
WHAT HAPPENS IF THE INVASION FAILS?
LOOK- IF YOU'RE GOING TO TALK CRAZY CEREBUS IS JUST GOING TO HAVE TO FIND SOMEONE ELSE FOR HIS INNER CIRCLE...
I'M SORRY! I'M SORRY! I WON'T DO IT AGAIN -- I PROMISE!

THANK YOU, MR. PRIME MINISTER! I'M SURE THIS GENEROUS CONTRIBUTION TO THE GOVERNMENT EMPLOYEES PENSION FUND WILL GO A LONG WAY TOWARDS SMOOTHING ANY RUFFLED BUREAUCRATIC FEATHERS ...
HEH HEH
A QUARTER OF A MILLION CROWNS!
BLESSED TARIM!
IF I ONLY SKIM OFF FIFTY THOUSAND FOR MYSELF, THAT WILL STILL LEAVE
EXCUSE ME...?
UH...
EXCUSE ME?
YES?
I JUST LEFT THE PRIME MINISTER AND... WELL... HE FORGOT TO SIGN THIS CHEQUE!
FINE.
IF YOU'LL LEAVE IT WITH ME, I'LL SEE THAT IT'S BROUGHT TO HIS ATTENTION
UH...
UH...
IS THERE SOMETHING ELSE?
UH-- I DON'T SUPPOSE YOU COULD ...
THAT HE WOULD ...
RIGHT NOW?
THE PRIME MINISTER IS VERY BUSY, I'M AFRAID ...
UH
WELL
DO YOU MIND IF I WAIT?
NOT AT ALL
I HOPE YOU BROUGHT A SLEEPING BAG.

HE'S GREEDY ENOUGH TO WAIT AT LEAST TWO DAYS FOR A SIGNATURE...
SO... THAT'S HOW LONG WE HAVE TO GET OUR HANDS ON THE LOWER FELDAN TREASURY... YOUR TROOP REPORT, BRAN
THE PIKE ARE IN POSITION?
YES, MR. PRIME MINISTER ...
THE CAVALRY?
YES, MR. PRIME MINISTER
THE CROSS-BOWMEN?
BRAN?
THAT'S ODD.
GREAT NEWS, MR. PRIME MINISTER!!
YOU FINALLY FOUND THE TIMES OFFICE AND SMASHED THE PRINTING PRESS?
BETTER THAN THAT!
I FOUND THE CRIMINAL WHO STOLE THE INAUGURATION JEWELS
HE SLUNK STEALTHILY FROM THE CITY-- THE MANTLE OF DARKNESS SHROUDING HIS EVERY MOVEMENT-- INVISIBLE TO ALL SAVE THE MERELY MAGNIFICENT MOON ROACH!
THE DARKNIGHT DO-GOODER FOLLOWED AT A DISCREET DISTANCE, WATCHING EACH SUBTLE MOVEMENT OF HIS FELONIOUS QUARRY, WHEN, VERY SUDDENLY...
SMAKT!
THE WORLD BROKE OUT IN STAR-SPANGLED FROSTONITE... THE ONLY SUBSTANCE THAT CAN NUM
CAN YOU STILL GET US THE CROSSBOWMEN?
HAVE YOU GOT ANY MORE FUZZY DETECTIVES?
NO.
I'LL DO MY BEST.

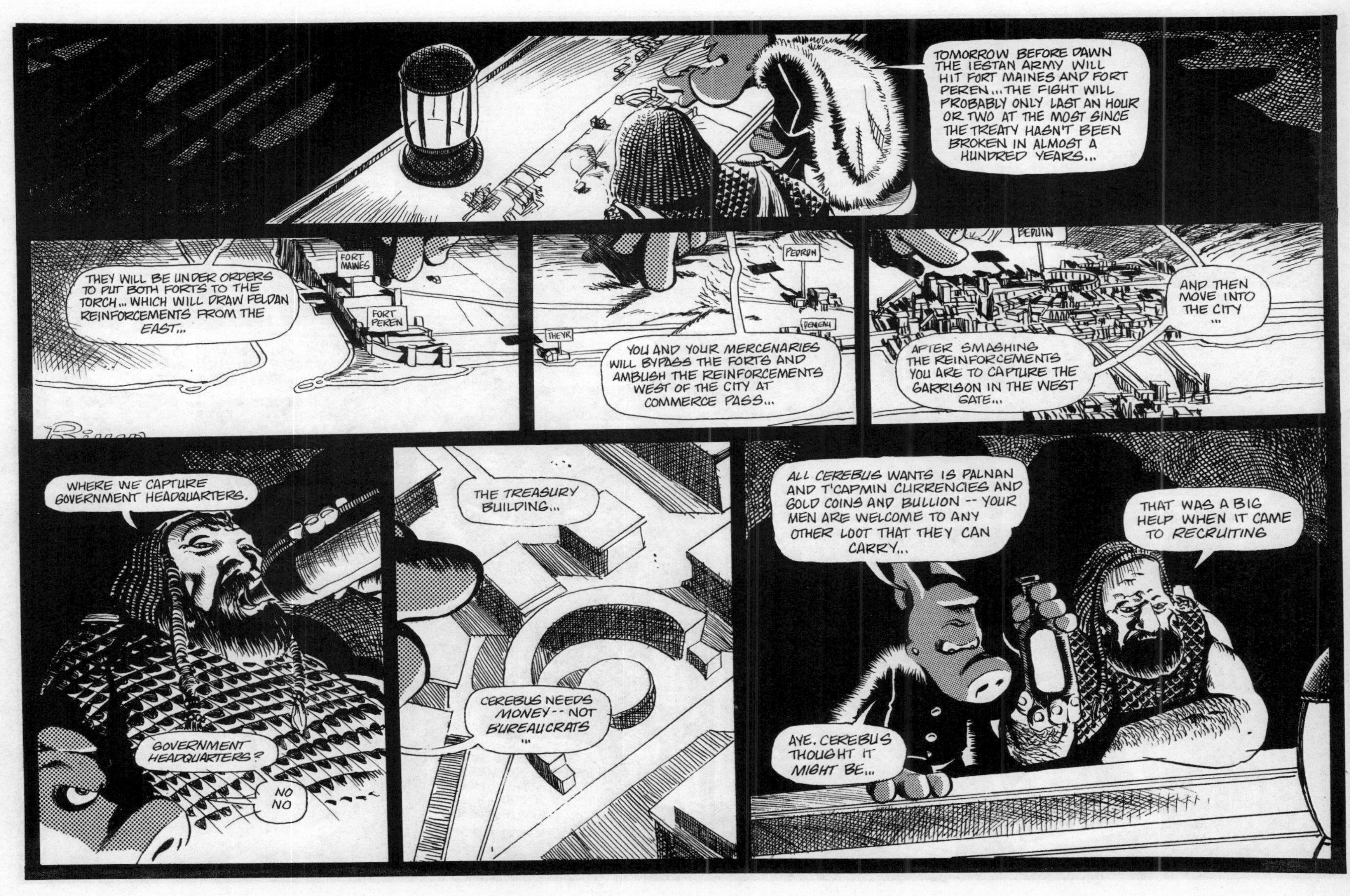
TOMORROW BEFORE DAWN THE IESTAN ARMY WILL HIT FORT MAINES AND FORT PEREN... THE FIGHT WILL PROBABLY ONLY LAST AN HOUR OR TWO AT THE MOST SINCE THE TREATY HASN'T BEEN BROKEN IN ALMOST A HUNDRED YEARS...
FORT MAINES
FORT PEREN
THEY WILL BE UNDER ORDERS TO PUT BOTH FORTS TO THE TORCH... WHICH WILL DRAW FELDAN REINFORCEMENTS FROM THE EAST...
THEYR
YOU AND YOUR MERCENARIES WILL BYPASS THE FORTS AND AMBUSH THE REINFORCEMENTS WEST OF THE CITY AT COMMERCE PASS...
AFTER SMASHING THE REINFORCEMENTS YOU ARE TO CAPTURE THE GARRISON IN THE WEST GATE...
AND THEN MOVE INTO THE CITY ...
WHERE WE CAPTURE GOVERNMENT HEADQUARTERS.
GOVERNMENT HEADQUARTERS?
NO NO
THE TREASURY BUILDING...
CEREBUS NEEDS MONEY -- NOT BUREAUCRATS ...
ALL CEREBUS WANTS IS PALNAN AND T'CAPMIN CURRENCIES AND GOLD COINS AND BULLION -- YOUR MEN ARE WELCOME TO ANY OTHER LOOT THAT THEY CAN CARRY...
THAT WAS A BIG HELP WHEN IT CAME TO RECRUITING
AYE. CEREBUS THOUGHT IT MIGHT BE...

ONCE WE HAVE BEDUIN, YOU SHOULD HAVE PLENTY OF TIME TO SHIP THE CURRENCY BACK HERE TO ME -- BUT I'LL NEED AN ACCURATE ACCOUNTING ALMOST IMMEDIATELY...
WHAT STORY ARE YOU GOING TO TELL THE POWDER-PUFFS TO GET THEM TO BREAK THE TREATY?
CEREBUS ALMOST FORGOT -- HE GOT A REPORT FROM THE EMBASSY ON POSSIBLE AREAS OF FRICTION ...
WHAT?
THIS IS AN OUTRAGE!
OUR RANKING DIPLOMATIC REPRESENTATIVE HAS BEEN AT THE BEDUIN POST FOR TWO YEARS!
AND THE MILITARY GOVERNMENT HASN'T ONCE INVITED HIM TO THEIR YEAR-END BANQUET!
OF COURSE THEY MUST REALIZE THIS MEANS WAR!
D'YOU GUYS REALLY TALK LIKE THAT?
SOMETIMES
REMEMBER TO BRING THAT LETTER WITH YOU WHEN YOU MAKE YOUR REPORT...

YOU KNOW, PINSHAW, I HAVEN'T A DECENT NIGHT'S SLEEP SINCE THAT REPORT ARRIVED BY COURIER... I LIE AWAKE BY THE HOUR THINKING ABOUT THE ABSOLUTE NERVE OF THOSE PEOPLE...
SLIMY LITTLE POWDERED AND PERFUMED GRAPE-STOMPERS, ALWAYS LOOKING DOWN THEIR NOSES AT WE DECENT AND HARD-WORKING FOLK
IT DOESN'T TAKE TOO MUCH IMAGINATION TO FIGURE OUT WHY THEY DID IT... YOU'VE HEARD THE WAY THEY TALK ABOUT US, HAVEN'T YOU, PINSHAW...?
"LET'S NOT INVITE THE IESTAN" ONE WOULD SNIFF. "YOU ARE ONLY TOO RIGHT" HIS FRIEND WOULD GIGGLE WHILE THEY SIP THAT VILE RIVER MUCK THEY CALL WINE.
"THOSE PEOPLE USE GOATS FOR WET-NURSES, DON'T THEY"
"EVEN WORSE, MY FRIEND, THE STUPID ORIFICES BREED THE SMELLY BEASTS"
"WHICH WOULD NOT BE BAD IF THEY WOULD BREED THEM TO EACH OTHER INSTEAD OF TO THEIR DAUGHTERS" THEY WOULD OF COURSE LAUGH AT THIS...
THEN THEY WOULD TURN AND CLEAR THEIR NOSTRILS IN THE DIRECTION OF THE IESTAN FLAG THEY USE TO CLEAN OUT THEIR FIRE PLACES...
"WHY NOT INVITE THE IESTAN'S WIFE ONLY, THEN?"
"HIS WIFE? BUT WHY INVITE HER, MY FRIEND?"
"SHE IS SUCH AN UGLY COW, SHE COULD GIVE US SOUR MILK WHICH WE COULD USE TO MAKE OUR DELICATE SNOBBISH SAUCES"...
EXCUSE ME, SIR!...
YEES, PINSHAW?
PERMIT ME TO CROSS THE RIVER AND WIPE OUT THE MANGY SCUM, SIR
WHAT A WONDERFUL IDEA... I HAVE SOME PLANS RIGHT OVER HERE...

REALLY, MR. PRIME MINISTER--
WOULDN'T IT BE EASIER TO JUST WRITE OUT ANOTHER ONE?
ASTORIA SAID SHE'D LEAVE IT ON HER DESK FOR ME TO SIGN... IT MUST BE HERE SOMEWHERE
JUST HAVE TO LOOK AROUND A BIT...
SIGH...
ODD... SOME SORT OF GLOW ON THE HORIZON...
A FIRE OR SOMETHING
MR. PRIME MINISTER --THERE'S SOME KIND OF...
EEEK!
WE CAPTURED THE CITY A FEW HOURS AGO
SORRY I'M SO LATE
WE WERE TORTURING PRISONERS AND I LOST TRACK OF THE TIME
YOU WANT US TO COUNT THE MONEY TONIGHT?
NO. TOMORROW WILL BE SOON ENOUGH...
WELL I'LL BE DARNED... YOUR CHEQUE WAS RIGHT IN FRONT OF ME THE WHOLE TIME.

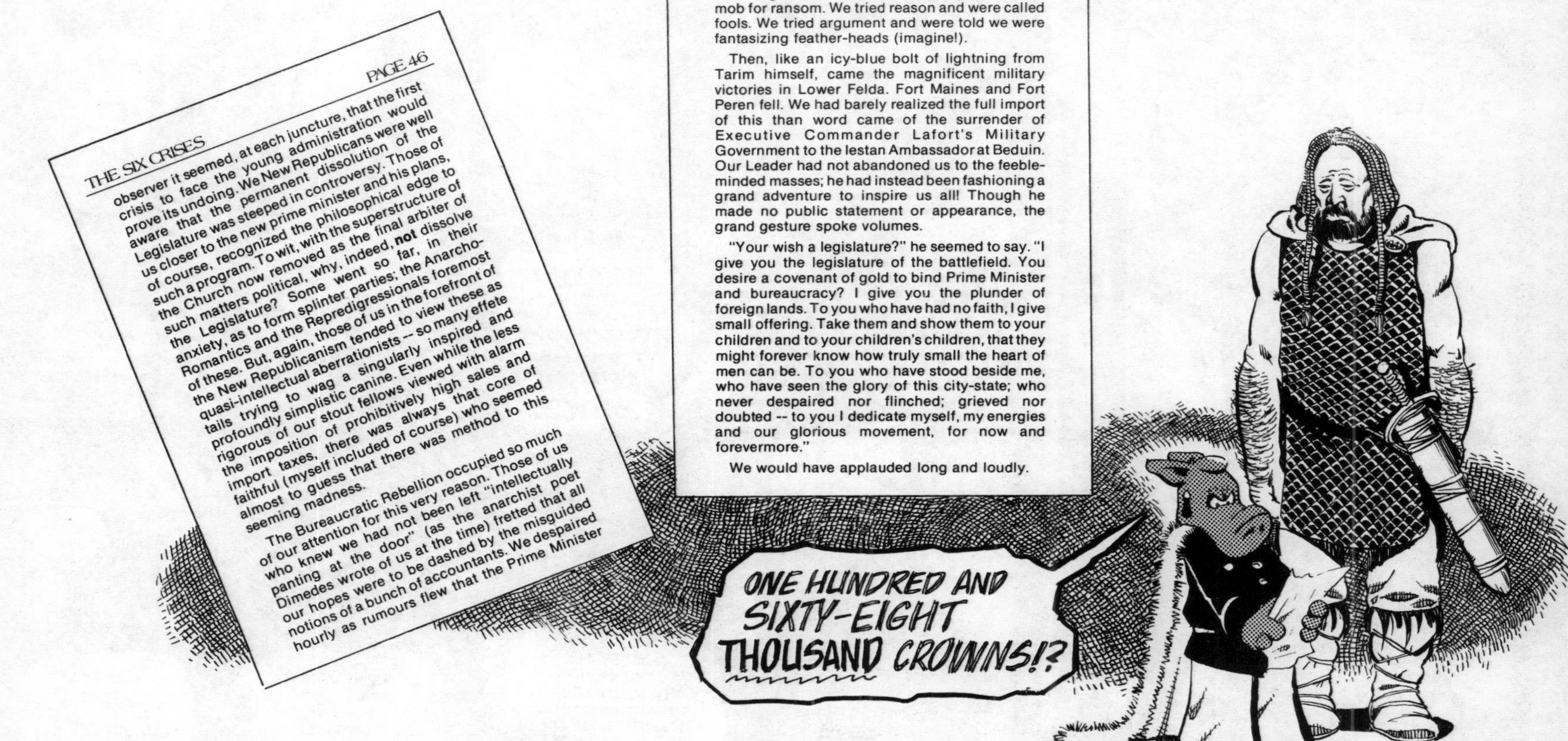

THE SIX CRISES PAGE 46

observer it seemed, at each juncture, that the first crisis to face the young administration would prove its undoing. We New Republicans were well aware that the permanent dissolution of the Legislature was steeped in controversy. Those of us closer to the new prime minister and his plans, of course, recognized the philosophical edge to such a program. To wit, with the superstructure of the Church now removed as the final arbiter of such matters political, why, indeed, **not** dissolve the Legislature? Some went so far, in their anxiety, as to form splinter parties; the Anarcho-Romantics and the Repredigressionals foremost of these. But, again, those of us in the forefront of the New Republicanism tended to view these as quasi-intellectual aberrationists -- so many effete tails trying to wag a singularly inspired and profoundly simplistic canine. Even while the less rigorous of our stout fellows viewed with alarm the imposition of prohibitively high sales and import taxes, there was always that core of faithful (myself included of course) who seemed almost to guess that there was method to this seeming madness.

The Bureaucratic Rebellion occupied so much of our attention for this very reason. Those of us who knew we had not been left "intellectually panting at the door" (as the anarchist poet Dimedes wrote of us at the time) fretted that all our hopes were to be dashed by the misguided notions of a bunch of accountants. We despaired hourly as rumours flew that the Prime Minister

THE SIX CRISES PAGE 47

had resigned, that Astoria was being held by the mob for ransom. We tried reason and were called fools. We tried argument and were told we were fantasizing feather-heads (imagine!).

Then, like an icy-blue bolt of lightning from Tarim himself, came the magnificent military victories in Lower Felda. Fort Maines and Fort Peren fell. We had barely realized the full import of this than word came of the surrender of Executive Commander Lafort's Military Government to the Iestan Ambassador at Beduin. Our Leader had not abandoned us to the feeble-minded masses; he had instead been fashioning a grand adventure to inspire us all! Though he made no public statement or appearance, the grand gesture spoke volumes.

"Your wish a legislature?" he seemed to say. "I give you the legislature of the battlefield. You desire a covenant of gold to bind Prime Minister and bureaucracy? I give you the plunder of foreign lands. To you who have had no faith, I give small offering. Take them and show them to your children and to your children's children, that they might forever know how truly small the heart of men can be. To you who have stood beside me, who have seen the glory of this city-state; who never despaired nor flinched; grieved nor doubted -- to you I dedicate myself, my energies and our glorious movement, for now and forevermore."

We would have applauded long and loudly.

ONE HUNDRED THOUSAND IN T'CAPMIN CURRENCY ...ANOTHER SIXTY EIGHT THOUSAND IN PALNAN CURRENCY
NO GOLD.
THAT'S ALL?!
THEY HAD TWENTY THOUSAND BOLTS OF BURLAP CLOTH, BUT I DIDN'T THINK YOU'D WANT THEM ...
THEY MUST HAVE HIDDEN ALL OF THEIR MONEY SOMEWHERE. THEY MUST HAVE...
WE TORTURED THE HEAD TREASURY GUY. ACCORDING TO HIM THE COUNTRY HAS BEEN BROKE FOR TEN YEARS ...
BROKE!?
THAT'S RIDICULOUS! HOW CAN A WHOLE COUNTRY BE BROKE?
OKAY! OKAY!
BUT WHY DID THAT COUNTRY HAVE TO BE BROKE?

AH! THERE YOU ARE, MR. PRIME MINISTER... I'VE BEEN TRYING TO FIND YOU...
A LETTER FROM LORD JULIUS JUST ARRIVED BY DIPLOMATIC MESSENGER
READ IT.
"CONGRATULATIONS ON YOUR SUPERB MILITARY VICTORY STOP YOUR MOTHER AND I ARE MIGHTY PROUD STOP WILL BE ARRIVING NEXT WEEK FOR TRILATERAL SUMMIT STOP ENCLOSED FIND BANK OF PALNU'S BILL FOR LOWER FELDA RE: FISCAL 1413 STOP SINCERELY DADDY"
BILL FOR...?
GIVE ME THAT!!
WHAT'S IT SAY?
"OUTSTANDING LOANS TO MILITARY GOVERNMENT OF LOWER FELDA.....689 MILLION CROWNS INTEREST PAYMENT OF 38 MILLION CROWNS DUE WITHIN 30 DAYS..."
DOES IT SAY ANYTHING ELSE?
HE ALSO SENT YOU A BOX OF CIGARS AND AN INVITATION TO THE FESTIVAL OF PETUNIAS
"NO CHEQUES PLEASE"

SO...!
LORD JULIUS THINKS I'M GOING TO ASSUME LOWER FELDA'S DEBTS JUST BECAUSE I'VE CAPTURED IT...
WELL, HE HAS A SURPRISE COMING AT NEXT WEEK'S SUMMIT...

HE'LL FIND THAT CEREBUS THE AARDVARK, THE EARTH-PIG BORN, PRIME MINISTER OF THE CITY-STATE OF IEST IS NOBODY'S...
bang!

...FOOL.

CEREBUS' SIX CRISES crisis number two

"A NIGHT in IEST"

OR

"SUMMIT ENCHANTED EVENING"

I'D LIKE TO WELCOME ALL THREE OF US TO THE FIFTH ANNUAL TRILATERAL SUMMIT AND BAKE-OFF AND I'D LIKE TO INTRODUCE OUR HOST FOR THIS EVENING...

PRIME MINISTER CEREBUS OF THE CITY-STATE OF IEST...

I'M THE FAST-TALKING SMOOTHIE FROM OVER THE MOUNTAINS AND THROUGH THE WOODS

AND THE WALKING EXAMPLE OF WHY COUSINS SHOULDN'T MARRY TO MY LEFT IS *DUKE LEONARDI* OF *NEW SEPRA*

WE WANT A GOOD CLEAN FIGHT. NO PINCHING NO KICKING NO GOUGING. ALL SALES ARE FINAL AND REMEMBER I'M NOT MAKING A HALF-CROWN ON THE DEAL

AS THE PERSON WHO HAD TO COME THE FARTHEST OVER THE WORST ROADS, I HAVE ELECTED TO THROW OUT THE FIRST ORDER OF BUSINESS

THE SECOND ORDER OF BUSINESS CONCERNS THE DIVISION OF CONQUERED TERRITORY IN ORDER TO MAINTAIN A BALANCE OF POWER IN THE FELD RIVER VALLEY AND TO KEEP CERTAIN SHORT AND GREY INDIVIDUALS FROM GETTING TOO BIG FOR MY BRITCHES ...
I THINK YOU BURNING YOU BRITCHES BEHIND YOU ...
LUCKILY, I HAVE A MAP OF LOWER FELDA RIGHT HERE...
IT LOOKSA LIKE A FAT TURKEY ...
RIGHT. THAT'S WHY I'M GOING TO CARVE IT UP...
WE'LL DIVIDE IT DOWN HERE AND HERE...
I'LL TAKE THE WEST, YOU TAKE THE MIDDLE, AND JUNIOR HERE CAN HAVE EVERYTHING ON THIS SIDE OF THE VIADUCT...
SHO'
ATSA FINE...
DON'T ASK ME WHY, BUT I WAS SURE HE WAS GOING TO SAY SOME-THING ELSE JUST THEN ...
I WANT MORE LAND ...
HOW D'YA LIKE THAT? HE CAN'T PAY THE INTEREST ON WHAT HE'S GOT, AND HE WANTS MORE!
'AT'S OKAY! I NO PAY MY RENT IN FINE MONTHS, AND I WANT MORE
HAVEN'T PAID YOUR RENT? WHO'S YOUR LANDLORD?
YOU ARE.
WELL, THAT EXPLAINS IT...

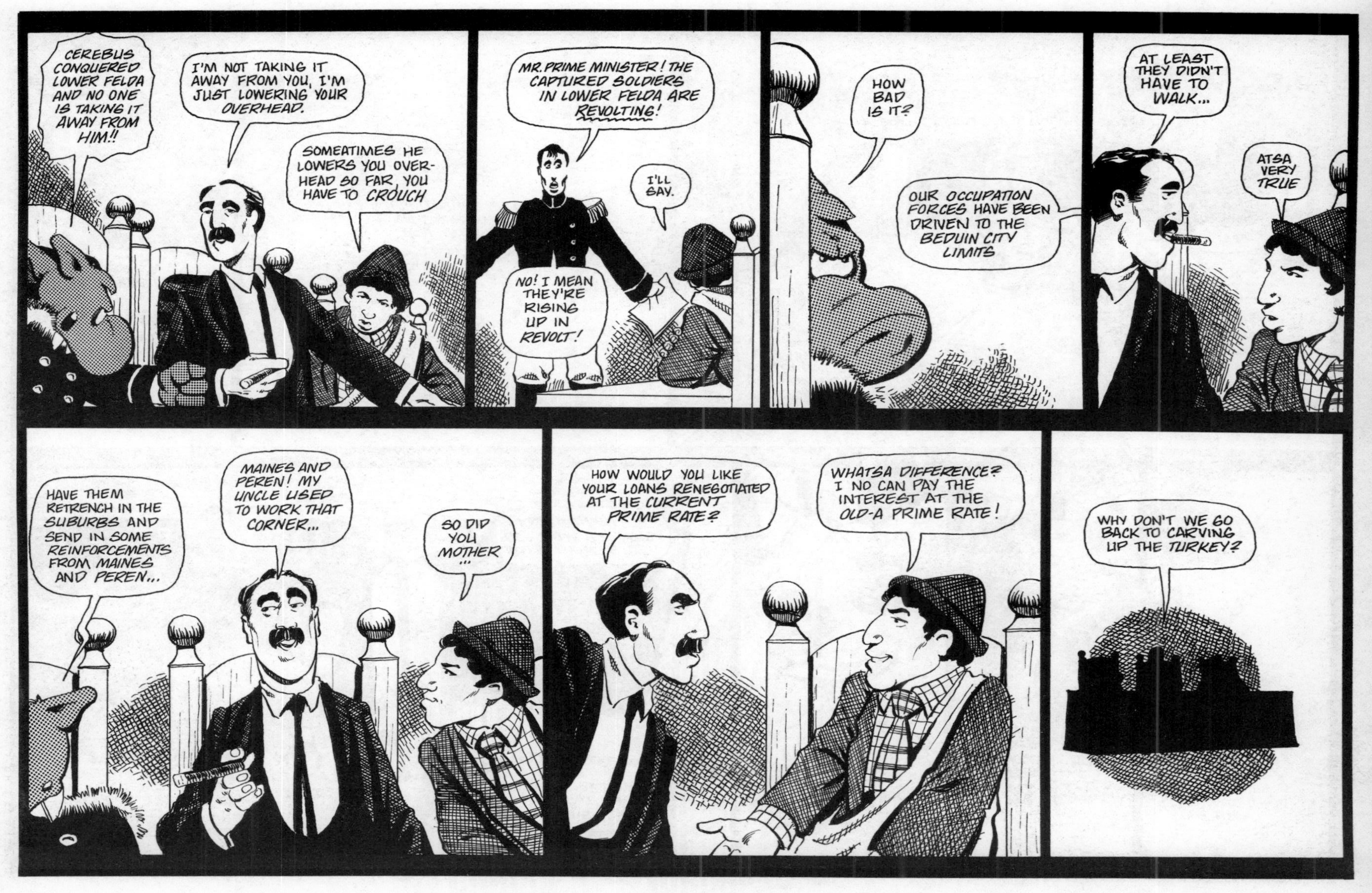
CEREBUS CONQUERED LOWER FELDA AND NO ONE IS TAKING IT AWAY FROM HIM!!
I'M NOT TAKING IT AWAY FROM YOU, I'M JUST LOWERING YOUR OVERHEAD.
SOMEATIMES HE LOWERS YOU OVER-HEAD SO FAR, YOU HAVE TO CROUCH
MR. PRIME MINISTER! THE CAPTURED SOLDIERS IN LOWER FELDA ARE REVOLTING!
I'LL SAY.
NO! I MEAN THEY'RE RISING UP IN REVOLT!
HOW BAD IS IT?
OUR OCCUPATION FORCES HAVE BEEN DRIVEN TO THE BEDUIN CITY LIMITS
AT LEAST THEY DIDN'T HAVE TO WALK...
ATSA VERY TRUE
HAVE THEM RETRENCH IN THE SUBURBS AND SEND IN SOME REINFORCEMENTS FROM MAINES AND PEREN...
MAINES AND PEREN! MY UNCLE USED TO WORK THAT CORNER...
SO DID YOU MOTHER ...
HOW WOULD YOU LIKE YOUR LOANS RENEGOTIATED AT THE CURRENT PRIME RATE?
WHATSA DIFFERENCE? I NO CAN PAY THE INTEREST AT THE OLD-A PRIME RATE!
WHY DON'T WE GO BACK TO CARVING UP THE TURKEY?

THE FELDANS ARE IN REVOLT IN YOUR TERRITORY, SO CEREBUS WILL TAKE THE WEST LIKE YOU SAID...
YOU TAKE THE WEST? NO, YOU TAKE THE EAST-- I GET THE WEST...
ALL I KNOW IS I GET BOTH BREASTS AND A THIGH...
I WOULDN'T TOUCH A STRAIGHT LINE LIKE THAT FOR A WEEKEND IN UNSHIB...
BIG DEAL.
I WOULDN'T TRADE A TOOTHACHE FOR A WEEKEND IN UNSHIB...
OH? HAVE YOU GOT A TOOTHACHE?
'AT DEPENDS.
DEPENDS ON WHAT?
ON WHETHER YOU CAN CHARGE A-ME INTEREST ON IT
...
OKAY -- I HAVE ANOTHER IDEA...
HOW ABOUT IF WE CARVE IT HORIZONTALLY INSTEAD OF VERTICALLY?
...
I'LL TAKE THE RIVER SECTION JUNIOR GETS THE MIDDLE SECTION AND YOU GET THE TOP SECTION...
'ATSA NO GOOD
WHY NOT?
YOU GET A RIVER AN' A HALF A CITY, HE GETS A MOUNTAIN PASS AN' A HALF A CITY AN' ALL I GET IS A LOTTA MOUNTAINS...

WHAT'S WRONG WITH THAT?
WHAT IF THERE'S AN AVALANCHE? ...
YOU KNOW WHAT THEY SAY-- AVALANCHE IS BETTER THAN NO LANCHE AT ALL
I NO THINK SO...
CEREBUS HAS CONTROL OF THE WHOLE COUNTRY...
NO DEALS.
MR. PRIME MINISTER!
OUR FORCES HAVE BEEN DRIVEN OUT OF THE SUBURBS!
YOU MUST SPEND A FORTUNE IN CABFARE...
HAVE THEM MEET THE REINFORCEMENTS IN THE MOUNTAIN PASS, THEN MARCH BACK INTO THE CITY... WE HAVE TO NIP THIS REBELLION IN THE BUD...
THAT SOUNDS LIKE A GOOD WAY TO GET RABIES ...
I GOT NIPPED IN THE BUD ONCE
I WAS IN BED FOR TWO WEEKS.
I'M TRYING TO DECIDE THE FUTURE SHAPE OF ESTARCION AND ALL HE WANTS TO DO IS DISCUSS HIS LOVE LIFE...

LOOK!...
THIS IS SUPPOSED TO BE A SUMMIT AND SO FAR ALL WE'VE TALKED ABOUT IS HOW TO DIVIDE CEREBUS' TERRITORY
WELL, WHAT DO YOU WANT TO TALK ABOUT?
HOW ABOUT INTEREST RATES?
HEY!
YEAH!
ATSA GOOD ONE!
OKAY.
LET'S TALK ABOUT INTEREST RATES ...
I THINK THEY'RE TOO HIGH!
ME TOO!
NOW THAT THAT'S OVER WITH ...
WAIT-A JUST A MINUTE! HE SAY HE THINK THE INTEREST RATE IS A TOO HIGH
I SAY I THINK THE INTEREST RATE IS A TOO HIGH...
ATSA MAJORITY!
IT CERTAINLY IS...
NOW ABOUT THIS TURKEY ...
I THINK THE INTEREST RATE SHOULD-A BE ...
... OH...

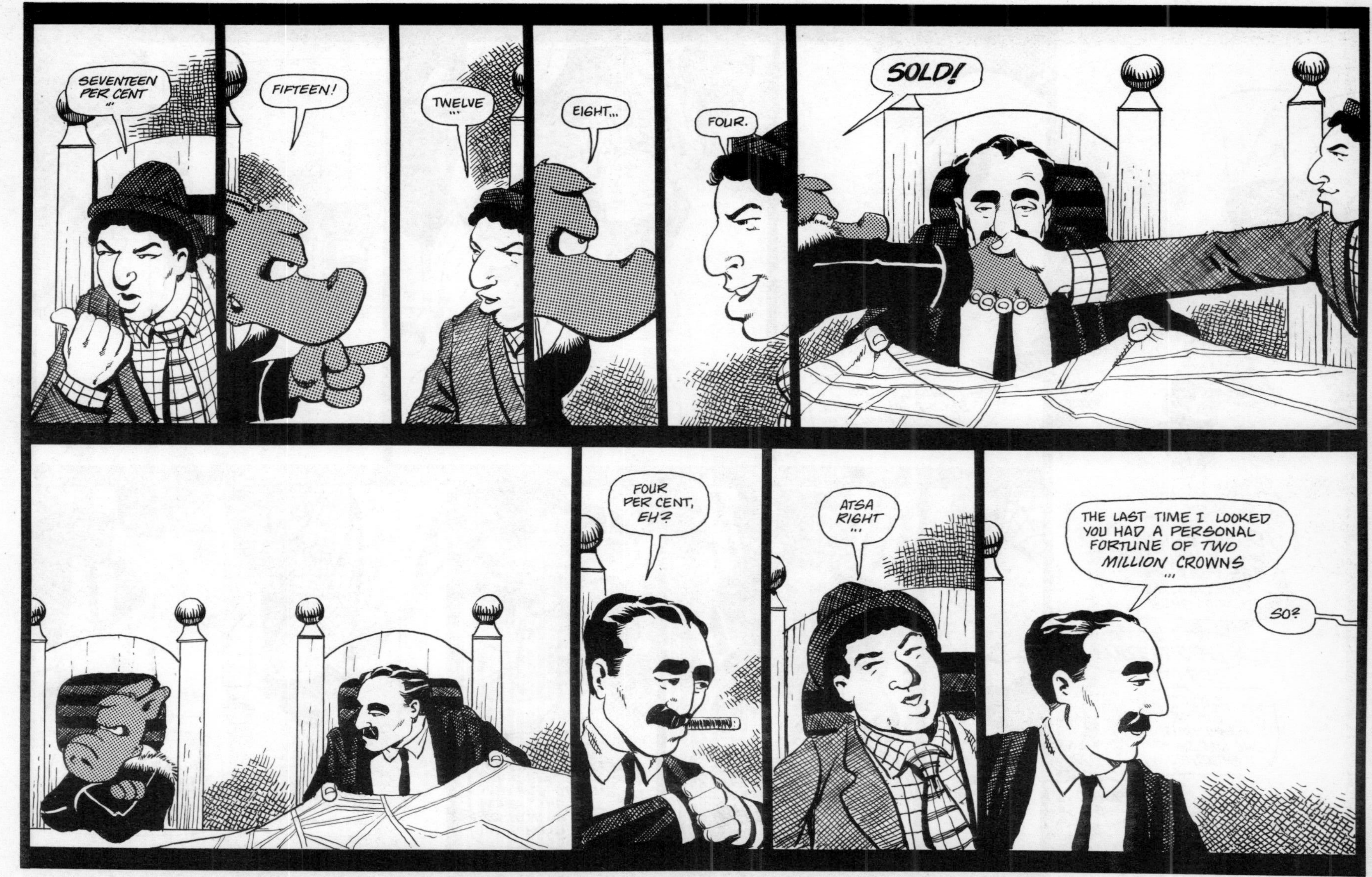
SEVENTEEN PER CENT ...
FIFTEEN!
TWELVE ...
EIGHT...
FOUR.
SOLD!
FOUR PER CENT, EH?
ATSA RIGHT ...
THE LAST TIME I LOOKED YOU HAD A PERSONAL FORTUNE OF TWO MILLION CROWNS ...
SO?

SO, HERE'S A BANK DRAUGHT FOR EIGHT THOUSAND CROWNS... I WANT TO BORROW ALL OF YOUR MONEY FOR A YEAR...
I'LL HAVE TO CHECK... I THINK MY MONEY IS BUSY THIS YEAR...
THAT'S PRETTY CLEVER... BORROW ALL HIS MONEY... THE FACT REMAINS THAT WE CAN'T AFFORD TO PAY YOUR INTEREST RATES!!
CEREBUS HAS DONE EVERYTHING HE CAN... HE EVEN CONQUERED A COUNTRY AND THEY OWE YOU MORE MONEY THAN CEREBUS DOES... THAT'S IT! CEREBUS GIVES UP!
CAN HE DO THAT?
OF COURSE!
CEREBUS CAN'T PAY THE INTEREST ON HIS LOANS!!
FORECLOSE!
TAKE THE COUNTRY AWAY! YOU'RE SO SMART, LET'S SEE YOU TURN A PROFIT ON THIS MESS!
I THINK HE'S SERIOUS, BOSS.
OF ALL THE UNGRATEFUL SWINE! WHO OFFERED TO STRETCH HIS PAYMENTS OUT OVER TWENTY FIVE YEARS?
I GIVE UP. WHO?
IS IT MY FAULT YOU PICKED THE WRONG COUNTRY TO INVADE?

DID YOU WRITE? WOULD IT HAVE KILLED YOU TO SEND A POSTCARD?
"DEAR DAD: THINKING OF A MILITARY ADVENTURE... KNOW ANY GOOD COUNTRIES? LOVE, JUNIOR"
IT'S A TERRIBLE THING WHEN A SON AND A FATHER DON'T COMMUNICATE
IT'S NOT ME I'M WORRIED ABOUT... IT'S YOUR POOR MOTHER...
PINING AWAY HER TWILIGHT YEARS...
IT'S A TERRIBLE THING WHEN A MOTHER SPENDS HER OLD AGE IN A PINE TREE
IT'S ALSO A TERRIBLE THING WHEN A WORLD LEADER ISN'T AS SMART AS A PINE TREE...
ATSA TRUE
WHAT DO YOU MEAN "INVADED THE WRONG COUNTRY"?
I SUPPOSE YOU HAD A BETTER CHOICE?!
THE EW-NAY EPRANS-SAY ARE ORE-MAY ULNERABLE -VAY

ULNERABLE-VAY?
ERY-VAY
ICH-RAY?
ILTHY-FAY
UPID-STAY, OO-TAY?
EXCUSE US -- WHEN WE GET TOGETHER WE LIKE TO TALK OVER OLD TIMES IN AN ANCIENT BOREALAN DIALECT...
ATSA FINE. DON'T MIND A-ME...
ULNERABLE-VAY, ICH-RAY AND UPID-STAY ...
YOU HAVE TO ADMIT IT'S AN ATTRACTIVE COMBINATION ...

THEY'VE BEEN WAITING FOR AN HOUR FOR YOU TO BRIEF THEM ON THE SUMMIT RESULTS
NOT NOW, ASTORIA! CEREBUS HAS PLANS HE HAS TO CHANGE IN THE WAR ROOM!
FINE, I'LL JUST TELL THEM THAT YOU'RE TOO BUSY TO SEE THEM ...
THEY'RE APT TO BE UPSET SINCE YOU'VE POSTPONED MEETING WITH THEM EIGHT TIMES SINCE THE ELECTION...
NOT TO MENTION THE FACT THAT THEY'RE YOUR ONLY ALLIES IN THE WHOLE BUREAUCRACY
I'LL JUST TELL THEM YOU'RE TOO BUSY TO SPARE AN HOUR TO BRIEF THEM ON THE FUTURE OF THEIR CITY-STATE AND...
OKAY! OKAY!!
CEREBUS SHOULD HAVE ABOLISHED CABINET MEETINGS WHEN HE DISSOLVED THE LEGISLATURE
MR. PRIME MINISTER... NOW THAT YOU HAVE MET WITH LORD JULIUS, WE WOULD VERY MUCH LIKE TO KNOW WHEN IESTANS CAN EXPECT AN ECONOMIC RECOVERY
THE DAY AFTER TOMORROW ...
I TOLD YOU WE SHOULD'VE HAD MORE QUESTIONS PREPARED...

THE BIGGEST PROBLEM WILL BE MOVING THE MERCENARIES THROUGH IEST
SECRECY WILL BE THE KEY, OF COURSE...
NO ONE WILL KNOW THEIR DESTINATION EXCEPT YOU, ME AND...
I'M SORRY--I SEEM TO HAVE INTERRUPTED SOMETHING...
I AM FATHER GESOLDE ... I AM AN OFFICIAL REPRESENTATIVE OF HIS HOLINESS' SACRED EMPIRE OF SEPRA...
I HAVE BEEN ASKED TO DELIVER A MESSAGE FROM HIS HOLINESS
IT IS TO BE READ ONLY IN THE PRESENCE OF THE ESTEEMED PRIME MINISTER...
OR, FAILING THAT, ONLY IN THE COMPANY OF THOSE WHOSE IGNORANCE WOULD PRECLUDE COMPREHENSION...
HUH?
MOST REASSURING ...

HIS HOLINESS WRITES AS FOLLOWS: "MY DEAR PRIME MINISTER, SINCE THE EXODUS INWARD OF OUR EASTERN BRETHREN IS NOW A REALITY, THE ALBATROSS BECOMES OF PARAMOUNT IMPORTANCE TO US BOTH..."
"WE PROPOSE, THEREFORE, THAT A PACT OF NON-AGGRESSION BE STRUCK, TO PREVENT THE UNLEASHING OF CHAOTIC FORCES SURE TO RESULT FROM ONE OR THE OTHER OF US SEEKING TO BECOME PREEMINENT..."
"WE HASTEN TO ADD THAT YOUR MILITARY SUCCESSES IN THE CULT-RIDDEN FELDWAR VALLEY HAVE PLEASED US GREATLY..."
"IT IS OUR FERVENT WISH THAT THE TRUE BELIEVERS AND FOLLOWERS OF THE SACRED TEXTS SHALL KEEP FOREVER AT BAY THE FORCES OF IGNORANCE AND BARBARISM..."
I AM INSTRUCTED TO AWAIT A REPLY...
MR. PRIME MINISTER?
UH...
TELL HIS HOLINESS THAT WE ARE PLEASED BY HIS EXPRESSIONS OF GOOD-WILL
AND TELL HIM WE ARE EQUALLY PLEASED TO FIND IMPLICIT IN HIS MESSAGE AN ADMISSION THAT HE DOES NOT POSSESS THE ALBATROSS...
TELL HIM ALSO THAT HE CAN REST ASSURED THAT HE WILL BE THE FIRST TO KNOW, SHOULD THE STATUE FIND ITS WAY TO THE CITY-STATE OF IEST...
HIS HOLINESS IS APT TO FIND YOUR ANSWER... AMBIGUOUS
YOU CAN TELL HIS HOLINESS THAT CEREBUS HAS FOUND AMBIGUITY TO BE THE VERY CORNERSTONE OF A SUCCESSFUL FOREIGN POLICY...
AS YOU WISH, MR. PRIME MINISTER ...

WHO'S THE HIGHEST RANKING CHURCH OFFICIAL NOT INVOLVED IN THE EXODUS INWARD?
MM?
THERE'RE A COUPLE OF BISHOPS LEFT IN THE LOWER CITY...
WHY?
CEREBUS HAS A COUPLE OF QUESTIONS FOR THEM ...
THEY'RE NOT KNOWN FOR BEING ENTHUSIASTIC CONVERSATIONALISTS ...
TRUE...
CEREBUS NEEDS SOMETHING THAT WILL MAKE THEM A LITTLE MORE ...
...TALKATIVE.

THIS RILLY IS EXC'LENT FRUIT PUNCH
WUDDID Y'SAY WUZZINIT?
OH... A LITTLE NUTMEG
A PINCH OF CINNAMON
SOME ORANGE PEEL ...
THAT MUS' BE IT
ORNCHES ALLUS MAKE ME DROWZEE ......
I SUPPOSE YOUR REVERENCES HAVE HEARD THE NEWS FROM SERREA? ...
NOOZE?!
NOOZE?!
IT SEEMS THAT HIS HOLINESS HAS FOUND A STATUE OF A WHITE BIRD ...
OH NO...!
THIS'S TERRBLE J'S TERRBLE
IS IT?
DEFIDENTLY!! MEANS HE C'N UNITE THE EAS'ERN 'N' WES'ERN CHURSHES UNNER HIS RULE!
F'REVER 'N' EVER 'N' EVER 'N' HIC EVER

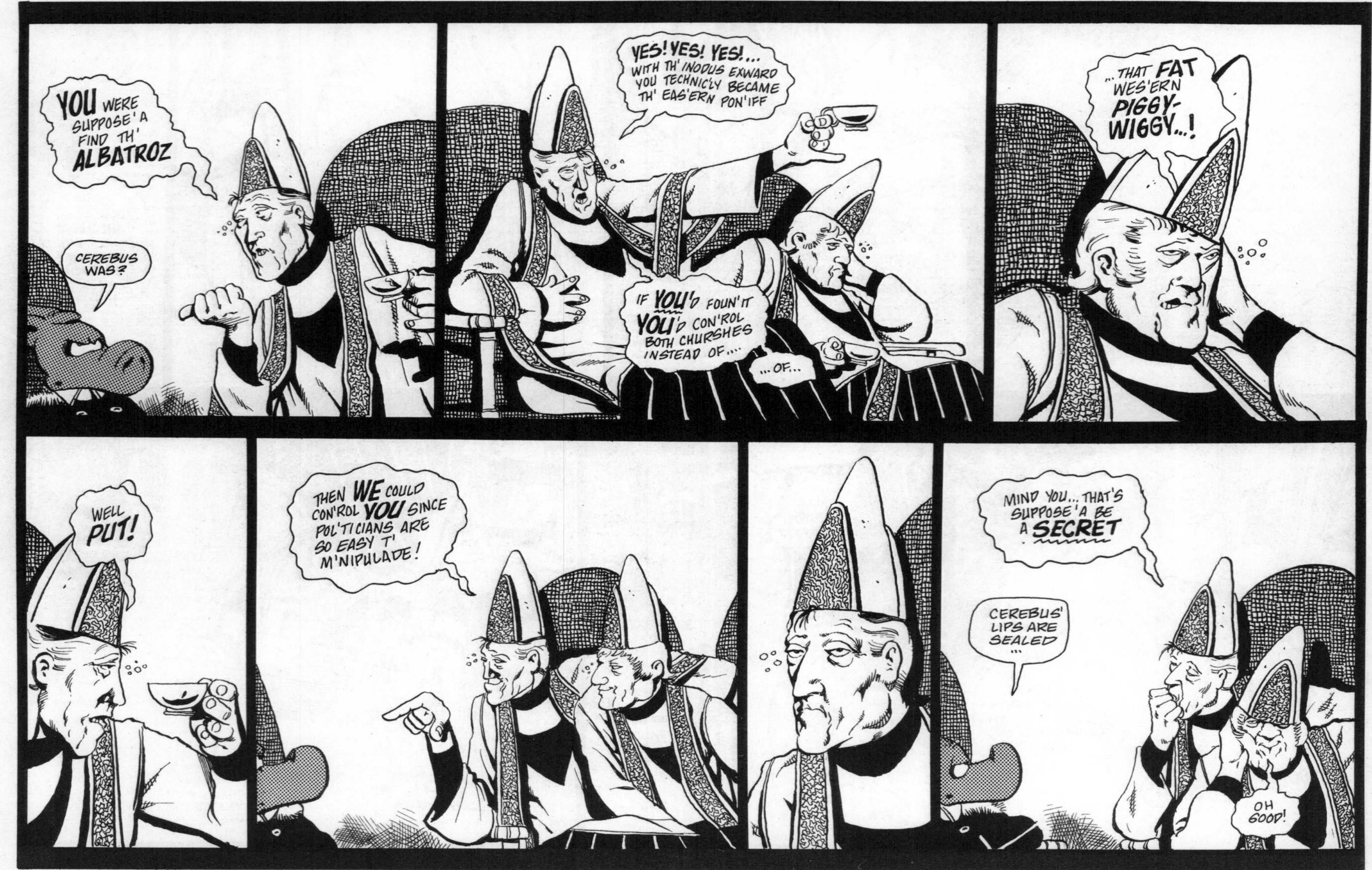
YOU WERE SUPPOSE'A FIND TH' ALBATROZ
CEREBUS WAS?
YES! YES! YES!... WITH TH' INODUS EXWARD YOU TECHNIC'LY BECAME TH' EAS'ERN PON'IFF
IF YOU'D FOUN' IT YOU'D CON'ROL BOTH CHURSHES INSTEAD OF....
...OF...
...THAT FAT WES'ERN PIGGY-WIGGY...!
WELL PUT!
THEN WE COULD CON'ROL YOU SINCE POL'TICIANS ARE SO EASY T' M'NIPULADE!
MIND YOU... THAT'S SUPPOSE'A BE A SECRET
CEREBUS' LIPS ARE SEALED ...
OH GOOD!

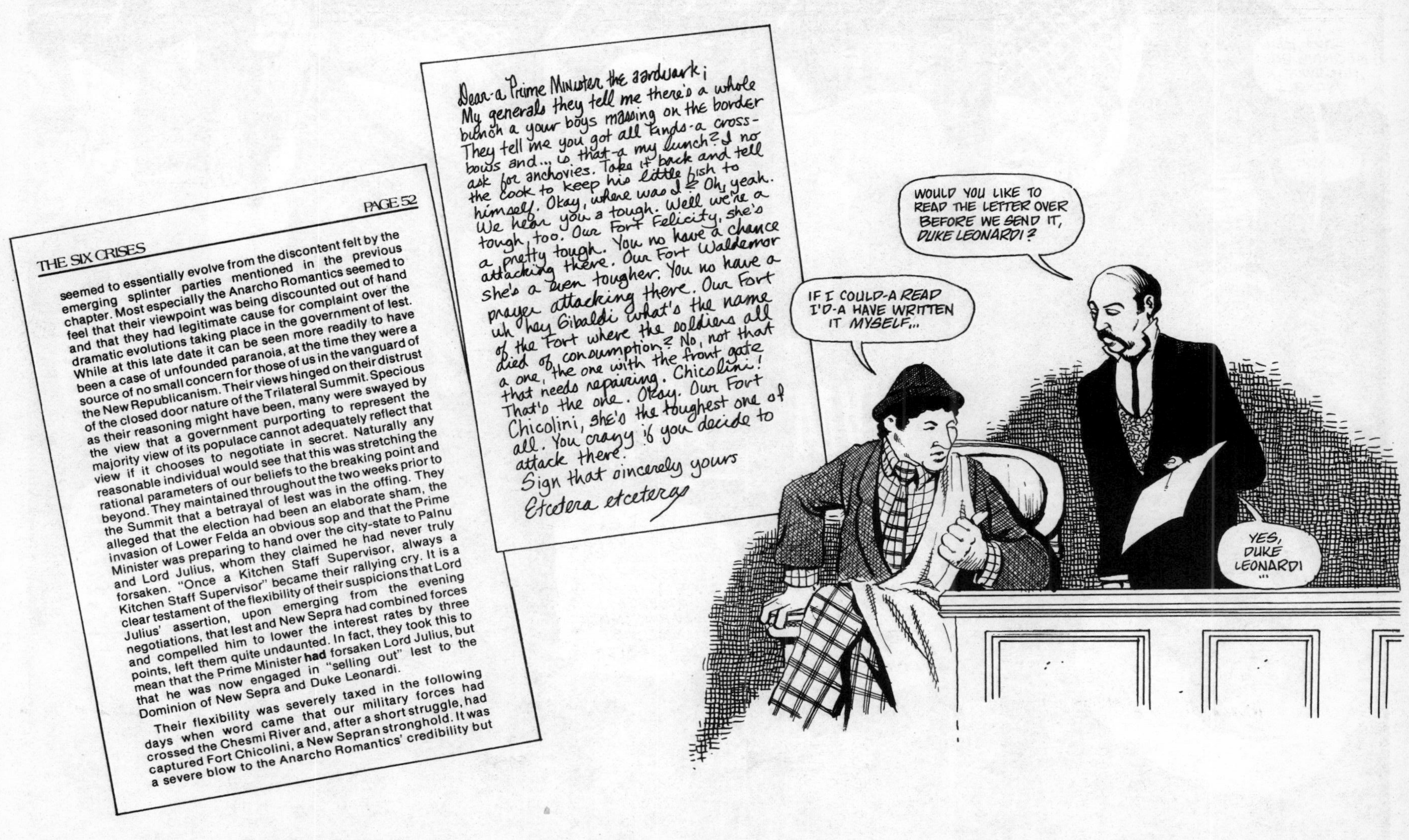

THE SIX CRISES PAGE 52

seemed to essentially evolve from the discontent felt by the emerging splinter parties mentioned in the previous chapter. Most especially the Anarcho Romantics seemed to feel that their viewpoint was being discounted out of hand and that they had legitimate cause for complaint over the dramatic evolutions taking place in the government of lest. While at this late date it can be seen more readily to have been a case of unfounded paranoia, at the time they were a source of no small concern for those of us in the vanguard of the New Republicanism. Their views hinged on their distrust of the closed door nature of the Trilateral Summit. Specious as their reasoning might have been, many were swayed by the view that a government purporting to represent the majority view of its populace cannot adequately reflect that view if it chooses to negotiate in secret. Naturally any reasonable individual would see that this was stretching the rational parameters of our beliefs to the breaking point and beyond. They maintained throughout the two weeks prior to the Summit that a betrayal of lest was in the offing. They alleged that the election had been an elaborate sham, the invasion of Lower Felda an obvious sop and that the Prime Minister was preparing to hand over the city-state to Palnu and Lord Julius, whom they claimed he had never truly forsaken. "Once a Kitchen Staff Supervisor, always a Kitchen Staff Supervisor" became their rallying cry. It is a clear testament of the flexibility of their suspicions that Lord Julius' assertion, upon emerging from the evening negotiations, that lest and New Sepra had combined forces and compelled him to lower the interest rates by three points, left them quite undaunted. In fact, they took this to mean that the Prime Minister **had** forsaken Lord Julius, but that he was now engaged in "selling out" lest to the Dominion of New Sepra and Duke Leonardi.

Their flexibility was severely taxed in the following days when word came that our military forces had crossed the Chesmi River and, after a short struggle, had captured Fort Chicolini, a New Sepran stronghold. It was a severe blow to the Anarcho Romantics' credibility but

Dear-a Prime Minister the aardvark;
My generals they tell me there's a whole bunch a your boys massing on the border. They tell me you got all kinds-a cross-bows and... is that-a my lunch? I no ask for anchovies. Take it back and tell the cook to keep his little fish to himself. Okay, where was I? Oh, yeah. We hear you a tough. Well we're a tough, too. Our Fort Felicity, she's a pretty tough. You no have a chance attacking there. Our Fort Waldemor she's a even tougher. You no have a prayer attacking there. Our Fort uh hey Gibaldi what's the name of the Fort where the soldiers all died of consumption? No, not that a one, the one with the front gate that needs repairing. Chicolini! That's the one. Okay. Our Fort Chicolini, she's the toughest one of all. You crazy if you decide to attack there.
Sign that sincerely yours
Etcetera etcetera

IF THE BLIZZARD HOLDS FOR ANOTHER WEEK, IT'S GOING TO COST CEREBUS TWENTY THOUSAND CROWNS IN PROVISIONS ALONE. IN THE MEANTIME, THE NEW SEPRANS HAVE TIME TO REINFORCE THEIR POSITIONS...
AND OUR MERCENARIES ARE STILL EIGHTY MILES FROM THE MOUNT SEPREA TREASURY. IF THE STORM BREAKS ANY TIME IN THE NEXT THREE...
STAND WHAR YER AT, Y'BIG FURRY VARMINT... AH'M DIRTY FLEAGLE McGREW--PERSONAL TYPE BODYGUARD T'HIS IMPOVERISHEDNESS--THE PRIME MINISTER O'
WAM
THAT WUZ A LUCKY PUNCH, Y'FLEA BITTEN, SLOPEY-BROWED GALOOT... BUT WHAR DIRTY FLEAGLE GOT SUCKERED, HIS BABY BROTHER DIRTY DREW IS-A GONNA...
WAM
IT'S MY ISSHURIAN CAVALRY COMMANDER ...
...ARNOLD.
HOWDY.
I BRUNG Y'SOMETHIN' WE FOUND IN TH' FORT...

THE WINTER PAYROLL FOR THE ENTIRE NEW SEPRAN ARMY...
I THOUGHT IT MIGHT COME IN HANDY...
THERE MUST BE...
...THREE...
...FOUR MILLION CROWNS IN NEW SEPRAN CURRENCY IN HERE
THREE MILLION SIX HUNDRED AND EIGHTY-FIVE THOUSAND TWO HUNDRED AND SIXTY-ONE.
CEREBUS SHOULD FIRE ALL HIS ACCOUNTANTS AND HIRE A MERCENARY TO KEEP TRACK OF HIS CASH...

THEY KEPT ALL OF THIS IN THEIR MOST VULNERABLE FORT?
UH-HUH. IN A ROOM MARKED "KEEP OUT SECRET PAYROLL ROOM"
UPID-STAY OR-FAY URE-SHAY ...
HUH?
NOTHING.
next: cerebus' two-front war

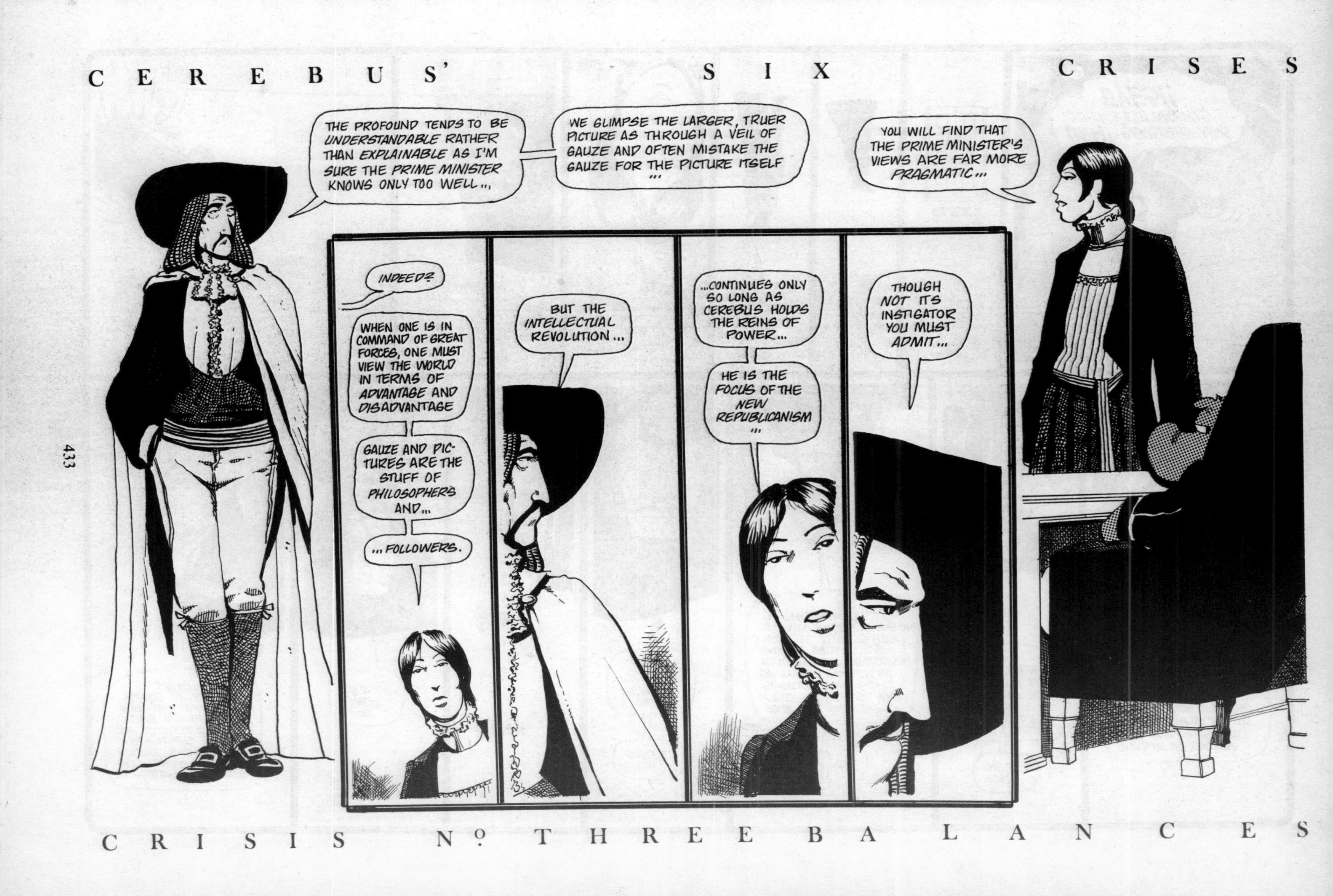

CRISIS Nº THREE BALANCES

IT COULD BE ARGUED THAT TARIM DIDN'T INSTIGATE THE TARIMIC DISCIPLINES SINCE THE SACRED TEXTS WERE NOT SET DOWN FOR ONE HUNDRED YEARS AFTER HIS DEATH...
...OR HER DEATH?
I'M SORRY.
I DIDN'T MEAN TO PROVOKE YOU...
DON'T WORRY. YOU DIDN'T.
YOUR JOB WILL BE TO WRITE SPEECHES, MANIFESTOS... THAT SORT OF THING. BASICALLY TO KEEP THE REVOLUTION UNITED WITH THIS OFFICE... AND TO HEAD OFF ANY MAJOR DIVISIONS IN THE PARTY...
VERY WELL...
BUT I WARN YOU THAT I DON'T INTEND TO BETRAY MY PRINCIPLES ...
HAD WE INTENDED FOR YOU TO BETRAY YOUR PRINCIPLES, WE WOULD HAVE OFFERED YOU A GOOD DEAL MORE THAN TWENTY CROWNS A WEEK...
WAIT OUTSIDE. I'LL SHOW YOU TO YOUR OFFICE...
I'LL TAKE MY LEAVE, THEN...
...MR. PRIME...
...MINISTER?
HE'S ...uh... MEDITATING ...
I SEE.
CLICK.
WAP
UNH! CEREBUS WAS JUST RESTING HIS EYES!!

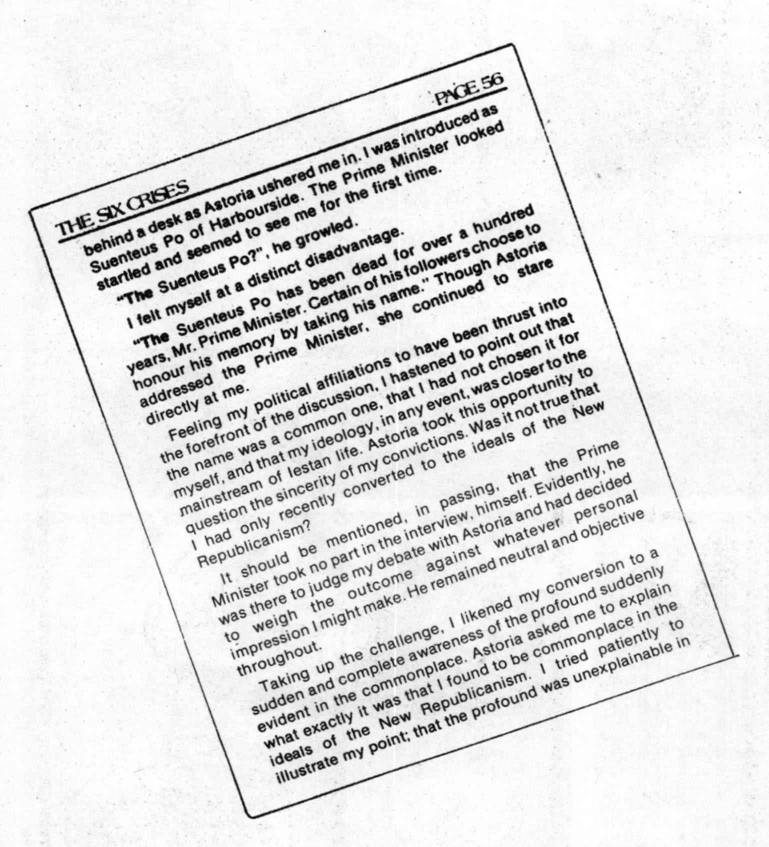

THE SIX CRISES PAGE 56

behind a desk as Astoria ushered me in. I was introduced as Suenteus Po of Harbourside. The Prime Minister looked startled and seemed to see me for the first time.

"The Suenteus Po?", he growled.

I felt myself at a distinct disadvantage.

"The Suenteus Po has been dead for over a hundred years, Mr. Prime Minister. Certain of his followers choose to honour his memory by taking his name." Though Astoria addressed the Prime Minister, she continued to stare directly at me.

Feeling my political affiliations to have been thrust into the forefront of the discussion, I hastened to point out that the name was a common one, that I had not chosen it for myself, and that my ideology, in any event, was closer to the mainstream of Iestan life. Astoria took this opportunity to question the sincerity of my convictions. Was it not true that I had only recently converted to the ideals of the New Republicanism?

It should be mentioned, in passing, that the Prime Minister took no part in the interview, himself. Evidently, he was there to judge my debate with Astoria and had decided to weigh the outcome against whatever personal impression I might make. He remained neutral and objective throughout.

Taking up the challenge, I likened my conversion to a sudden and complete awareness of the profound suddenly evident in the commonplace. Astoria asked me to explain what exactly it was that I found to be commonplace in the ideals of the New Republicanism. I tried patiently to illustrate my point; that the profound was unexplainable in

I SAY IT'S TIME FOR A SHOW OF FORCE ...
OTHERWISE, HE'LL RUN RIGHT OVER US...
DON'T BE STUPID.
SO HE RAISED TAXES... EVERY PRIME MINISTER RAISES TAXES...

THE DOOR BUCKLES INWARD WITH THE SOUND OF SPLINTERING WOOD
SMASH!!
"I'M SERGEANT PRESTON OF THE NORTHERN IESTAN MOUNTED POLICE" HE ANNOUNCES...
"I DON'T HAVE THE AUTHORITY TO ARREST YOU..."

"SO I'M JUST GOING TO ROUGH YOU UP A BIT, INSTEAD!"

"LOUSY STINKING RADICALS," HE OPINES, "FIGURE THE LAW IS THERE FOR YOU TO HIDE BEHIND..."
"WELL, THE LAW ISN'T THERE FOR YOU TO HIDE BEHIND-- IT'S THERE FOR US TO HIDE BEHIND..."
"THE GOOD AND DECENT LAW-ABIDING PEOPLE OF THIS GREAT CITY-STATE"
HIS FISTS ARE LIKE TWIN SLEDGEHAMMERS DEALING OUT PURE AND RIGHTEOUS JUSTICE...
"YOU'RE EITHER WITH US OR AGAINST US, VERMIN..."
"THAT'S WHAT FREEDOM'S ALL ABOUT"

HIS ROACH-SENSE FLOODS THE ROOM...
PING!
PING!
PING!
AND DETECTS THE PRESENCE OF A HEAVILY UNARMED MALCONTENT...
"TASTE BOOT, SCUM..."

LIKE ALL COWARDLY VERMIN SCUM SLIME RAT PUKE, THEY HAVE THE "COURAGE" TO WRITE ABOUT REVOLUTION, BUT WHEN IT COMES DOWN TO DUKING IT OUT... MAN TO MAN... GOOD VERSUS EVIL ...
HE SEIZES THEIR CRAVEN LEADER BY THE TONSILS...
GULK!

AND TOSSES HIM AT ONE OF HIS HALF-WITTED DUPES...

THE FINAL MISCREANT FALLS ...
ONCE MORE HAS BRUTE FORCE AND GOODNESS WON OUT...
OVER WEAKNESS AND EVIL! HSSS!

"THE WEED OF REVOLUTION BEARS BITTER FRUIT"
THE MOON ROACH KNOWS ...
HSSSS!
WEEDS AREN'T FRUIT-BEARING ARE THEY?
SHHH...
DON'T PROVOKE HIM...

THERE'S A CHANCE THAT LOWER FELDA IS JUST MAKING A WHOLE LOTTA NOISE ABOUT ...
MR. PRIME MINISTER? THERE'S A "MISTER THE ISSHURIAN" HERE TO SEE YOU...
HAVE HIM COME RIGHT IN...

WE CAPTURED THE NEW SEPRAN TREASURY ...
AND...?
EMPTY. THEY'VE MOVED ALL THEIR MONEY BACK TO THEIR RED MARCHES OUTPOST...
SO HOW MUCH IS IT GOING TO COST CEREBUS TO HAVE YOUR MEN GO AND GET IT?
MMM.
ROUGHLY.
ROUGHLY? I'D SAY...ohhh...
THREE MILLION SIX HUNDRED AND EIGHTY FIVE THOUSAND TWO HUNDRED AND SIXTY NEW SEPRAN CROWNS
CEREBUS THOUGHT IT WAS THREE MILLION SIX HUNDRED AND EIGHTY-FIVE THOUSAND TWO HUNDRED AND SIXTY ONE...
YOU SAID "ROUGHLY."
MR. PRIME MINISTER...THIS URGENT MESSAGE JUST CAME IN FROM PALNU...
RIP!
WONDERFUL.
WHAT'S IT SAY?

"IN LIGHT OF THE FACT THAT THE GOVERNMENTS OF ESTARCION HAVE BASED THE MARKET VALUE OF THE NEW SEPRAN CROWN ON THE ABILITY OF THE NEW SEPRAN MILITARY FORCES TO HOLD THE BORDERS OF THE DOMINION OF NEW SEPRA SECURE AND UNBREECHED, AND IN LIGHT OF SAID BORDERS BEING VIOLATED WITH DECIDED EASE IN RECENT DAYS BY FORCES UNKNOWN, WE, THE UNDER-SIGNED, HEREBY SERVE NOTICE OF THE IMMEDIATE DEVALUATION OF THE NEW SEPRAN CROWN TO ONE-ONE HUNDREDTH OF ITS CURRENT MARKET VALUE..."

"FORCES UNKNOWN"?
CAPTAIN ARNOLD AND HIS ARMPIT AVENGERS ARE "FORCES UNKNOWN"?

SO WHAT KIND OF MILITARY ACTION CAN CEREBUS GET FOR THIRTY-SIX THOUSAND EIGHT HUNDRED AND FIFTY TWO NEWER SEPRAN CROWNS...
A GOOD SNOW-BALL FIGHT IF THEY TRY TO RECAPTURE FORT CHICOLINI...

HAVE YOUR MEN SIT TIGHT.... CEREBUS WILL GET BACK TO YOU...
OKEY-DOKEY

THE WAY CEREBUS FIGURES IT, LORD JULIUS IS BEHIND THE DEVALUATION -- HE WANTS CEREBUS TO STOP GOING AFTER THE NEW SEPRAN TREASURY ...
HE FIGURES CEREBUS WILL GIVE UP INSTEAD OF GOING AFTER A TREASURY FULL OF DEVALUED CURRENCY...
WHICH MEANS THE TREASURY PROBABLY CONTAINS FOREIGN CURRENCY AND GOLD OR ENOUGH DEVALUED CURRENCY SO THAT EVEN AT REDUCED VALUE IT'S STILL WORTH A KING'S RANSOM!...
IF THAT'S TRUE, WHY DID LORD JULIUS TELL YOU NEW SEPRA WAS RICH AND VULNERABLE?
RIGHT. RIGHT.
AH! BUT! WHAT IF THAT WAS A DIVERSION? HE DIDN'T WANT CEREBUS TO INVADE, SO HE TOLD CEREBUS TO INVADE, WHICH MADE CEREBUS DECIDE TO INVADE...
WHICH MEANS THAT LORD JULIUS GOT WHAT HE WANTED AND I GOT WHAT I WANTED WHICH MEANS LORD JULIUS...

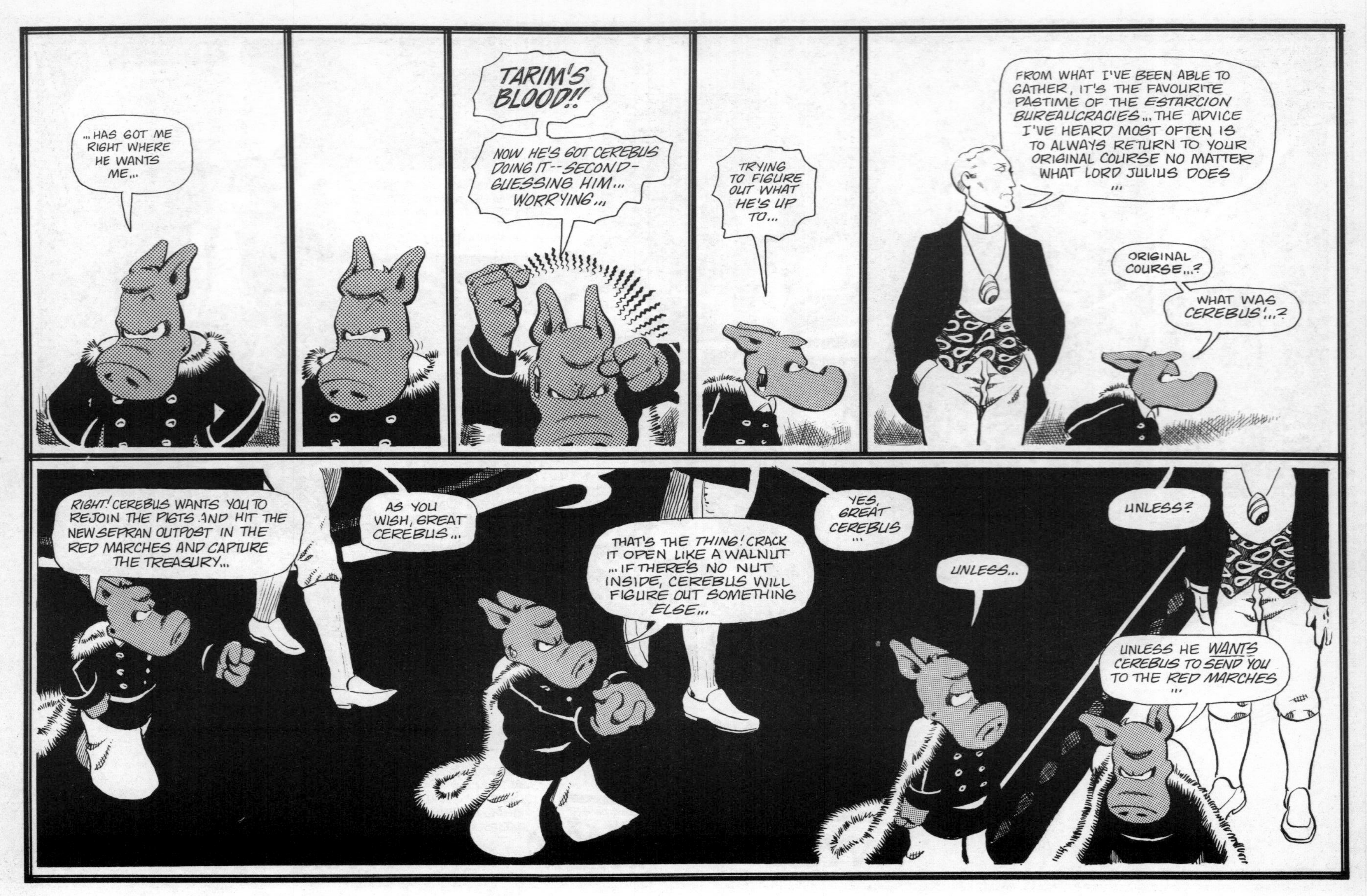

...HAS GOT ME RIGHT WHERE HE WANTS ME...
TARIM'S BLOOD!!
NOW HE'S GOT CEREBUS DOING IT--SECOND-GUESSING HIM... WORRYING...
TRYING TO FIGURE OUT WHAT HE'S UP TO...
FROM WHAT I'VE BEEN ABLE TO GATHER, IT'S THE FAVOURITE PASTIME OF THE ESTARCION BUREAUCRACIES... THE ADVICE I'VE HEARD MOST OFTEN IS TO ALWAYS RETURN TO YOUR ORIGINAL COURSE NO MATTER WHAT LORD JULIUS DOES ...
ORIGINAL COURSE...?
WHAT WAS CEREBUS'...?
RIGHT! CEREBUS WANTS YOU TO REJOIN THE PIGTS AND HIT THE NEW SEPRAN OUTPOST IN THE RED MARCHES AND CAPTURE THE TREASURY...
AS YOU WISH, GREAT CEREBUS...
THAT'S THE THING! CRACK IT OPEN LIKE A WALNUT ...IF THERE'S NO NUT INSIDE, CEREBUS WILL FIGURE OUT SOMETHING ELSE...
YES, GREAT CEREBUS ...
UNLESS...
UNLESS?
UNLESS HE WANTS CEREBUS TO SEND YOU TO THE RED MARCHES ...

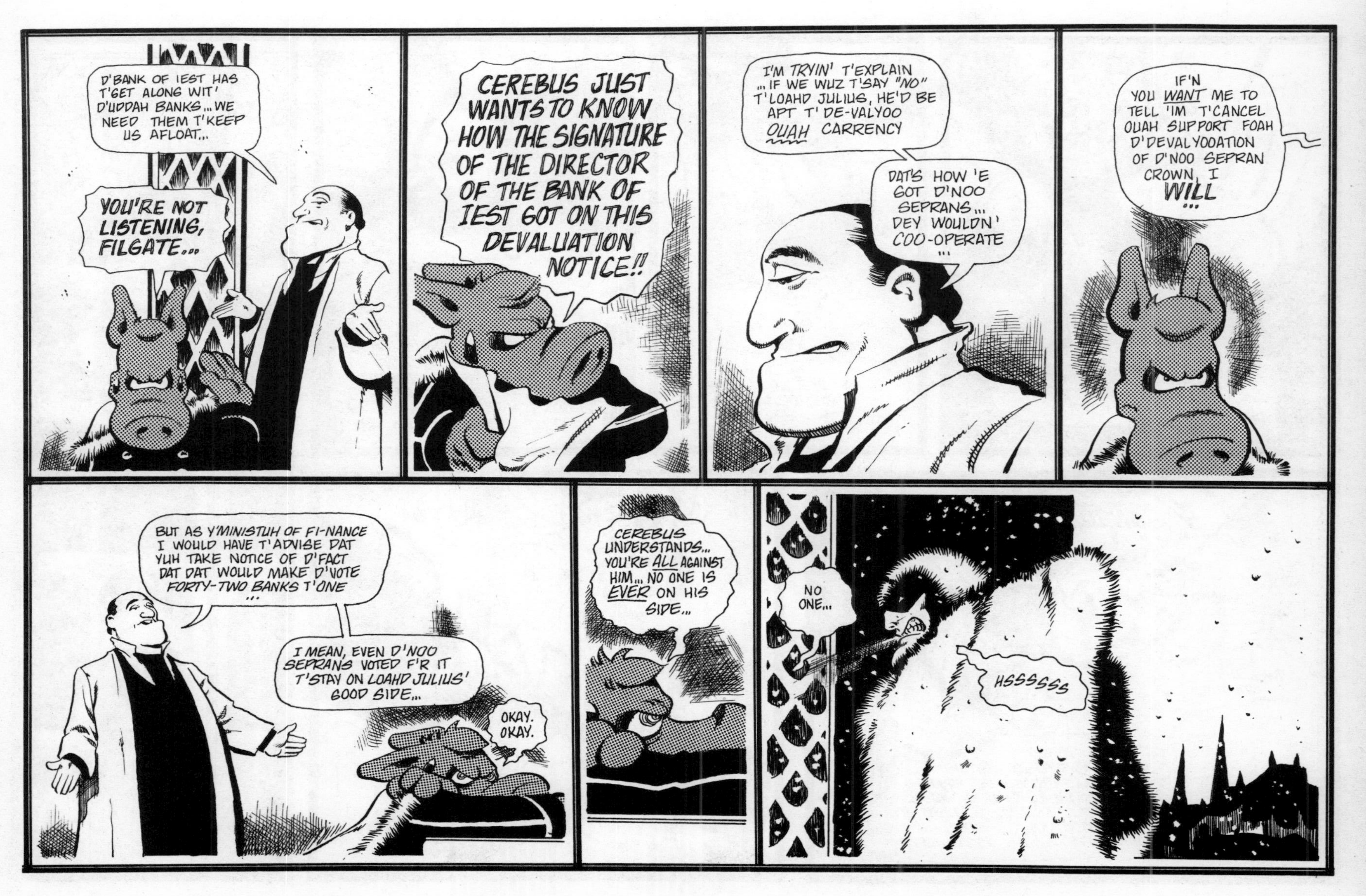

D'BANK OF IEST HAS T'GET ALONG WIT' D'UDDAH BANKS... WE NEED THEM T'KEEP US AFLOAT...
YOU'RE NOT LISTENING, FILGATE...
CEREBUS JUST WANTS TO KNOW HOW THE SIGNATURE OF THE DIRECTOR OF THE BANK OF IEST GOT ON THIS DEVALUATION NOTICE!!
I'M TRYIN' T'EXPLAIN ... IF WE WUZ T'SAY "NO" T'LOAHD JULIUS, HE'D BE APT T' DE-VALYOO OUAH CARRENCY
DAT'S HOW 'E GOT D'NOO SEPRANS... DEY WOULDN' COO-OPERATE ...
IF'N YOU WANT ME TO TELL 'IM T'CANCEL OUAH SUPPORT FOAH D'DEVALYOOATION OF D'NOO SEPRAN CROWN, I WILL ...
BUT AS Y'MINISTUH OF FI-NANCE I WOULD HAVE T'ADVISE DAT YUH TAKE NOTICE OF D'FACT DAT DAT WOULD MAKE D'VOTE FORTY-TWO BANKS T'ONE ...
I MEAN, EVEN D'NOO SEPRANS VOTED F'R IT T'STAY ON LOAHD JULIUS' GOOD SIDE...
OKAY. OKAY.
CEREBUS UNDERSTANDS... YOU'RE ALL AGAINST HIM... NO ONE IS EVER ON HIS SIDE...
NO ONE...
HSSSSSS

ODD. I THOUGHT I SAW A ...

HALT, VILE TRAITOR!!
OH, MY ...

YOU WORTHLESS, SCUMMY, VERMINOUS, STOMACH-TURNING, ORDUROUS BIT OF USELESS CRUD -- I OUGHT TO GRIND YOU INTO A LITTLE BLACK QUIVERING SPOT ON THE TOP OF THIS CRUMMY DESK...
W-WHO ARE Y-YOU? ...
A FRIEND!

SEE THIS? THIS IS A LOYALTY OATH SWEARING THAT YOU WILL NEVER EVER DO ANYTHING THE PRIME MINISTER DOESN'T WANT YOU TO DO AND THAT YOU WILL IMMEDIATELY DO ANYTHING THAT HE DOES WANT YOU TO DO!!

YOU CAN EITHER SIGN IT OR EAT IT...!!
I--I'LL SIGN

M.... T.... HOWE.... DI.... RECTOR... ....BANK.... OF.... THAT'S IT...

THAT DOCUMENT WON'T DO THE PRIME MINISTER ANY GOOD -- IT WAS SIGNED UNDER DURESS!
THERE ISN'T A COURT IN THIS CITY-STATE THAT WOULD CONSIDER IT BINDING...!

OF ...MY.... OWN..... FREE ...WILL....WITH ...OUT.... ANY ...THREAT... OF... PHYSICAL ...PHYS.... IC.... AL..... HARM .....SIGNED....

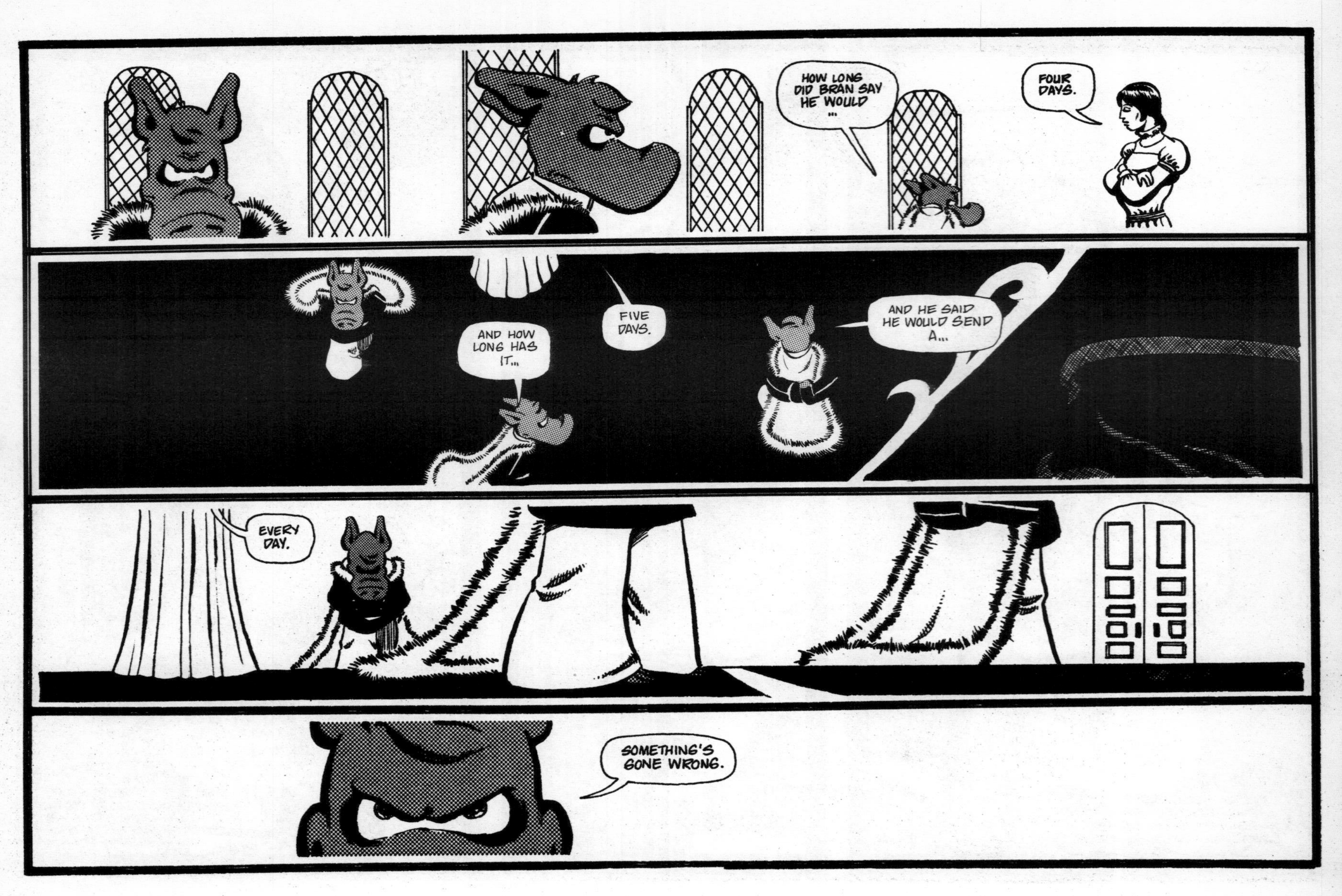
HOW LONG DID BRAN SAY HE WOULD ...
FOUR DAYS.
AND HOW LONG HAS IT...
FIVE DAYS.
AND HE SAID HE WOULD SEND A...
EVERY DAY.
SOMETHING'S GONE WRONG.

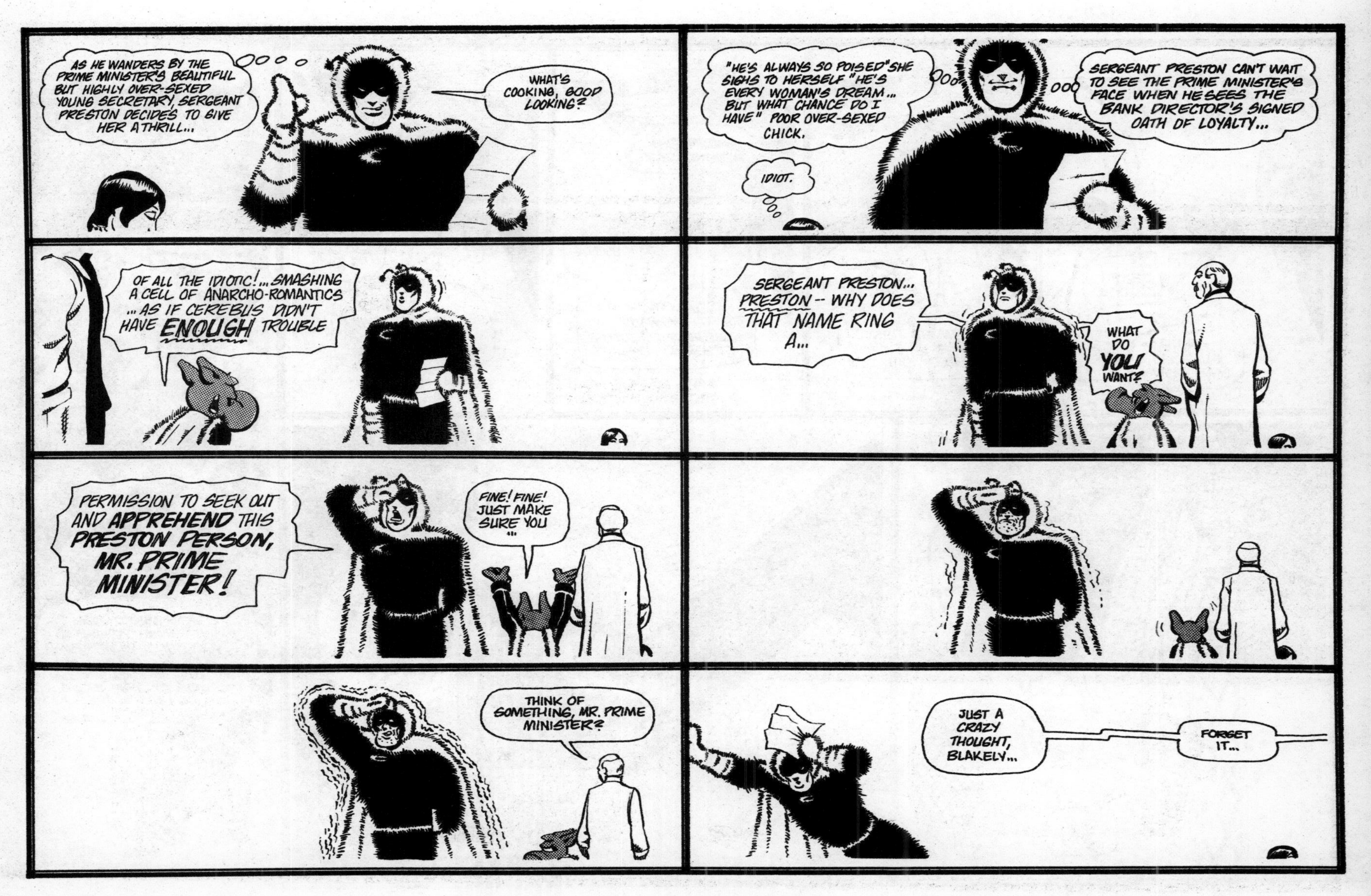

AS HE WANDERS BY THE PRIME MINISTER'S BEAUTIFUL BUT HIGHLY OVER-SEXED YOUNG SECRETARY, SERGEANT PRESTON DECIDES TO GIVE HER A THRILL...
WHAT'S COOKING, GOOD LOOKING?
"HE'S ALWAYS SO POISED" SHE SIGHS TO HERSELF "HE'S EVERY WOMAN'S DREAM... BUT WHAT CHANCE DO I HAVE" POOR OVER-SEXED CHICK.
IDIOT.
SERGEANT PRESTON CAN'T WAIT TO SEE THE PRIME MINISTER'S FACE WHEN HE SEES THE BANK DIRECTOR'S SIGNED OATH OF LOYALTY...
OF ALL THE IDIOTIC!... SMASHING A CELL OF ANARCHO-ROMANTICS ...AS IF CEREBUS DIDN'T HAVE ENOUGH TROUBLE
SERGEANT PRESTON... PRESTON -- WHY DOES THAT NAME RING A...
WHAT DO YOU WANT?
PERMISSION TO SEEK OUT AND APPREHEND THIS PRESTON PERSON, MR. PRIME MINISTER!
FINE! FINE! JUST MAKE SURE YOU ...
THINK OF SOMETHING, MR. PRIME MINISTER?
JUST A CRAZY THOUGHT, BLAKELY...
FORGET IT...

I'M NOT KIDDIN'! DIS IS D'MOST UPSET I EVUH SEEN D'BANK UF IEST... IF DIS "SAHJINT PRESTON" WAS LOAHD JULIUS' IDEA, IT WOIKED... HOWE WANTS Y'HEAD ONNAH SILVER...
ALLRIGHT! ALLRIGHT! WHAT DO YOU THINK WE SHOULD DO?

THEY'VE BEEN PUSHIN' F'R A DISCRETIONARY DISBURSEMENTS COUNCIL F'YEARS... A GROUP O'BANKUHS DAT WOULD DECIDE WHEN AN' HOW D'PROIME MINISTUH CAN SPEND PUBLIC FUNDS...
WHAT IF CEREBUS DOESN'T GO ALONG WITH THEM...?
IN D'CASE O'DAT EVENTOOALITY HAPPENIN' DEY INTEND T'PETITION LOAHD JULIUS T'DEVALYOO D'IESTAN CROWN RIGHT OUT O' EXISTENCE
SWELL.
HERE'S D'REPORT ...
TELL THEM CEREBUS IS FORMING A COMMITEE TO STUDY...
DEY ADVISE YOUSE T'SAY "YES"
TELL THEM CEREBUS WANTS TO CONSULT HIS ADVISORY COUNCIL ON ECONOMIC...
DEY ADVISE Y'T'SAY "YES" ALTSO ...
TELL THEM CEREBUS HAS A BLUE RIBBON PANEL HE WANTS TO...
RIGHT HERE ...
WHERE DOES CEREBUS SIGN?

PINSHAW! COME IN! COME IN!
SO WE'RE HOLDING THEM AT THE PASS ARE WE?

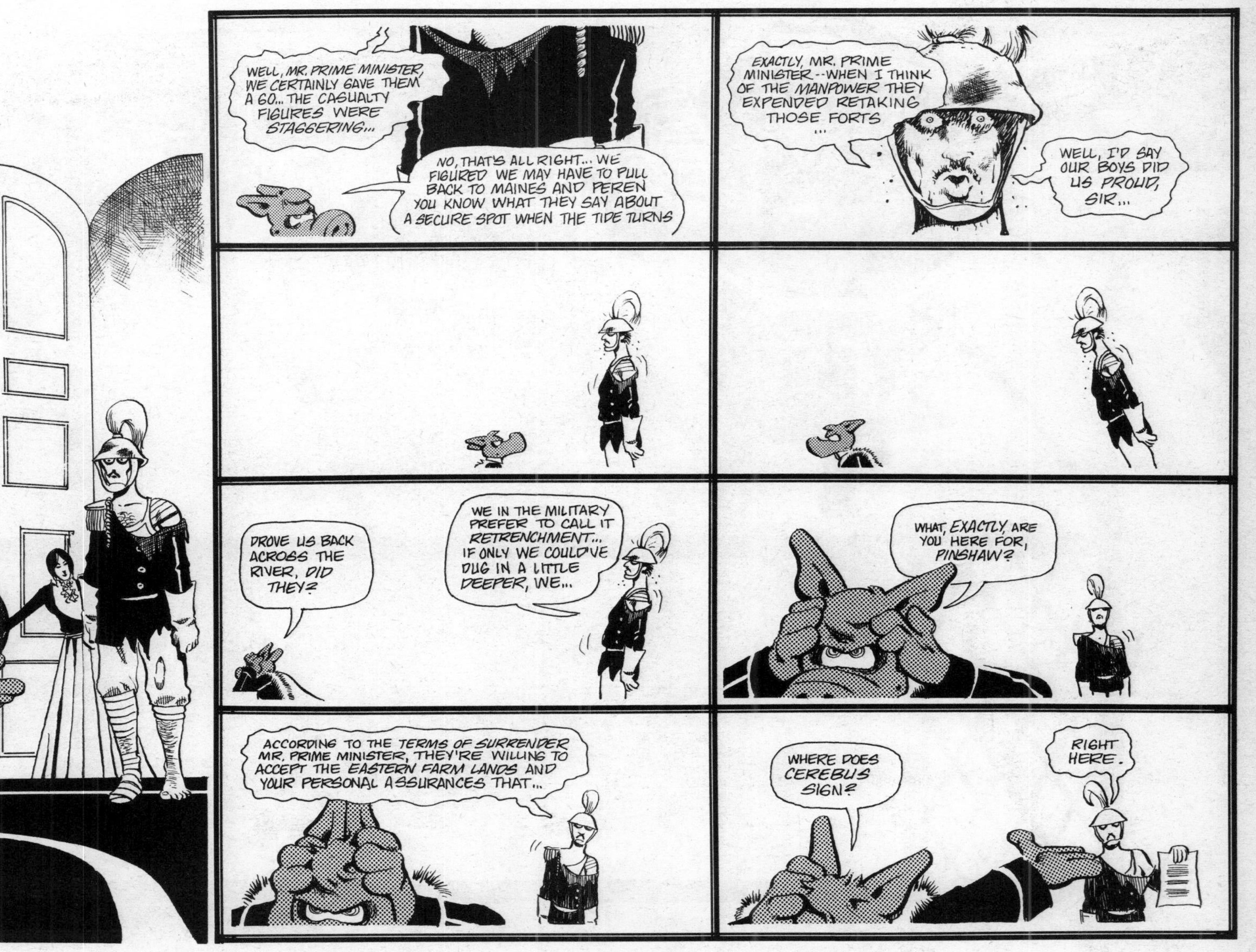

WELL, MR. PRIME MINISTER, WE CERTAINLY GAVE THEM A GO... THE CASUALTY FIGURES WERE STAGGERING...
NO, THAT'S ALL RIGHT... WE FIGURED WE MAY HAVE TO PULL BACK TO MAINES AND PEREN YOU KNOW WHAT THEY SAY ABOUT A SECURE SPOT WHEN THE TIDE TURNS
EXACTLY, MR. PRIME MINISTER --WHEN I THINK OF THE MANPOWER THEY EXPENDED RETAKING THOSE FORTS ...
WELL, I'D SAY OUR BOYS DID US PROUD, SIR...
DROVE US BACK ACROSS THE RIVER, DID THEY?
WE IN THE MILITARY PREFER TO CALL IT RETRENCHMENT... IF ONLY WE COULD'VE DUG IN A LITTLE DEEPER, WE...
WHAT, EXACTLY, ARE YOU HERE FOR, PINSHAW?
ACCORDING TO THE TERMS OF SURRENDER MR. PRIME MINISTER, THEY'RE WILLING TO ACCEPT THE EASTERN FARM LANDS AND YOUR PERSONAL ASSURANCES THAT...
WHERE DOES CEREBUS SIGN?
RIGHT HERE.

AND SHOULD YOU CHOOSE TO IGNORE OUR "APPEAL" TO PLACE AN INDIVIDUAL CHOSEN BY THE ANARCHO-ROMANTICS' STEERING COMMITEE IN THE POSITION VACATED BY MR. MAC MUFIN, WE SHALL BE FORCED TO TAKE EVEN MORE DRASTIC ACTION IN ALL DISTRICTS OF THE LOWER CITY...
... THIS, OF COURSE, IS IN ADDITION TO OUR "APPEAL" THAT YOU DISBAND THE NORTHERN IESTAN MOUNTED POLICE AND FIRE YOUR "SERGEANT PRESTON"
WHERE DOES CEREBUS SIGN...?
RIGHT HERE.

MR. PRIME MINISTER....?
WHERE DOES CEREBUS SIGN...?

IT'S NOTHING YOU HAVE TO SIGN, SIR, IT'S A MESSAGE FROM GARRISON...
WHAT'S IT SAY?

AN ARMY MARCHING UNDER UNKNOWN COLOURS IS A DAY'S RIDE AWAY FROM GARRISON
COMMANDER LESLA REQUESTS YOUR INSTRUCTIONS ...

BRAN.
HE MADE IT...!

TELL COMMANDER LESLA THAT MR. MACMUFIN AND HIS ARMY ARE TO BE GIVEN A FULL MILITARY ESCORT ...
TELL HIM THEY ARE TO BE BROUGHT THROUGH THE PLAZA TO MY OFFICIAL RESIDENCE FOR MY OFFICIAL GREETINGS ...

NEXT: HSIFFIES

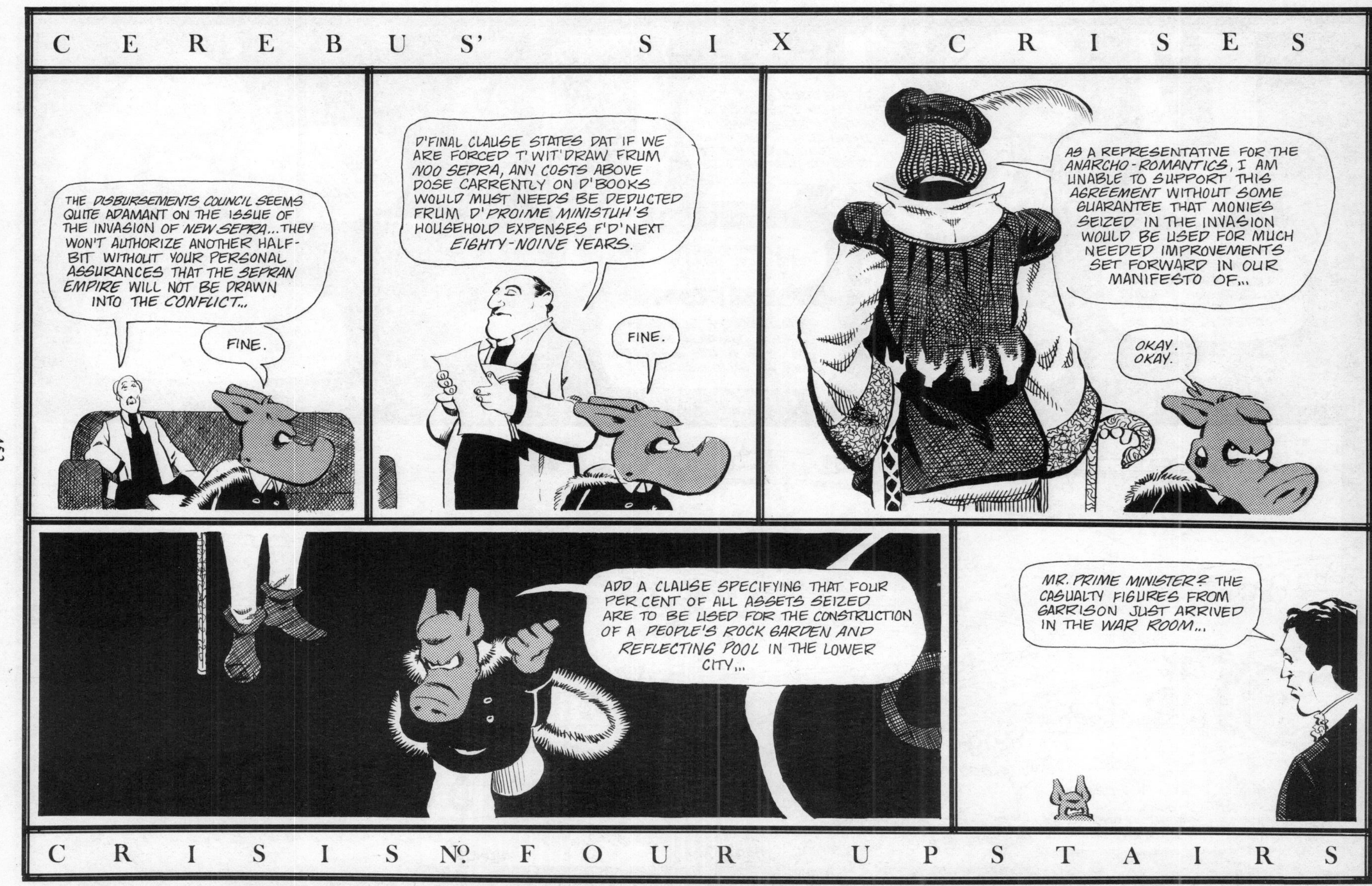
CEREBUS' SIX CRISES
THE DISBURSEMENTS COUNCIL SEEMS QUITE ADAMANT ON THE ISSUE OF THE INVASION OF NEW SEPRA... THEY WON'T AUTHORIZE ANOTHER HALF-BIT WITHOUT YOUR PERSONAL ASSURANCES THAT THE SEPRAN EMPIRE WILL NOT BE DRAWN INTO THE CONFLICT...
FINE.
D'FINAL CLAUSE STATES DAT IF WE ARE FORCED T'WIT'DRAW FRUM NOO SEPRA, ANY COSTS ABOVE DOSE CARRENTLY ON D'BOOKS WOULD MUST NEEDS BE DEDUCTED FRUM D'PROIME MINISTUH'S HOUSEHOLD EXPENSES F'D'NEXT EIGHTY-NOINE YEARS.
FINE.
AS A REPRESENTATIVE FOR THE ANARCHO-ROMANTICS, I AM UNABLE TO SUPPORT THIS AGREEMENT WITHOUT SOME GUARANTEE THAT MONIES SEIZED IN THE INVASION WOULD BE USED FOR MUCH NEEDED IMPROVEMENTS SET FORWARD IN OUR MANIFESTO OF...
OKAY. OKAY.
ADD A CLAUSE SPECIFYING THAT FOUR PER CENT OF ALL ASSETS SEIZED ARE TO BE USED FOR THE CONSTRUCTION OF A PEOPLE'S ROCK GARDEN AND REFLECTING POOL IN THE LOWER CITY...
MR. PRIME MINISTER? THE CASUALTY FIGURES FROM GARRISON JUST ARRIVED IN THE WAR ROOM...
CRISIS No. FOUR UPSTAIRS

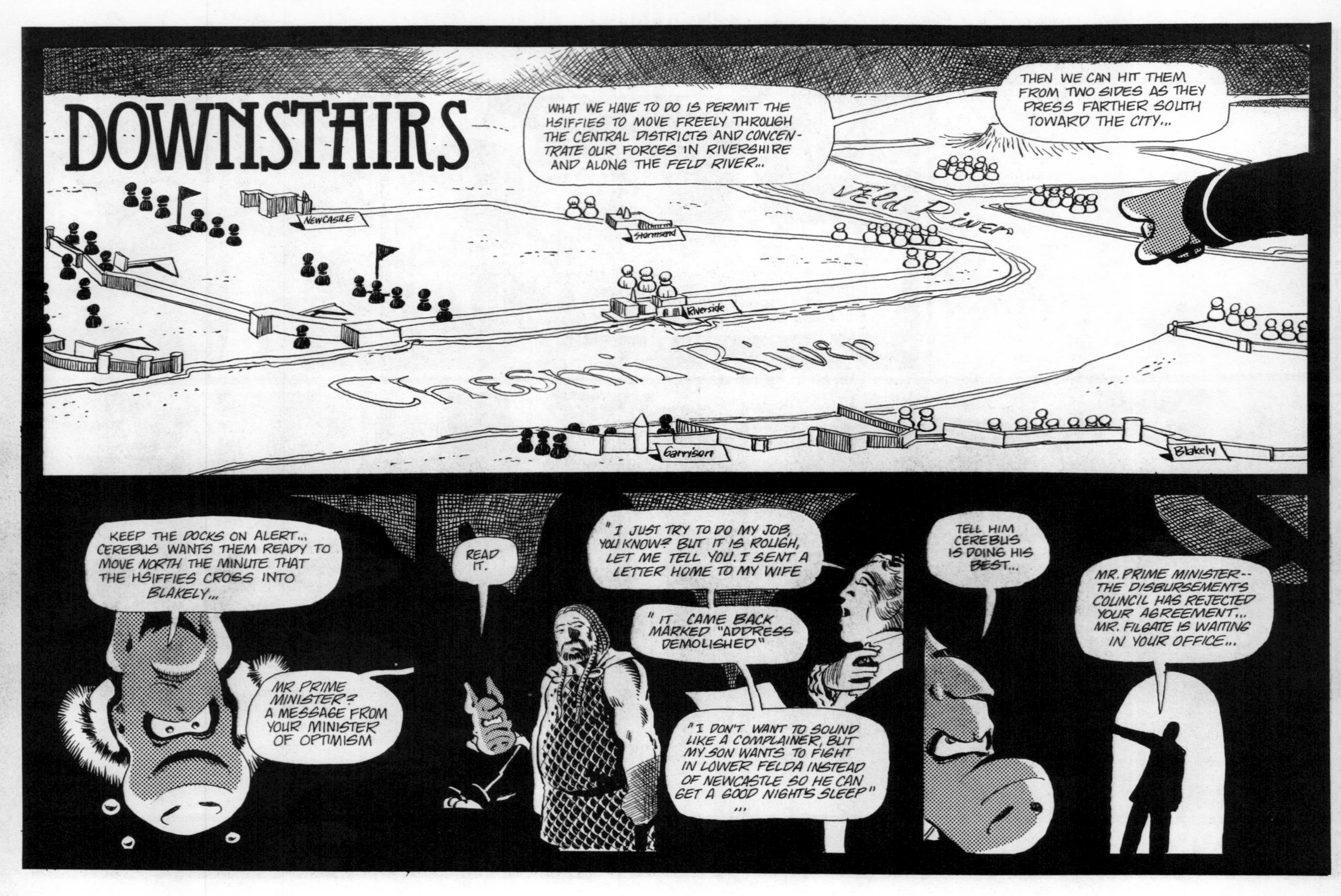
DOWNSTAIRS
WHAT WE HAVE TO DO IS PERMIT THE HSIFFIES TO MOVE FREELY THROUGH THE CENTRAL DISTRICTS AND CONCENTRATE OUR FORCES IN RIVERSHIRE AND ALONG THE FELD RIVER...
THEN WE CAN HIT THEM FROM TWO SIDES AS THEY PRESS FARTHER SOUTH TOWARD THE CITY...
Feld River
Newcastle
Riverside
Chesmi River
Garrison
Blakely
KEEP THE DOCKS ON ALERT... CEREBUS WANTS THEM READY TO MOVE NORTH THE MINUTE THAT THE HSIFFIES CROSS INTO BLAKELY...
MR PRIME MINISTER? A MESSAGE FROM YOUR MINISTER OF OPTIMISM
READ IT.
"I JUST TRY TO DO MY JOB, YOU KNOW? BUT IT IS ROUGH, LET ME TELL YOU. I SENT A LETTER HOME TO MY WIFE
"IT CAME BACK MARKED "ADDRESS DEMOLISHED"
"I DON'T WANT TO SOUND LIKE A COMPLAINER, BUT MY SON WANTS TO FIGHT IN LOWER FELDA INSTEAD OF NEWCASTLE SO HE CAN GET A GOOD NIGHT'S SLEEP" ...
TELL HIM CEREBUS IS DOING HIS BEST...
MR. PRIME MINISTER-- THE DISBURSEMENTS COUNCIL HAS REJECTED YOUR AGREEMENT... MR. FILGATE IS WAITING IN YOUR OFFICE...

HOWE SEZ HE'S ON BOARD WIT' D'NOO SEPRAN CONCESSIONS... D'ASSOCIATE DIRECTUH WANTS T'KNOW WHY D' ROCK GAHDEN 'N' RUHFLECTIN' POOL CAN'T BE ERECTED IN D'BOROUGH O' HARNE OF WHICH HE IS, CO-INCUHDENT'LY, D'COMMISSIONUH O'PUBLIC WORKS...
INSTEAD OF IN D' BOROUGH OF T'AGATH WHICH HE CLAIMS IS A WELL-KNOWN PIG-STY.
THE REGIONAL DIRECTOR IS, COINCIDENTALLY, THE COMMISSIONER OF PUBLIC WORKS FOR THE WELL-KNOWN PIG-STY... HE IS WITH YOU SO LONG AS THE WELL-KNOWN PIG-STY REMAINS THE CHOSEN SITE...
DON'T THOSE IDIOTS REALIZE THAT THE WHOLE PROJECT IS NOTHING MORE THAN A STUPID AND NEEDLESS EXTRAVAGANCE TO KEEP THE DAMN ANARCHO-ROMANTICS IN LINE!?!
DEY ARE WELL AWARE DAT IT IS A STOOPID 'N' NEEDLESS EXTRAVAGUNCE... WHUT DEY ARE DEBATIN' IS WHOSE STOOPID 'N' NEEDLESS EXTRAVAGUNCE IT IS GOIN' T'BE...
IDIOTS!
SOMETHING SHOULD BE ...
"SHOULD BE..." WHAT, MR. PRIME MINISTER?
NOTHING.
CEREBUS WAS JUST THINKING OUT LOUD ...
SERGEANT PRESTON STANDS POISED IN MID-LEAP, AWAITING THE COMPLETION OF THE PRIME MINISTER'S CODED PSIONIC INSTRUCTIONS... ALL FIFTY-SIX ROACH SENSES HUMMING...
"FIFTY-SEVEN" SAYS KEVITCH, CORRECTING HIM...
AND RIGHT HE IS, TOO, FOR SERGEANT PRESTON HAS FORGOTTEN HIS MERELY MAGNIFICENT ROACH STABILITY SENSE WHICH TELLS HIM WHEN HE IS DANGEROUSLY OVER-BALANCE...
TELL THEM CEREBUS HAS DECIDED ON A REFLECTING POOL CONNECTING THE TWO BOROUGHS WITH SOME ROCKS AND PLANTS AND FOUNTAINS AT EITHER END...
A MR. THE ISSHURIAN IS WAITING FOR YOU WITH A REPORT FROM FORT CHICOLINI, MR. PRIME MINISTER...

WE HAVE A SMALL PROBLEM ...SOME OF MY MEN WANT TO LEAVE, WORK SOME-PLACE ELSE, INSTEAD OF "SITTING TIGHT" AT CHICOLINI....
CEREBUS IS WORKING ON THE FINANCING FOR A PUSH INTO THE RED MARCHES TO SEIZE THE NEW SEPRAN TREASURY... HOW MUCH WOULD YOU NEED TO BRING IT OFF?
A HALF MILLION, GIVE OR TAKE TEN THOUSAND... MORE IF IT TOOK LONGER THAN TEN DAYS...
FINE.
CEREBUS WILL HAVE THE CASH READY IN A FEW HOURS... YOU CAPTURE THE TREASURY ...IF THERE'S ENOUGH CURRENCY THERE, YOU CAN DIVIDE IT UP AND THEN COME BACK TO HELP US REPEL THE HSIFFY INVASION ...
WHAT IF THERE ISN'T ENOUGH CURRENCY?
THEN YOU'RE ALL FREE TO GO ON YOUR MERRY WAY...
AND CEREBUS WILL BE THE ONE WITH THE SMALL PROBLEM.

IS DIS SOME KINDA JOKE, HARGRAVES?
MOST ASSUREDLY NOT, MR. FILGATE. IT IS A SIMPLE REJECTION OF THE REVISED AGREEMENT BY THE ANARCHO-ROMANTIC STEERING COMMITEE...
IT IS OUR CONSIDERED OPINION THAT THE TWO ROCK GARDENS AND ADJOINING REFLECTING POOL ARE NOT SUFFICIENT COMPENSATION. WE REQUIRE A MORE MEANINGFUL AND IMPORTANT ROLE FOR OUR MOVEMENT IN THIS ADMINISTRATION ...
AND WHAT MEANINGFUL AND IMPORTANT ROLE DO YOU FORESEE FOR A BUNCH OF PERFUMED, POSTURING...
NOW, BLAKELY-- HE'S GOT A GOOD POINT ...
WE'VE BEEN TRYING TO BUY HIS SUPPORT WITH MINOR CONCESSIONS ...
AS LONG AS HE'S HERE, WE SHOULD BE USING HIS ABILITIES AND SKILLS TO THEIR BEST ADVANTAGE
ASTORIA?
NOTIFY THE MINISTRY OF DEFENCE THAT OUR FRONT LINE OF INVASION TROOPS INTO NEW SEPRA WILL BE ANARCHO-ROMANTICS
YES, MR. PRIME MINISTER ...
...HAND-PICKED AND LED BY MR. HARGRAVES HERE ...
...BUT...
...BUT...
I SIMPLY MUST TELL THE LADS IN THE WAR ROOM...THEY HAVEN'T HAD A GOOD LAUGH IN WEEKS...

BUT--YOU CAN'T
I MEAN I CAN'T
I MEAN
THERE MUST BE SOME OTHER WAY!
WELL...
IT WOULD MEAN COMPROMISING THE INTEGRITY OF YOUR MOVEMENT ...
BUT IF YOU COULD SEE YOUR WAY CLEAR TO SIGNING THE REVISED AGREEMENT ...
WHERE DO I SIGN?
WHERE?!
MM. NO.
CEREBUS CAN'T LET YOU BETRAY YOUR MOVEMENT.
YOU'D BE THROWING AWAY YOUR CAREER...
PLEASE LET ME! I WANT TO!
HOWEVER. IF YOU COULD CONVERT THE MOVEMENT TO CEREBUS' SIDE
SAY-- A HUNDRED OF THEM?
EACH WILLING TO PAY THE TEN THOUSAND CROWN JOINER FEE...
TEN THOUSAND CROWNS?
WHO WOULD BE WILLING TO PART WITH THAT MUCH MONEY?!
WHY-- ANYONE WHO DOESN'T WANT TO JOIN YOU ON THE FRONT LINES, OF COURSE
NO RUSH ...
ANYTIME BEFORE MIDNIGHT TOMORROW WILL BE FINE ...

WE'LL HAVE A RELAY OF MESSENGERS IN PLACE AS FAR AS CHICOLINI -- IT'LL BE YOUR JOB TO KEEP A LINE OF COMMUNICATION OPEN THROUGHOUT THE ATTACK...
AS SOON AS YOU TAKE THE TREASURY, CEREBUS NEEDS TO KNOW HOW...
SO!
IF TISN'T THE PRIMINISTER 'MSELF... S'THIS'S WHERE YOU DO Y'R MILILITARY PLANNING...
I HOPE YOU'RE NOT PLANNING T'SPEND 'NUTHER MILLION CROWNS CAUSE Y'AIN'T GETT'N'IT ...
YEWW THINK YEWWR SOOO SMART--
WELL, Y'R NOT-- I TALKED T'EVERY ANTARCHTIC ROMANO I KNEW 'N' EVEN SOME I DINT!
AND GUESSWHUT? THEY'RE AAALLL BROKE
NOT ONE OF'M COULD GIMME A THOUS'N'CROWNS... NOT EVEN'A ONES INNA BIG HOUSES....
Y'R WHOLE STINKY BIG OUTHOUSE OF A STINKY CITY-STATE IS BROKE
AND D'YEW KNOW WHAT THAT MEANS, MINISTER PRIME MISTER? D'YEW? WELL'LL TELLYEW...

IT MEANS TH'T T'MORROW I LEAD TH' INVASION INNA NEW SEPRA... WE SHALL THROW 'RSELVES 'PON TH' PIDDYLESS FOE
RENT LIMBFRUMLIMB WE SHALL DIE IN TH' NAME 'F' OUR GLOOORIOUS MOVEMENT ...
YEWERE RIGHT! TH'TIME'S COME F'RACTION!
DANGER!
DEATH!
TONIGHT WE'DRINK DEEP TH'SWEET WINE OF LIFE F'T'MORROW WE DIE
I WOULDN' SIGN Y'LOUSY 'GREEMENT IF Y'BEGGED ME! Y'HEAR ME, Y'L'IL SOD?... TH' MADN'SS OF BATTLE 'SUPON ME—I'VE B'COME A WILD BEAST!! TEARIN' OFF GREAT CHUNKS O'LIFE...HOV'RIN' AT THE VERY EDGE O' THE ABYSS! UNTAMED! TH' THIN VENEER O' CIVILISATION STRIP'DAWAY
SIP
OH THANK YEW THANK YEW MINISTER PRIME MISTER THANK YEW!!
SKRTCHA SKRTCHA
THANK YEW THANK YEW THANK YEW THANK YEW
DON'T ASK.

THIS IS THE WAR ROOM, BLAKELY...
WITH ALL OF CEREBUS' COMMANDERS IN THE FIELD, WE NEED YOU TO BE HERE AT ALL TIMES ...
ALL INCOMING MESSAGES ARE IN CODE... THE MASTER CODE IS LOCKED IN THIS DRAWER... ONLY YOU AND CEREBUS WILL HAVE KEYS
YOU'RE TO DECODE ANY MESSAGE IMMEDIATELY AND SEND A COPY TO MY OFFICE...
IF IT DESCRIBES ANY CHANGE IN TROOP POSITION ...
YOU'RE TO MAKE THE APPROPRIATE CHANGES ON THE SITUATION BOARD...
THE WHITE MARKERS ARE OURS... EACH ONE DENOTES FIVE HUNDRED MEN
EACH BLACK MARKER DENOTES APPROXIMATELY SEVEN HUNDRED HSIFFIES ...
THE BROWN ONES ARE THE MERCENARIES INVADING NEW SEPRA...
LOOKING AT THE BOARD, NOW, BLAKELY--FOR THE FIRST TIME, CAN YOU SEE ANYTHING I MIGHT HAVE OVERLOOKED?
AS LONG AS YOU'RE ASKING MR. PRIME MINISTER ...THERE IS ONE THING
THE ENTIRE ROOM IS ABSOLUTELY FILTHY!
EVERY INCH OF SURFACE IS COVERED WITH A LAYER OF DUST...
YOU, THERE! YES, BOY, YOU! RUN AND FETCH THE HEAD OF THE HOUSEKEEPING STAFF...
TELL HIM THE PRIME MINISTER'S SENIOR DOMESTIC AFFAIRS ADVISOR WANTS A WORD WITH HIM.

LOOKS LIKE I FINALLY FOUND A JOB FOR OLD BLAKELY HE CAN HANDLE -- THE END OF HIS FIRST DAY IN THE WAR ROOM AND CEREBUS HASN'T HEARD FROM HIM ...
MR. PRIME MINISTER -- OLDCASTLE HAS BEEN CAPTURED... STORM'SEND MANOR IS UNDER SIEGE
RIVERSHIRE'S BEEN TAKEN ... THE NORTHERN PROVINCES ARE EVACUATING SOUTH TO THE RIVER...
THE DISPATCHES ALL CAME IN EARLY THIS MORNING...!
THIS MORNING!?
MR. BLAKELY WOULDN'T LET ME BRING THEM TO YOU UNTIL I POLISHED THE WAR ROOM FLOOR...
YOU CAN'T KILL YOUR DOMESTIC AFFAIRS ADVISOR-- THINK OF THE BAD PUBLICITY

POST NOTICES THAT THE REFUGEES FROM THE NORTHERN PROVINCES ARE TO BE SPLIT UP INTO PRIVATE HOMES
IF WE KEEP THEM TOGETHER, THEY'LL JUST SPREAD PANIC...
D'MAIN BODY OF D'INVADIN' FORCE IS MOVIN' EAST...
SEND A MESSAGE TO LOWER FELDA THAT THE HSIFFIES ARE HEADED FOR THE OESIS... GET THEM TO SEND MILITARY AID...
THERE'S SOME RIOTING IN THE DOCKS AND ALONG THE RIVERFRONT OF THE LOWER CITY...
FIND THE LEADERS AND HAVE THEM EXECUTED ON THE SPOT...
DISBURSE THE REST ...
D'LOWAH FELDANS RUHFYOOZ T'HELP, BUT DEY ARE WILLIN' T'OFFUH YOU P'LITICAL ASSOYLUM IF D'HSIFFIES DECOIDE T'CROSS D' FELD RIVUH...
SWELL.
THE DOCKS THREATEN TO CUT ALL TIES WITH THE UPPER CITY IF YOU DON'T RESIGN AND APPOINT FILGATE YOUR SUCCESSOR ...
" I CANNOT EMPHASIZE TOO STRONGLY THE NEED FOR UNITY IN THIS TIME OF DANGER. I DO NOT SEEK, AND IF OFFERED, WILL NOT ACCEPT THE POSITION OF PRIME MINISTER. CEREBUS IS OUR PRIME MINISTER, AND IT IS ONLY WITH ALL OF OUR SUPPORT THAT HE WILL LEAD US TO SURE VICTORY. SINCERELY, EULING S. FILGATE, MINISTER OF FINANCE."
NOW, WHO CAN WE SEND IT TO IN THE DOCKS?
IT HAS TO BE SOMEONE WHO CAN READ ...
CHEE-- DAT'S A TOUGHIE ...

D'MOICENARIES INVADIN' NOO SEPRA RAN INTAN AMBUSH... FORTUNATELY, DEY WAS ONLY OUT-NUMBUHED FIVE TUH ONE SO DEY MANAGED TUH WRAP UP DUH BATTLE OVUH LUNCH ...
THE DOCK POLICE REPORT ALL QUIET IN THE LOWER CITY
FIVE ANARCHO-ROMANTICS DEAD.
A DOZEN UNDER ARREST
D'HSIFFIES ON D'UDDAH SIDE O'D'CHESMI HAVE MOVED INTA BLAKELY PROVINCE...
THAT'S OKAY. THE NATIVES WILL DAMP-MOP THEM TO DEATH.
ALERT THE DOCKS TO START MOVING THEIR FORCES NORTH.
HARGRAVES WISHES TO STRONGLY PROTEST THE ARREST AND EXECUTION OF ANARCHO-ROMANTICS ...
UNLESS IT MEANS HE HAS TO LEAD AN IN-VASION SOMEWHERE, IN WHICH CASE, WHAT-EVER YOU WANT TO DO IS FINE BY HIM.
D'MOICENARIES ARE CLOSIN' IN ON D'RED MAHCHES ...
D'NOO SEPRAN OUTPOST IS IN SIGHT ...
SOME PRIESTS IN THE LOWER CITY ARE PREACHING THAT THE END OF THE WORLD IS AT HAND... THEY SAY THE INVASION IS THE WILL OF TARIM ...
LET THEM PREACH, BUT HAVE THE POLICE KEEP AN EYE ON THEM...
IF ANY OF THEM STARTS TO DEVELOP A LARGER FOLLOWING THAN THE OTHERS, HAVE HIM EXECUTED...
MR. PRIME MINISTER?
WHAT IS IT?
THERE'S A MISTRESS JAKA HERE TO SEE YOU...

JAKA?
CEREBUS THOUGHT YOU LEFT ...
I AM LEAVING. TONIGHT.
FOR GOOD.
YOU DON'T HAVE TO. YOU CAN STAY HERE. WITH CEREBUS.
I'M LEAVING.
...AND I WANT YOU TO COME WITH ME. YOU'RE IN TERRIBLE DANGER HERE.
DANGER? OF COURSE CEREBUS IS IN DANGER ...
...THAT'S CEREBUS' JOB...
MR. PRIME MINISTER?
COMMANDERS JOHNS AND HYANNS HAVE ARRIVED WITH THE NORTHERN REFUGEES ...

HAVE THEM WAIT FOR CEREBUS IN THE WAR ROOM.

JAKA...
CEREBUS IS...

WE CAN TRAVEL.
LIKE YOU SAID.
THE WALL OF TSI... THE T'CAPMIN KINGDOMS ...

CEREBUS IS THE PRIME MINISTER ...
CEREBUS HAS TO STAY HERE.

NO ONE IS GOING TO COME AND TELL YOU TO TAKE A VACATION!
CAN'T YOU SEE?!
YOU'RE NOT ONE OF THEM!
THEY'RE GOING TO THROW YOU TO THE WOLVES ...

WHAT ARE YOU TALKING ABOUT?

IT'S ALL GONE WRONG.
THERE WAS A FIFTY-FIFTY CHANCE THAT YOU WOULD WORK OUT AND NOW IT'S ALL FALLING APART
...AND YOU'RE BEING WRITTEN OFF... NO ONE IS GOING TO HELP YOU...
WHO'S WRITTEN CEREBUS OFF?
WHO ARE YOU TALKING ABOUT...
ALL OF THEM... I CAN'T EXPLAIN. IT'S TOO COMPLICATED, BUT YOU MUST BELIEVE ME!
IT'S ALL COMING TO AN END ...
...SOON.
THE HSIFFIES, YOU MEAN?
WE'RE RETRENCHING THAT'S ALL.
THEY WON'T CROSS THE RIVER...
BUT THEY WILL! THEY WILL!
YOU HAVE TO...
MR. PRIME MINISTER? THE MERCENARIES HAVE CAPTURED THE RED MARCHES. THEY EXPECT TO HAVE SOMETHING TO REPORT WITHIN THE HOUR...
FINE.
FINE. THANK YOU.

DO YOU DISCUSS YOUR PLANS WITH ASTORIA?
ASTORIA?
WHAT HAS ASTORIA GOT TO DO WITH ALL THIS?
NOTHING.
EVERYTHING.
DO YOU?
ASTORIA IS CEREBUS' SECRETARY ...
SHE HAS NOTHING TO DO WITH CEREBUS' PLANS ...
WHAT DO YOU SUPPOSE SHE WOULD DO IF YOU TOLD HER YOU WERE LEAVING ...
... RESIGNING.
DO?
GET A JOB AS A SECRETARY SOMEWHERE ELSE ...
I SUPPOSE.
I DON'T KNOW. WHAT DIFFERENCE DOES IT...
TELL HER YOU'RE LEAVING...
YOU DON'T HAVE TO ACTUALLY LEAVE...
JUST TELL HER YOU ARE.

BUT...
WHY?
YOU'RE NOT MAKING ANY SENSE ...
BECAUSE I WANT YOU TO LIVE.
BECAUSE I WANT TO BE WITH YOU...
I WANT US TO LEAVE...
NOW.
I LOVE YOU.

MR. PRIME MINISTER? THE DOCKS FORCES HAVE SUFFERED A MAJOR DEFEAT IN BLAKELY...
THE HSIFFIES ARE MOVING SOUTH ...
CEREBUS WILL BE THERE IN A MINUTE...
SUCH A WASTE. SUCH A...
SO YOU CAN BE THERE WHEN THEY BREAK THE DOORS DOWN...

SO NO ONE WILL CALL YOU A COWARD...
STOP IT.

SO YOU CAN BE IN YOUR OFFICE WHEN THEY COME FOR YOU...
STOP IT, JAKA!
SO YOU CAN BE THERE TO...

STOP IT!
SLAP

JAKA.
BUT
DON'T APOLOGIZE...
I UNDERSTAND ...
I HAVE TO LEAVE ...
I'M SORRY...

NEXT: The Last Stand

cerebus' six crises
crisis no.5
the Last Stand
WE SHOULD BE GETTING NEW INFORMATION SOON...
WHUT I'M SAYIN' IS WE SHOULD HIT DEM ON DIS SIDE...
BE A GOOD LAD AND FIND ME A DAMP MOP, MM?
IF YOU WERE TO ASK ME, IT'S THE FAULT OF TH' BLEEDIN' BUREAUCRACY, DRAGGIN' THEIR FEET LIKE SOME RETARDED GREAT OAF WITH A BRAIN OF PUNGENT AND OVER-RIPE CHEESE ...
NEW REPORTS FROM OLDHAM, ASTORIA...
MM
REMOVE ANOTHER OF OLDHAM'S WHITE MARKERS, THERESA.
ANY SIGN OF THOSE RESERVE CAVALRY, M'LAD?
NO SIR...

I'VE BEEN ASKED TO GET THE *PRIME MINISTER'S* SIGNATURE ON THOSE, AS WELL...
OH.
YES. OF COURSE ...

WAIT HERE.
MR. PRIME MINISTER?

I'M *TERRIBLY* SORRY TO DISTURB YOU...

NO, SIR...
JUST A COUPLE OF SIGNATURES ...

THANK YOU, MR. PRIME MINISTER ...

WE CAN'T KEEP THIS UP FOREVER, YOU KNOW...
THANK YOU, MR. BLAKELY... I WAS JUST WONDERIN HOW LONG WE CAN'T KEEP THIS UP, AND NOW I KNOW THE ANSWER --FOREVER.
I'M SERIOUS... WE HAVEN'T GOT THE AUTHORITY...
MR BLAKELY, AS I SEE IT, I HAVE TWO OPTIONS ...
ONE, IS TO INFORM A PANIC-STRICKEN CITY FACING A MAJOR INVASION THAT ITS CHIEF EXECUTIVE IS SLEEPING OFF THE EFFECTS OF THE BETTER PART OF FOUR BOTTLES OF TWELVE YEAR OLD BOREALAN WHISKEY...
...AND THE OTHER IS TO KEEP THAT LITTLE GEM OF INFORMATION TO MYSELF...
IF I HAVE, THROUGH OVERSIGHT, MISSED SEEING SOME OBVIOUS AND VIABLE THIRD OPTION, I WOULD BE DELIGHTED TO ACT UPON ANY KEEN INSIGHTS YOU MIGHT WISH TO SHARE WITH ME...
YOU THERE!
YOU!
YOU'RE JUST SWISHING THE MUD AROUND...
HASN'T ANYONE EVER SHOWED YOU HOW TO USE A MOP!?

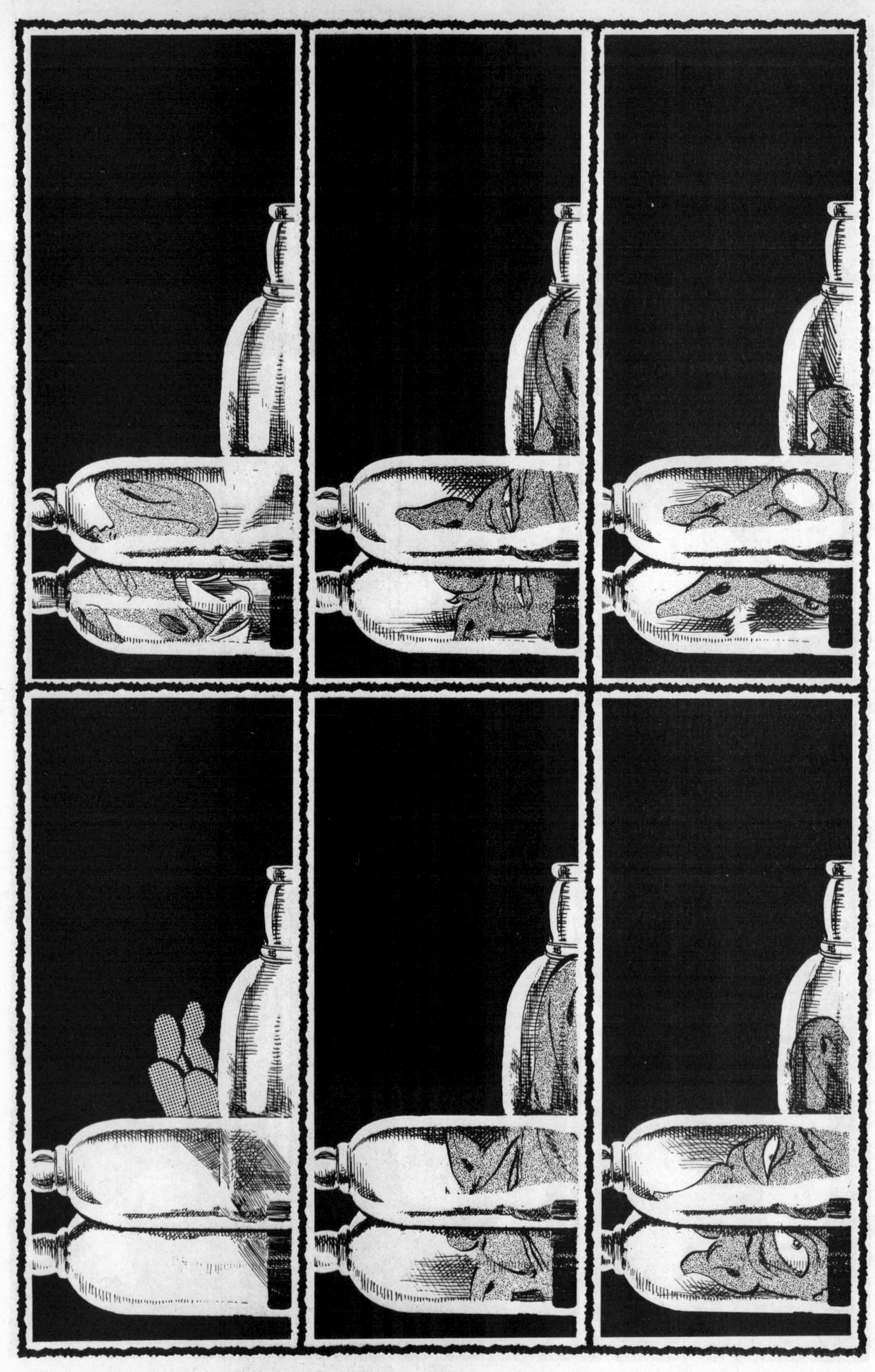

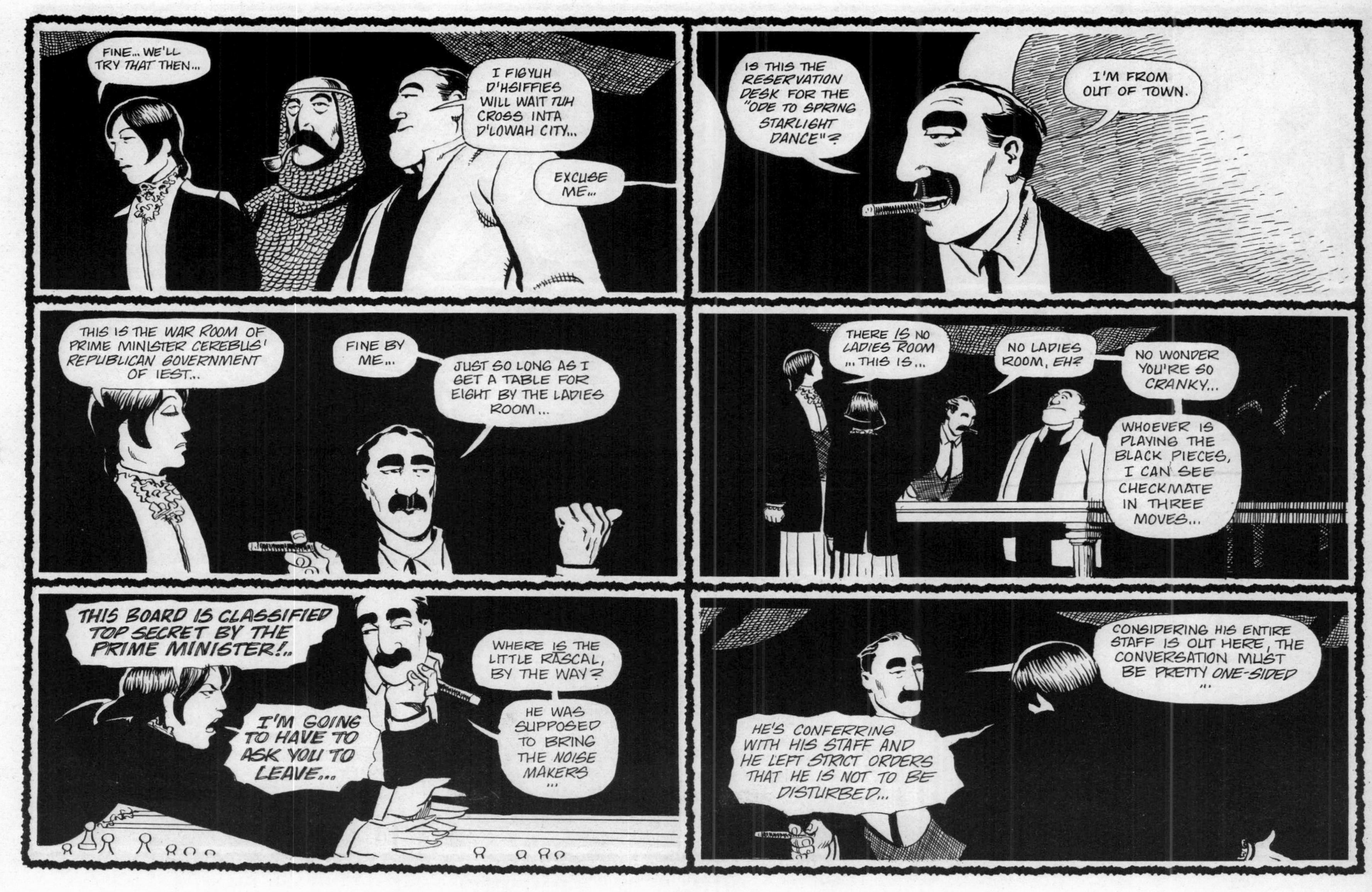
FINE... WE'LL TRY THAT THEN...
I FIGYUH D'HSIFFIES WILL WAIT TUH CROSS INTA D'LOWAH CITY...
EXCUSE ME...
IS THIS THE RESERVATION DESK FOR THE "ODE TO SPRING STARLIGHT DANCE"?
I'M FROM OUT OF TOWN.
THIS IS THE WAR ROOM OF PRIME MINISTER CEREBUS' REPUBLICAN GOVERNMENT OF IEST...
FINE BY ME...
JUST SO LONG AS I GET A TABLE FOR EIGHT BY THE LADIES ROOM...
THERE IS NO LADIES ROOM ... THIS IS...
NO LADIES ROOM, EH?
NO WONDER YOU'RE SO CRANKY...
WHOEVER IS PLAYING THE BLACK PIECES, I CAN SEE CHECKMATE IN THREE MOVES...
THIS BOARD IS CLASSIFIED TOP SECRET BY THE PRIME MINISTER!..
I'M GOING TO HAVE TO ASK YOU TO LEAVE...
WHERE IS THE LITTLE RASCAL, BY THE WAY?
HE WAS SUPPOSED TO BRING THE NOISE MAKERS ...
HE'S CONFERRING WITH HIS STAFF AND HE LEFT STRICT ORDERS THAT HE IS NOT TO BE DISTURBED...
CONSIDERING HIS ENTIRE STAFF IS OUT HERE, THE CONVERSATION MUST BE PRETTY ONE-SIDED ...

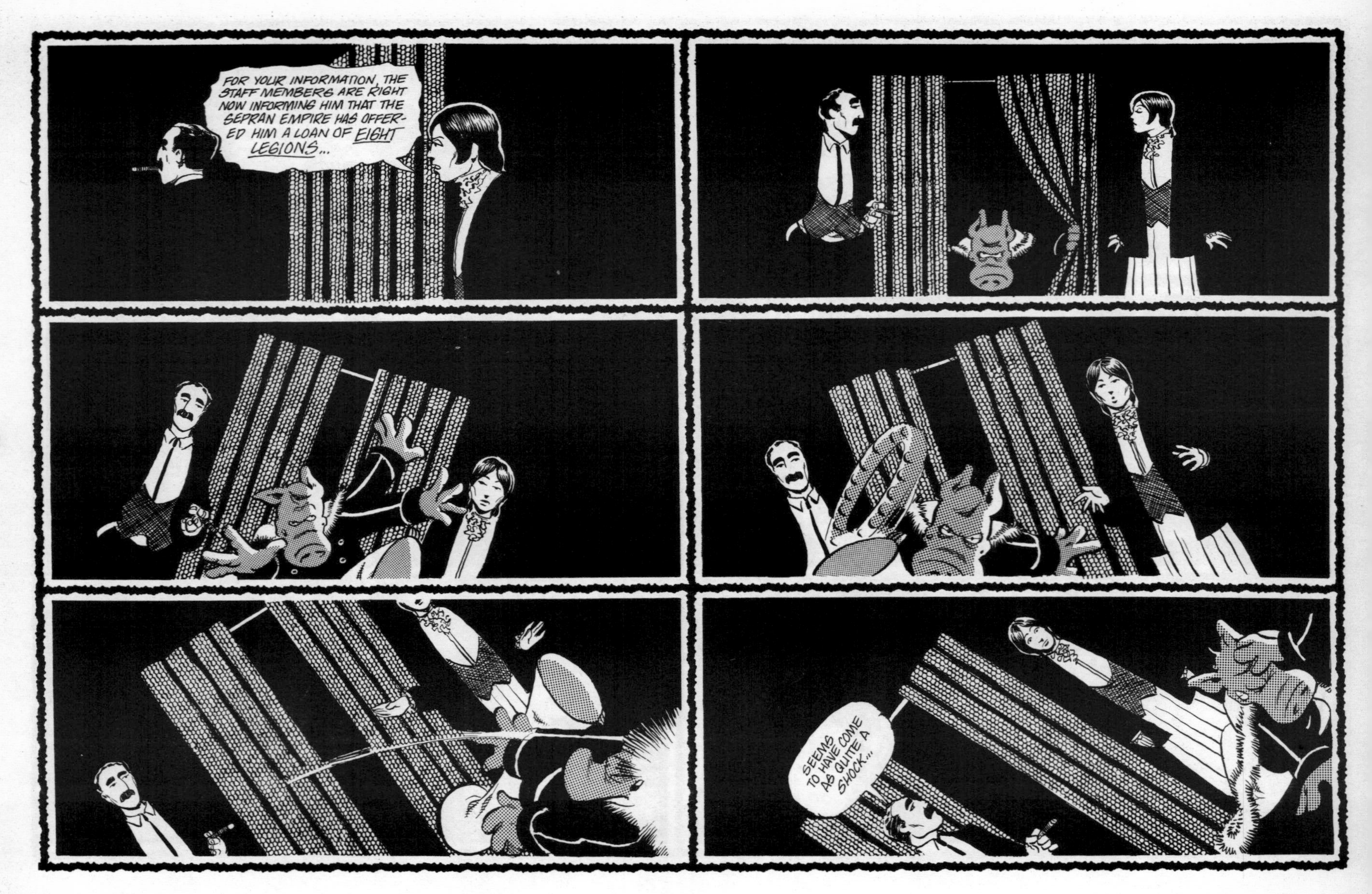

FOR YOUR INFORMATION, THE STAFF MEMBERS ARE RIGHT NOW INFORMING HIM THAT THE SEPRAN EMPIRE HAS OFFERED HIM A LOAN OF EIGHT LEGIONS...
SEEMS TO HAVE COME AS QUITE A SHOCK...

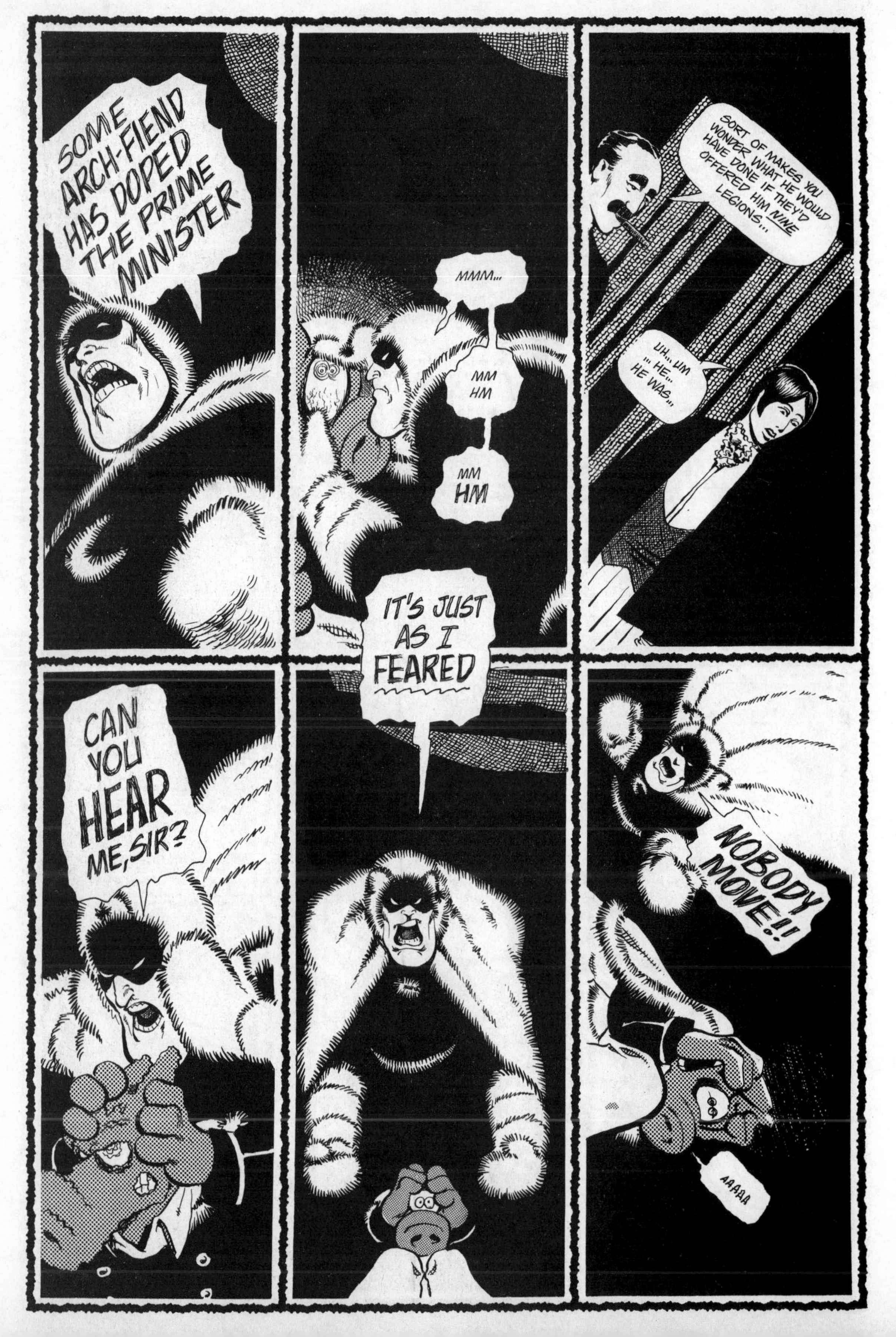
SOME ARCH-FIEND HAS DOPED THE PRIME MINISTER
MMM...
MM HM
MM HM
IT'S JUST AS I FEARED
SORT OF MAKES YOU WONDER WHAT HE WOULD HAVE DONE IF THEY'D OFFERED HIM NINE LEGIONS...
UH...UM ..."HE"... HE WAS...
CAN YOU HEAR ME, SIR?
NOBODY MOVE!!
AAAAA

LISTEN, YOU PEOPLE--IF HE FALLS ASLEEP HE WILL DIE
WE MUST KEEP HIM AWAKE

YOU THERE! YELL AT HIM! HIT HIM IF YOU HAVE TO...
I'LL BE BACK IN A MINUTE

MR. PRIME MINI
GUMP

ALL EIGHTY-SEVEN OF HIS ROACH SENSES SCAN THE ROOM FOR WHAT HE SEEKS
PING
PING
PING...
COFF COFF

AHA!
FROSTONITE IN LIQUID FORM, THE IDEAL THING ...
HEY! THAT'S MY WASH BUCKET! WHAT ARE YOU...

SEIZING THE RED CLAW TROUBLEMAKER'S NOSE WITH HIS ROACH MIT, SERGEANT PRESTON MAKES IT CLEAR HE HAS NO TIME FOR INTERRUPTIONS
OW OW OW

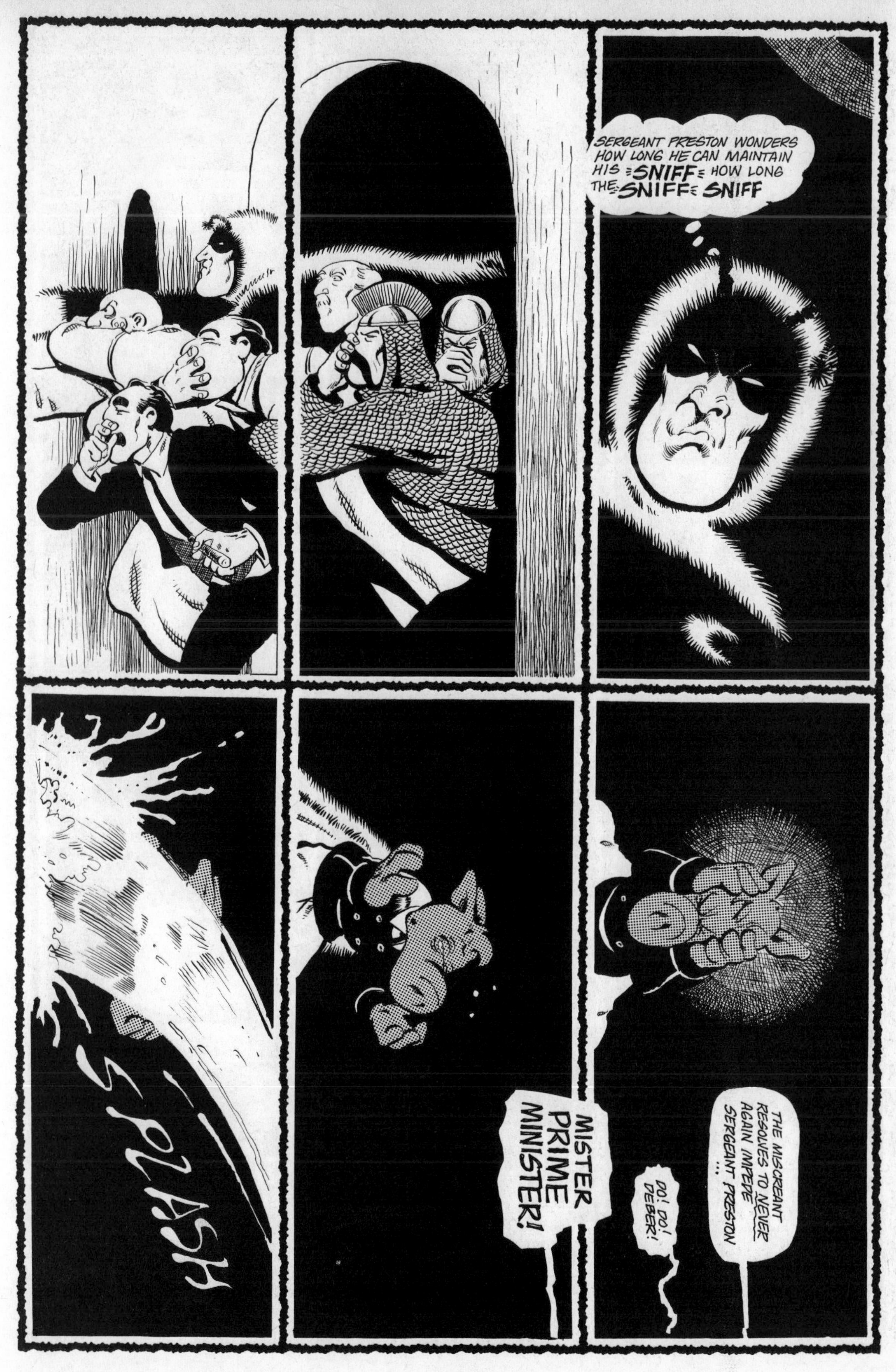
SERGEANT PRESTON WONDERS HOW LONG HE CAN MAINTAIN HIS SNIFF HOW LONG THE SNIFF SNIFF
SPLASH
MISTER PRIME MINISTER!
THE MISCREANT RESOLVES TO NEVER AGAIN IMPEDE SERGEANT PRESTON ...
DO! DO! DEBER!

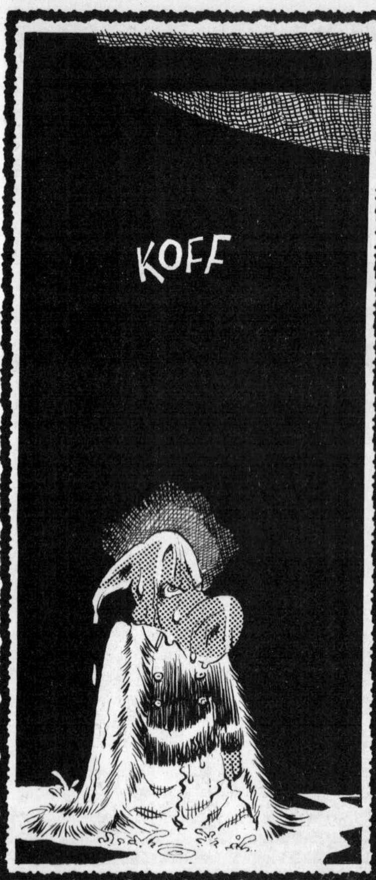
KOFF

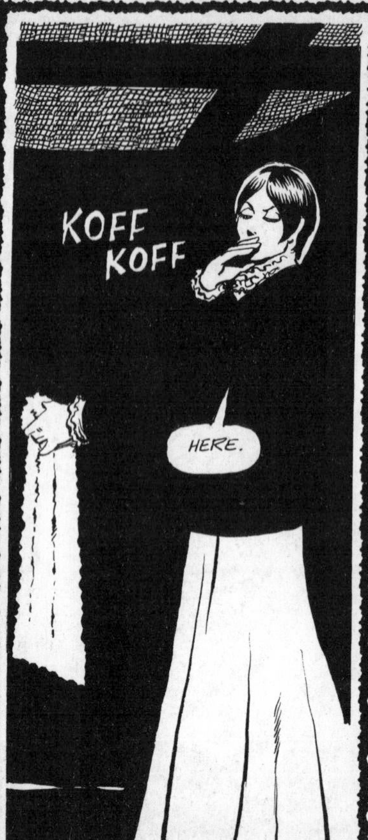
KOFF
KOFF
HERE.

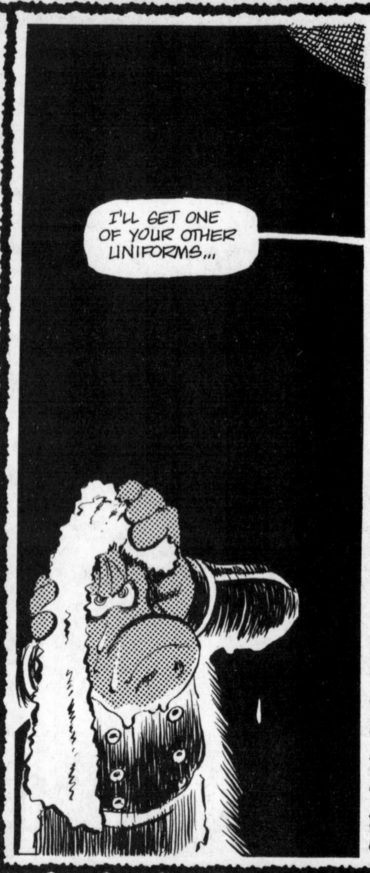
I'LL GET ONE OF YOUR OTHER UNIFORMS...

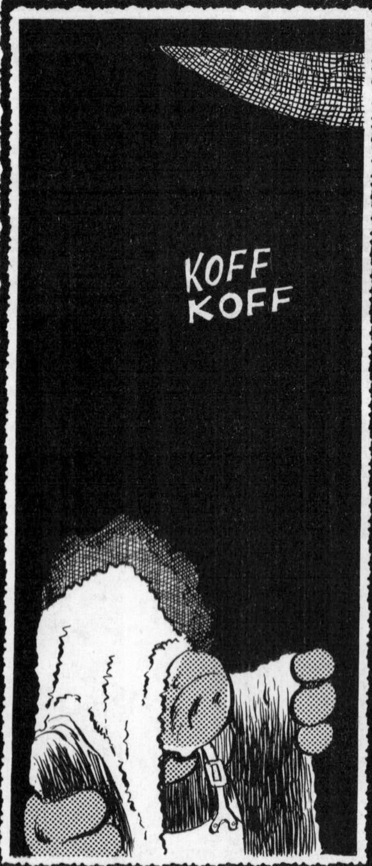
KOFF
KOFF

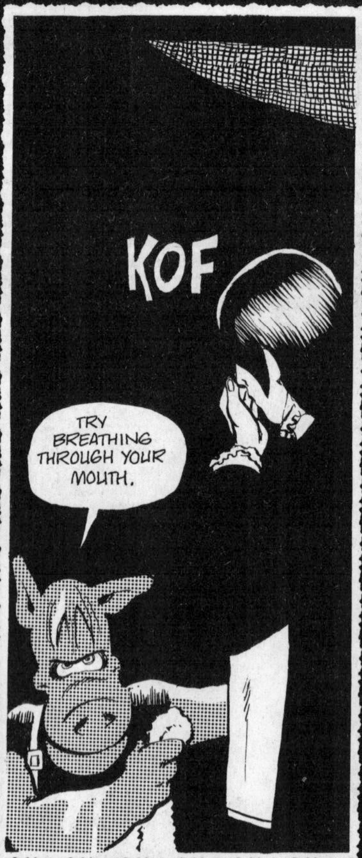
KOF
TRY BREATHING THROUGH YOUR MOUTH.

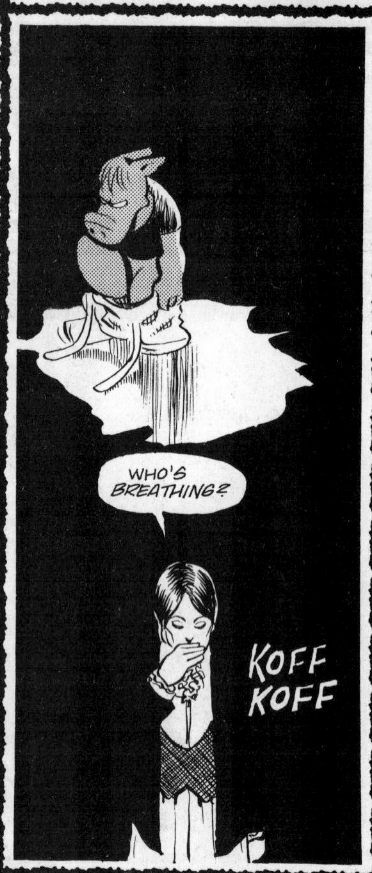
WHO'S BREATHING?
KOFF
KOFF

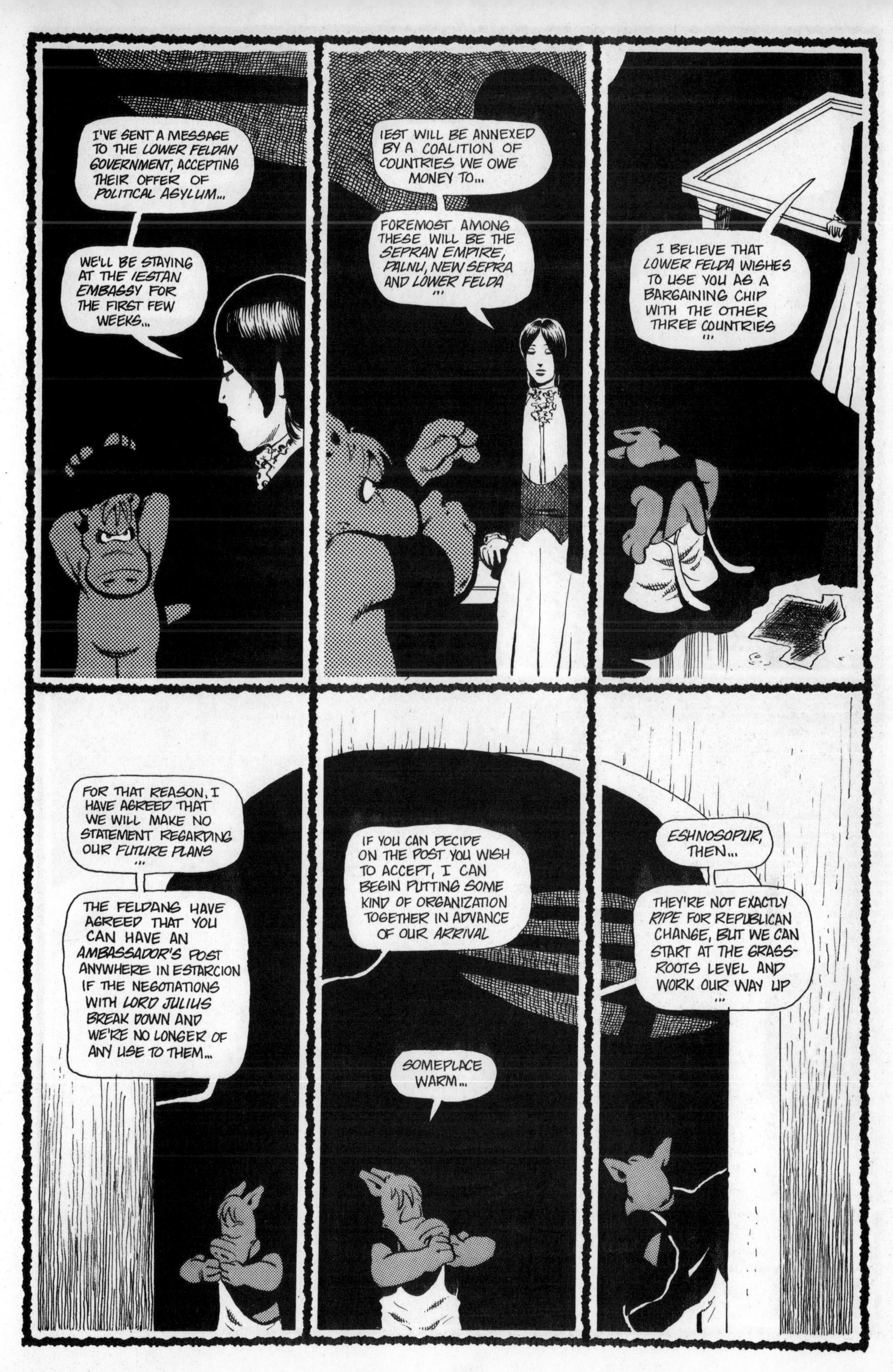
I'VE SENT A MESSAGE TO THE LOWER FELDAN GOVERNMENT, ACCEPTING THEIR OFFER OF POLITICAL ASYLUM...
WE'LL BE STAYING AT THE IESTAN EMBASSY FOR THE FIRST FEW WEEKS...
IEST WILL BE ANNEXED BY A COALITION OF COUNTRIES WE OWE MONEY TO...
FOREMOST AMONG THESE WILL BE THE SEPRAN EMPIRE, PALNU, NEW SEPRA AND LOWER FELDA ...
I BELIEVE THAT LOWER FELDA WISHES TO USE YOU AS A BARGAINING CHIP WITH THE OTHER THREE COUNTRIES ...
FOR THAT REASON, I HAVE AGREED THAT WE WILL MAKE NO STATEMENT REGARDING OUR FUTURE PLANS ...
THE FELDANS HAVE AGREED THAT YOU CAN HAVE AN AMBASSADOR'S POST ANYWHERE IN ESTARCION IF THE NEGOTIATIONS WITH LORD JULIUS BREAK DOWN AND WE'RE NO LONGER OF ANY USE TO THEM...
IF YOU CAN DECIDE ON THE POST YOU WISH TO ACCEPT, I CAN BEGIN PUTTING SOME KIND OF ORGANIZATION TOGETHER IN ADVANCE OF OUR ARRIVAL
SOMEPLACE WARM...
ESHNOSOPUR, THEN...
THEY'RE NOT EXACTLY RIPE FOR REPUBLICAN CHANGE, BUT WE CAN START AT THE GRASS-ROOTS LEVEL AND WORK OUR WAY UP ...

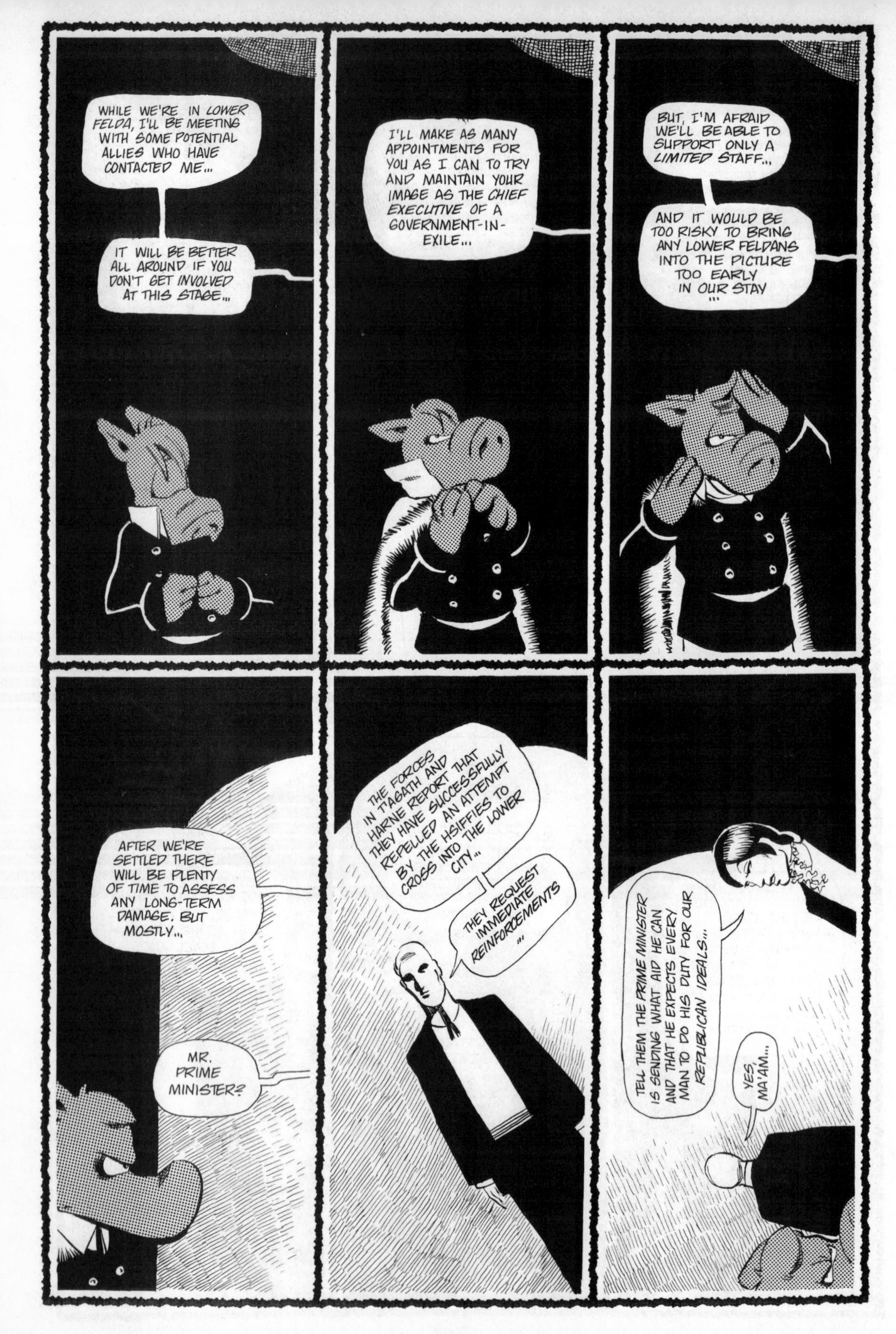
WHILE WE'RE IN LOWER FELDA, I'LL BE MEETING WITH SOME POTENTIAL ALLIES WHO HAVE CONTACTED ME...
IT WILL BE BETTER ALL AROUND IF YOU DON'T GET INVOLVED AT THIS STAGE...
I'LL MAKE AS MANY APPOINTMENTS FOR YOU AS I CAN TO TRY AND MAINTAIN YOUR IMAGE AS THE CHIEF EXECUTIVE OF A GOVERNMENT-IN-EXILE...
BUT, I'M AFRAID WE'LL BE ABLE TO SUPPORT ONLY A LIMITED STAFF...
AND IT WOULD BE TOO RISKY TO BRING ANY LOWER FELDANS INTO THE PICTURE TOO EARLY IN OUR STAY...
AFTER WE'RE SETTLED THERE WILL BE PLENTY OF TIME TO ASSESS ANY LONG-TERM DAMAGE. BUT MOSTLY...
MR. PRIME MINISTER?
THE FORCES IN T'AGATH AND HARNE REPORT THAT THEY HAVE SUCCESSFULLY REPELLED AN ATTEMPT BY THE HSIFFIES TO CROSS INTO THE LOWER CITY...
THEY REQUEST IMMEDIATE REINFORCEMENTS...
TELL THEM THE PRIME MINISTER IS SENDING WHAT AID HE CAN AND THAT HE EXPECTS EVERY MAN TO DO HIS DUTY FOR OUR REPUBLICAN IDEALS...
YES, MA'AM...

MAYBE THIS IS A *MISTAKE*... MAYBE CEREBUS IS LEAVING TOO SOON...
THESE GO WITH THE *FINANCIAL RECORDS*...
YES, MA'AM
MAYBE THE LOWER CITY WILL PROVE TO BE THE *TURNING POINT*...
MAYBE ALL THAT'S NEEDED NOW IS TO MAKE USE OF THE FORCES AT HAND ...
MAYBE IT'S TIME TO TRY FOR A FULL MOBILIZATION OF THOSE CLOSEST TO THE *PRIME* MINISTER'S OFFICE TOWARDS *TOTAL-WIN*...
"LONG LIVE THE *HSIFANS*"
"NO YEO ...DESE *TAOSAN*"
"LONG LIVE THE *KHANATE*"
"NO YEO DES *DAOSAN*"
"PLEASE DON'T SET FIRE TO MY BROTHER"
"DONO TANWA IMPRESH YON ENWA"
ON THE OTHER HAND

HOURS LATER
MR. PRIME MINISTER?
THEY'VE BROKEN THROUGH OUR DEFENCES... ONLY TOKEN RESISTANCE IS EXPECTED IN THE LOWER CITY...
HAVE TWO OF YOUR MEN GET OUR BAGS, COMMANDER ...
IT'S TIME TO GO.
CEREBUS?
IT'S TIME TO GO...
CEREBUS ISN'T LEAVING UNTIL THE HSIFFIES GET HERE...
WHAT?!

CEREBUS!
DON'T BE AN IDIOT!
COMMANDER!
STOP HIM!
DO YOU TAKE ORDERS FROM SECRETARIES, NOW, COMMANDER?
NO, SIR! ...
COME BACK HERE! BOTH OF YOU!
YES SIR ...
FINE...
LET'S HAVE A LOOK AT THESE "INVADERS" THEN...

DUSK.
THIS IS INSANE!
WHAT IF THEY CUT OFF OUR ESCAPE ROUTE?
IF WE DON'T LEAVE RIGHT NOW WE'RE JUST ASKING TO BE TRAPPED BY A BUNCH OF IGNORANT SAVAGES!
LOOKS LIKE THEY'RE HERE, SIR...
UH HUH.
WONDERFUL...
YOU'VE SEEN THEM! NOW CAN WE GET OUT OF HERE BEFORE ...
I'LL NEED YOUR SWORD, COMMANDER
YES, SIR.
WHAT?!

CEREBUS!
WHAT ARE YOU GOING TO...
CEREBUS
CER E BUS!
IF ALL THAT SCREECHING STARTS TO BOTHER YOU, COMMANDER, FEEL FREE TO TURN HER UPSIDE-DOWN IN A SNOW-BANK SOMEWHERE
YES, SIR.
CEREBUS!
LISTEN TO ME!

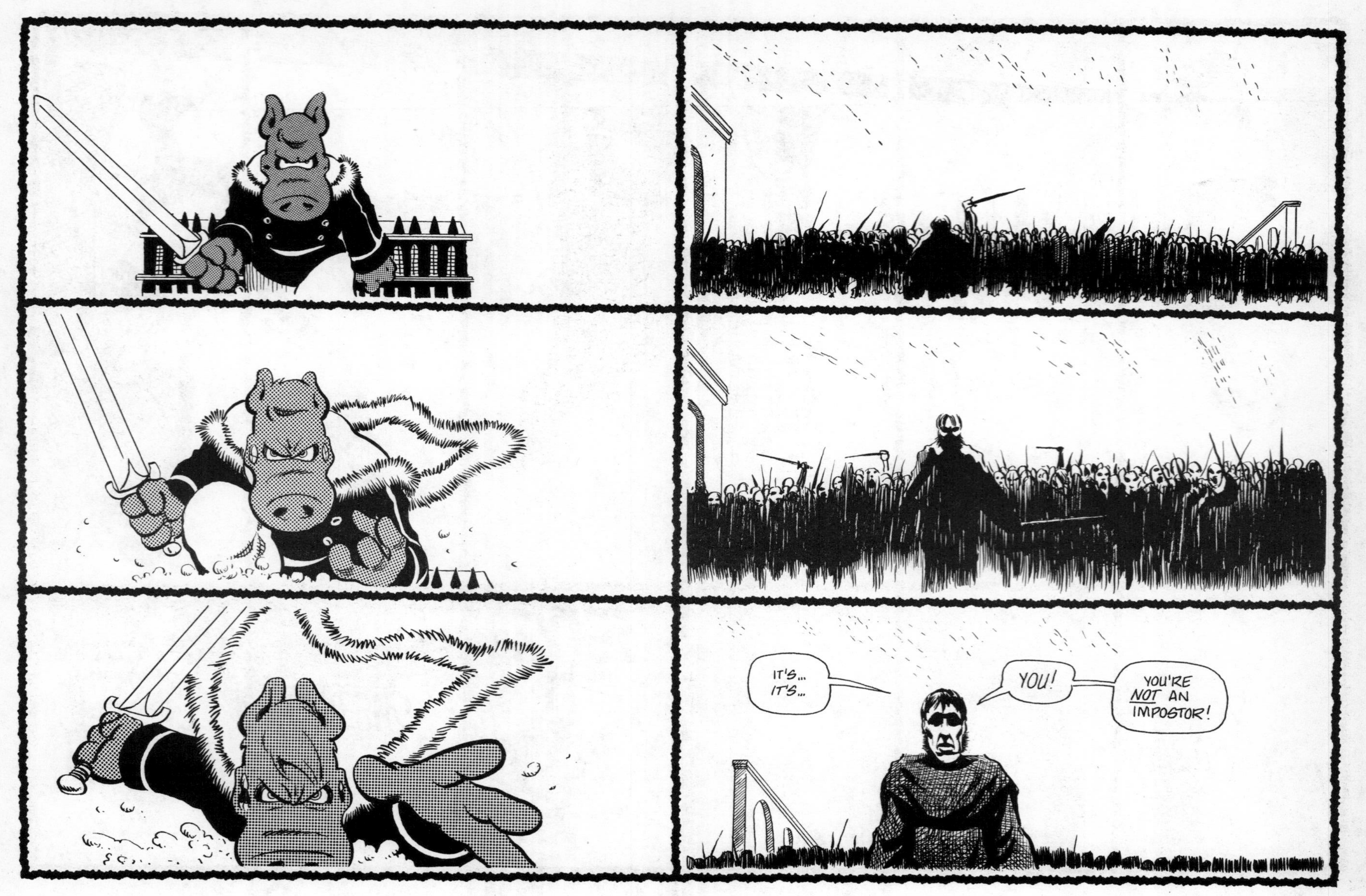
IT'S... IT'S...
YOU!
YOU'RE NOT AN IMPOSTOR!

MEN! IT'S HIM!
IT'S REALLY CEREBUS!
MIGHT FOR RIGHT
MIGHT FOR MIGHT
RIGHT FOR MIGHT
FIGHT! FIGHT! FIGHT!

NEXT: DENOUEMENT

cerebus' six crises
crisis Nº6
DENOUEMENT
HEY!
'EY

WHERE IS EVERYBODY
ODY
Y

IF THIS IS SOMEONE'S IDEA OF A JOKE...!
THERE'S NO NEED TO SHOUT...
I'M RIGHT HERE ...

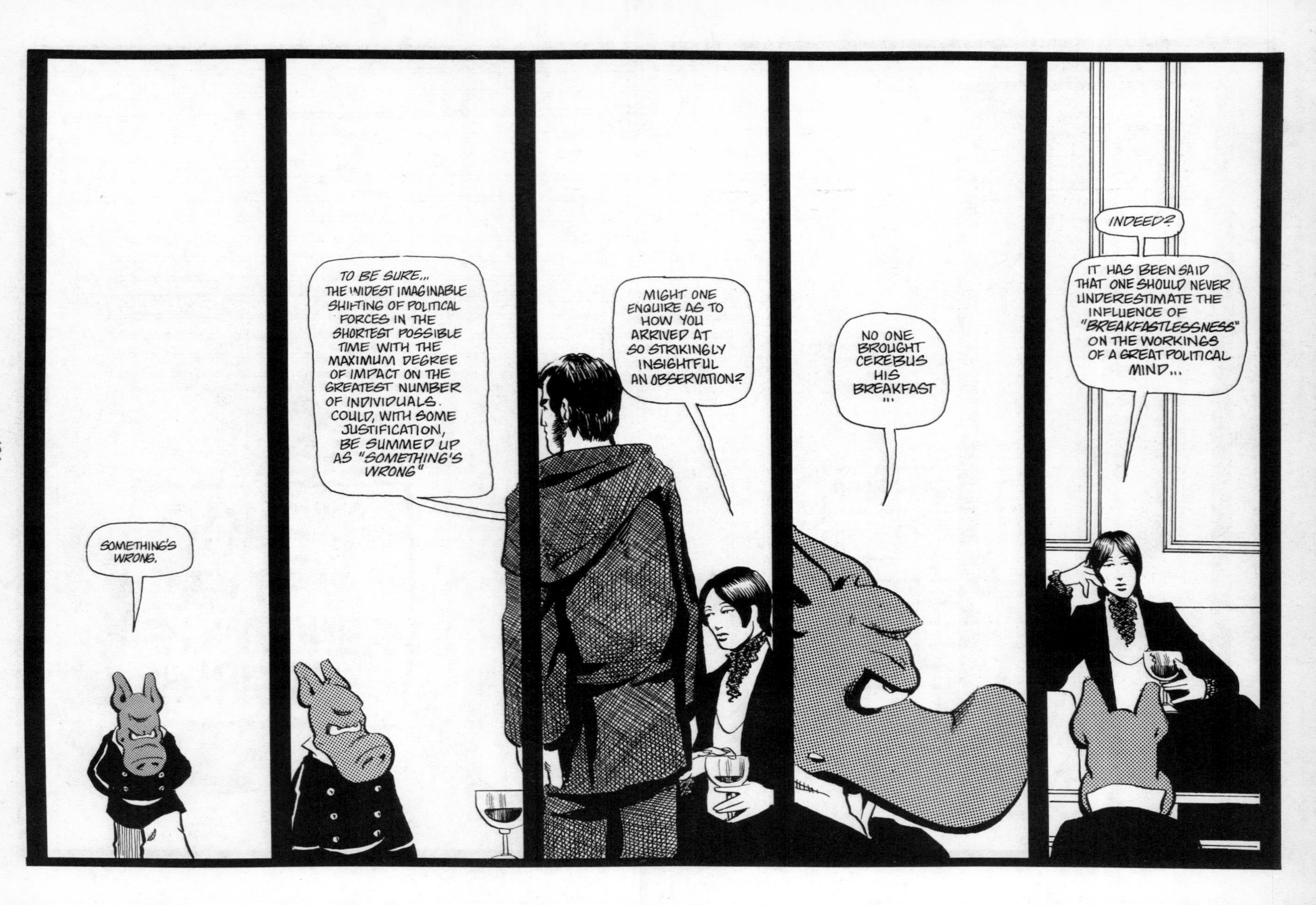
SOMETHING'S WRONG.
TO BE SURE... THE WIDEST IMAGINABLE SHIFTING OF POLITICAL FORCES IN THE SHORTEST POSSIBLE TIME WITH THE MAXIMUM DEGREE OF IMPACT ON THE GREATEST NUMBER OF INDIVIDUALS. COULD, WITH SOME JUSTIFICATION, BE SUMMED UP AS "SOMETHING'S WRONG"
MIGHT ONE ENQUIRE AS TO HOW YOU ARRIVED AT SO STRIKINGLY INSIGHTFUL AN OBSERVATION?
NO ONE BROUGHT CEREBUS HIS BREAKFAST ...
INDEED?
IT HAS BEEN SAID THAT ONE SHOULD NEVER UNDERESTIMATE THE INFLUENCE OF "BREAKFASTLESSNESS" ON THE WORKINGS OF A GREAT POLITICAL MIND...

AS I WAS TELLING YOUR CONNIPTIN FRIEND HERE, THOUGH I DOUBT HE UNDERSTOOD A WORD OF IT...
THE EXODUS INWARD HAS ENDED...
WHAT ARE YOU TALKING ABOUT?
THE PONTIFF IS DEAD...
... LONG LIVE THE NEW PONTIFF.
HAVE YOU LOOKED OUTSIDE?
IT'S QUITE IMPRESSIVE, REALLY.
THE PERSONAL GUARD OF HIS HOLINESS, THE EASTERN PONTIFF -- ASSIGNED TO SECURE THE EXECUTIVE MANSION...
WHERE ARE BLAKELY AND FILGATE?
WE NEED TO PLAN SOME STRATEGY...
"AND HE SAID TO THE PEOPLE; KEEP YOUR DISCIPLINES AND YOUR LESSONS ALL YOUR DAYS"
NOW THAT THE CONNIPTINS ARE HERE, WE HAVE THE MILITARY STRENGTH WE NEEDED ALL ALONG...

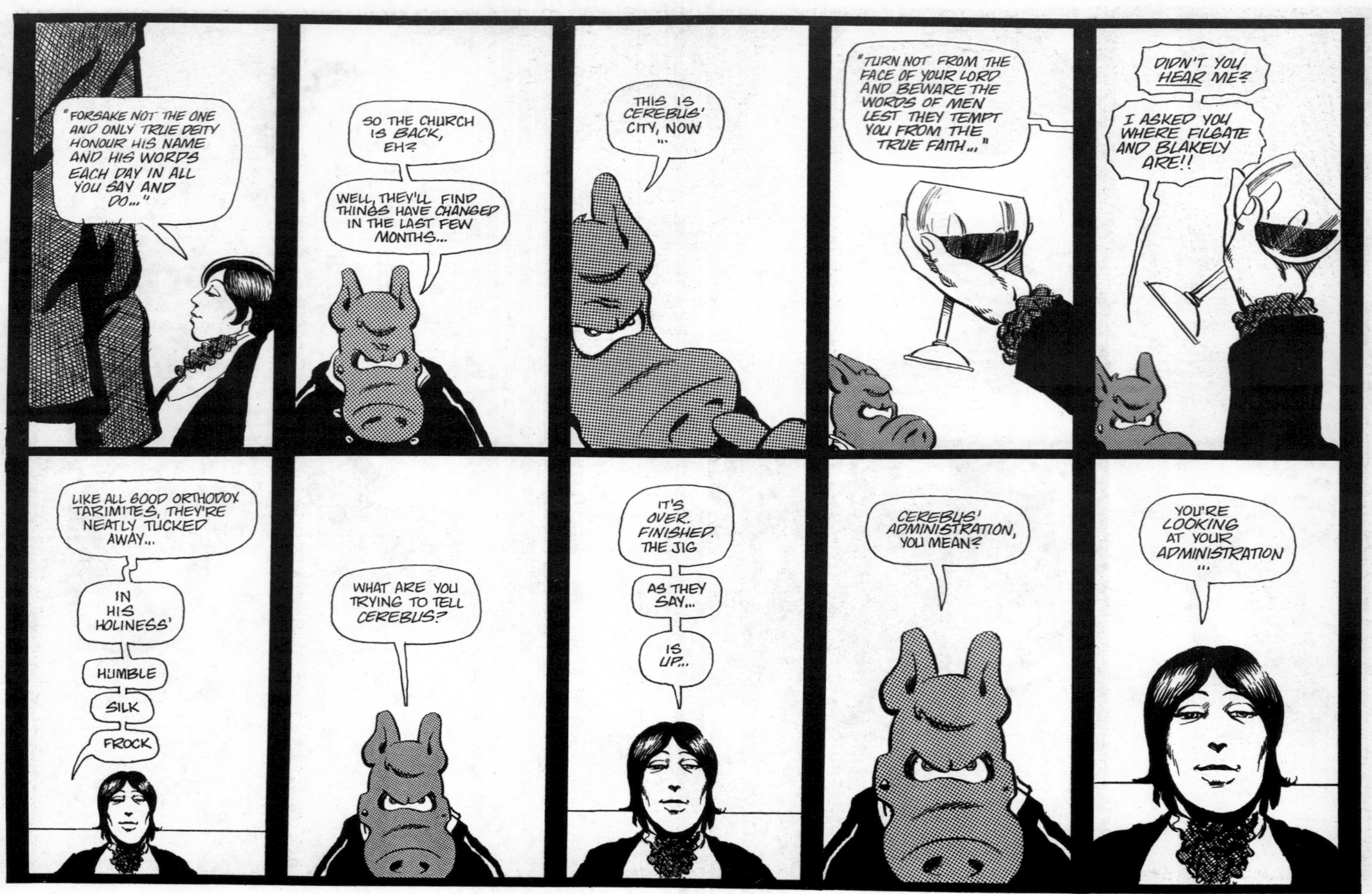
"FORSAKE NOT THE ONE AND ONLY TRUE DEITY HONOUR HIS NAME AND HIS WORDS EACH DAY IN ALL YOU SAY AND DO..."
SO THE CHURCH IS BACK, EH?
WELL, THEY'LL FIND THINGS HAVE CHANGED IN THE LAST FEW MONTHS...
THIS IS CEREBUS' CITY, NOW ...
"TURN NOT FROM THE FACE OF YOUR LORD AND BEWARE THE WORDS OF MEN LEST THEY TEMPT YOU FROM THE TRUE FAITH..."
DIDN'T YOU HEAR ME?
I ASKED YOU WHERE FILGATE AND BLAKELY ARE!!
LIKE ALL GOOD ORTHODOX TARIMITES, THEY'RE NEATLY TUCKED AWAY...
IN HIS HOLINESS'
HUMBLE
SILK
FROCK
WHAT ARE YOU TRYING TO TELL CEREBUS?
IT'S OVER. FINISHED. THE JIG
AS THEY SAY...
IS UP...
CEREBUS' ADMINISTRATION, YOU MEAN?
YOU'RE LOOKING AT YOUR ADMINISTRATION ...

WHAT ABOUT COMMANDERS JOHNS AND HYANNS...
OR WHAT'S-HIS-NAME FROM OLDCASTLE...?
THE CHURCH IS BACK...
...AND, AS I SAID, THEY'RE ALL VERY LOYAL ORTHODOX...
HARGRAVES?
SURELY THE ANARCHO-ROMANTICS...
THEY'RE ALL EITHER UNDER ARREST AND AWAITING TRIAL ...
OR ARE ACTIVELY BEGGING HIS HOLINESS' OFFICIAL FORGIVENESS ...
TRAITORS!
TRAITORS? THAT'S QUITE FUNNY COMING FROM THE PERSON THEY ABANDONED THEIR FAITH TO FOLLOW...
...ON THE OFFHAND CHANCE THAT THE ALBATROSS COULD BE FOUND BEFORE THE EXODUS ENDED... AND MADE IT A WORTHLESS TRINKET AGAIN...
COMMANDER!
YES, MY LORD CEREBUS?
THOSE MEN IN THE COURTYARD-- HOW LONG WOULD IT TAKE YOU TO CUT THEM TO RIBBONS!?
MM. LIGHT CAVALRY...
PIKE.

A FEW HOURS AT THE MOST ...
DARE I ASK WHAT YOU HAVE IN MIND?
THEY WANT A FIGHT?
THEY'LL GET ONE...
AND HOW LONG WOULD IT TAKE YOU TO DEFEAT FOUR OF THE WESTERN PONTIFF'S ELITE LEGIONS, COMMANDER?
THE WESTERN PONTIFF? ...
"HIS HOLINESS, THE NEW IESTAN PONTIFF WISHES TO ANNOUNCE THE REUN-ITING OF THE EASTERN AND WESTERN CHURCHES UNDER ONE FLAG--THE GLORIOUS BANNER OF THE LION OF TARIM -- THE MOST PIOUS SEPRAN EMPIRE"
THE LEGIONS ARRIVE AT DAWN.
SEPRA
AN ALLIANCE?
IT WILL NEVER LAST...
YOU'RE PROBABLY RIGHT. BUT IT WILL LAST LONG ENOUGH TO SEE EVERY CONNIPTIN IN THE UPPER CITY REDUCED TO A FEW POUNDS OF GROUND MEAT...
WHICH IS ALL HIS HOLINESS IS COUNTING ON...
YOU MIGHT LIKE TO READ THE FORMAL AGREEMENT...
THE NEW PONTIFF IS SO EAGER TO HAVE YOU EJECTED FROM THE CITY, HE HAS VIRTUALLY HANDED IEST TO THE EMPIRE ON A SILVER PLATTER ...
SEPRA
WE'LL SMASH HIS PERSONAL GUARD!
THE PEOPLE WILL SEE THAT CEREBUS IS STRONGER AND FLOCK TO HIS SIDE!

MY LORD CEREBUS -- MY MEN ARE READY...
DO YOU WISH THEM TO ATTACK?
DO YOU, "MY LORD CEREBUS"? SUPPOSE YOU DO RECAPTURE THE CITY...
SUPPOSE YOU EVEN MANAGE TO REPEL THE WESTERN LEGIONS WHEN THEY ARRIVE...
HOW DO YOU PROPOSE TO REPAY THE CITY'S DEBTS? ...
NEW SEPRA ...
THE EMPIRE...
LOWER FELDA. LORD JULIUS.
THEY'LL ALL BE UNITED AGAINST YOU...
OR DO YOU PLAN TO DEFEAT ALL OF ESTARCION WITH YOUR RAGGED LITTLE BAND OF NORTHLANDERS?
MY LORD CEREBUS ...
SHUT UP!
I SUPPOSE YOU HAVE A BETTER IDEA?
WE CAN GO TO LOWER FELDA... THEY'RE WILLING TO SUPPORT YOU AS IESTAN PRIME MINISTER-IN-EXILE...
TO EMBARRASS THE CHURCH ...

WHAT THEN? THAT DOESN'T SOUND LIKE MUCH OF A PLAN!
WE START CONVERTING PEOPLE...
... MAKING INROADS FOR REPUBLICANISM ...
REPUBLICANISM! AND WHAT GOOD DOES THAT DO? HUH?
WHY ARE YOU SO BLOODY INTERESTED IN IT?
YOU REALLY WANT TO KNOW?
YES!
I BELIEVE, IN TIME, THAT IT CAN LEAD TO WOMEN GETTING THE RIGHT TO VOTE...
WOMEN?
YES.
THE RIGHT TO VOTE?!
AND WHY NOT?
WOMEN COOK...
CLEAN...
HAVE BABIES.
SOME DO...

OTHERS FIND CAST-OFF KITCHEN STAFF SUPERVISORS AND MAKE PRIME MINISTERS OUT OF THEM...
CEREBUS WON THE ELECTION.
CEREBUS MADE THE DECISIONS
OF COURSE YOU DID
IF WE LEAVE FOR LOWER FELDA TOMORROW AT DAWN...
YES, DEAR.
WE WON'T BE ABLE TO CARRY MUCH LUGGAGE...
CEREBUS WAS THE BOSS!
I'M AGREEING WITH YOU...
NOW...
WHEN WE GET TO LOWER FELDA...
EGHNOSOPUR.
I BEG YOUR PARDON?

CEREBUS HAS DECIDED WE'RE GOING TO ESHNOSOPUR INSTEAD!
THEY HAVEN'T OFFERED YOU A POSITION.
IT'S WARMER THERE...
SO...WHAT.
RIPP!
CEREBUS IS LEAVING!
DON'T BE AN IDIOT!
CEREBUS ISN'T AN IDIOT!
CEREBUS HAS HAD ENOUGH
WHERE WILL YOU GO?
WHAT WILL YOU DO?
CEREBUS HAS SOMEONE HE HAS TO FIND...
JAKA?
POSSIBLY.

THERE ARE THINGS YOU DON'T KNOW ABOUT HER...
YOU MEAN LIKE THE FACT THAT SHE'S LORD JULIUS' NIECE?
YOU'RE NOT THE ONLY ONE WHO KNOWS A FEW SECRETS AROUND HERE, ASTORIA...
I WAS LORD JULIUS' "NIECE" ONCE...
HE'S HAD QUITE A NUMBER OF "NIECES" OVER THE YEARS...
THE ONLY DIFFERENCE WAS THAT HE MARRIED ME!
GOODBYE, ASTORIA...
I WOULDN'T LEAVE IF I WERE YOU...

NO ONE WALKS OUT ON ME CEREBUS!
DO YOU HEAR ME?
NO ONE WALKS OUT ON

CLIK

The Regency
IT JUST ISN'T FAIR...
YOU WERE THE BEST PRIME MINISTER IEST EVER HAD ...
EVER!
YEAH...
NO ONE EVEN LIKES THE CRUMMY OL' CHURCH...
IT'LL SERVE THEM RIGHT ...
WHAT'S THAT?
STAYING HERE THE REST OF YOUR LIFE AND PLAYING "WICKETS" ...
YEAH--IT'LL SERVE THEM RIGHT FOR CEREBUS TO STAY HERE FOR ...
NICE TRY, ELF...
BUT YOU'VE GOT TO STAY HERE ... YOU'VE GOT TO!

NO?
NO.
WILL YOU COME BACK AND SEE ME...?
SOMETIME?
SOMETIME.
NOT SOON... BUT SOMET✲
I'M GOING TO MISS YOU... ARE YOU GOING TO MISS ME?
CEREBUS?
CEREBUS?
ARE YOU CRYING?
DON'T BE RIDICULOUS I JUST GOT SOME SOOT IN M✲

IT'S OKAY, ELF ...THE SOOT'S GONE NOW ...
I DON'T KNOW. FOR A WHILE THERE CEREBUS THOUGHT HE COULD...MAKE A DIFFERENCE...
AND HERE I AM... RIGHT BACK WHERE I STARTED...
YOU GOT YOUR SWORD BACK...
YEAH--I GOT MY SWORD BACK...
AND I'VE GOT MY VEST ...
AND MY MEDALLIONS
AND THIS...
THIS SACK OF JUNK I GOT FROM THAT ...
KICK!

ARTIST...
OH DEAR

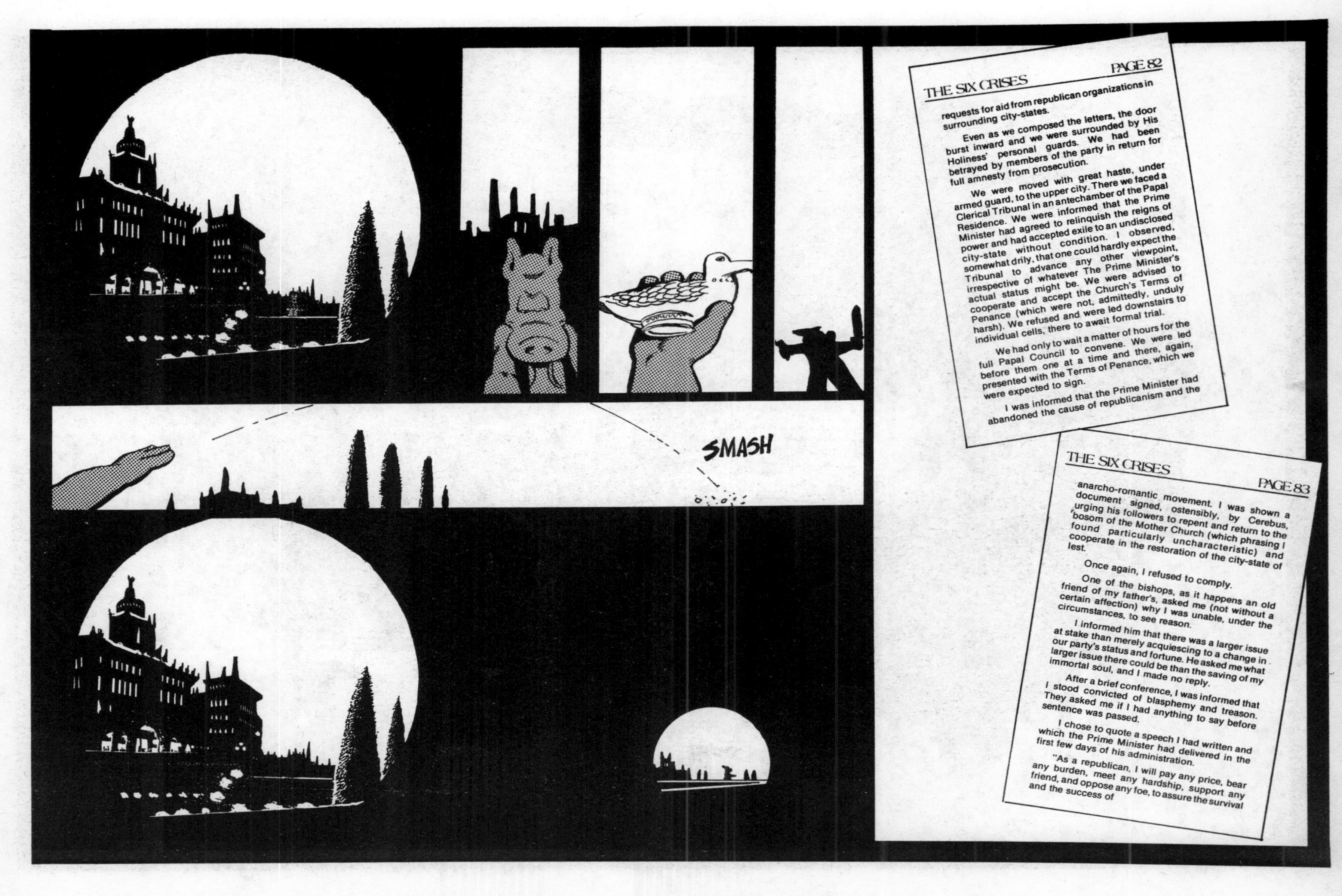

THE SIX CRISES PAGE 82

requests for aid from republican organizations in surrounding city-states.

Even as we composed the letters, the door burst inward and we were surrounded by His Holiness' personal guards. We had been betrayed by members of the party in return for full amnesty from prosecution.

We were moved with great haste, under armed guard, to the upper city. There we faced a Clerical Tribunal in an antechamber of the Papal Residence. We were informed that the Prime Minister had agreed to relinquish the reigns of power and had accepted exile to an undisclosed city-state without condition. I observed, somewhat drily, that one could hardly expect the Tribunal to advance any other viewpoint, irrespective of whatever The Prime Minister's actual status might be. We were advised to cooperate and accept the Church's Terms of Penance (which were not, admittedly, unduly harsh). We refused and were led downstairs to individual cells, there to await formal trial.

We had only to wait a matter of hours for the full Papal Council to convene. We were led before them one at a time and there, again, presented with the Terms of Penance, which we were expected to sign.

I was informed that the Prime Minister had abandoned the cause of republicanism and the

THE SIX CRISES PAGE 83

anarcho-romantic movement. I was shown a document signed, ostensibly, by Cerebus, urging his followers to repent and return to the 'bosom of the Mother Church (which phrasing I found particularly uncharacteristic) and cooperate in the restoration of the city-state of Iest.

Once again, I refused to comply.

One of the bishops, as it happens an old friend of my father's, asked me (not without a certain affection) why I was unable, under the circumstances, to see reason.

I informed him that there was a larger issue at stake than merely acquiescing to a change in our party's status and fortune. He asked me what larger issue there could be than the saving of my immortal soul, and I made no reply.

After a brief conference, I was informed that I stood convicted of blasphemy and treason. They asked me if I had anything to say before sentence was passed.

I chose to quote a speech I had written and which the Prime Minister had delivered in the first few days of his administration.

"As a republican, I will pay any price, bear any burden, meet any hardship, support any friend, and oppose any foe, to assure the survival and the success of

Liberty